PLANT AND ANIMAL
GEOGRAPHY

PLANT AND ANIMAL GEOGRAPHY

by

MARION I. NEWBIGIN

With 39 Illustrations and Maps

LONDON : METHUEN & CO. LTD.
NEW YORK : E. P. DUTTON & CO. INC.

First published September 10th 1936
Reprinted three times
Reprinted 1957 and 1960

3·3

CATALOGUE NO. 2/3656/10 (METHUEN)

PRINTED IN GREAT BRITAIN BY
WILLMER BROTHERS AND HARAM LTD
BIRKENHEAD

PREFACE

THIS book was being prepared for the press by the late Dr. Marion I. Newbigin at the time of her death. It is partly based on a series of lectures given over a number of years to the students of Bedford College, London, and is an attempt to show, as the result of many years' work as zoologist, botanist and geographer, the meaning of Biogeography treated on broad and general lines. This subject corresponds to a large extent to what botanists call Ecology—that is, the study of living organisms in relation to their environment, the latter including questions of relief, climate and soil. It remains to add that the complex subject of man is of necessity omitted.

To the kindness of Professor H. J. Fleure, School of Geography, University of Manchester, I am deeply indebted for the help he has given me in revising the manuscript throughout and completing the portions left unfinished. To Miss Margaret Dunlop, B.A., Assistant Secretary of the Manchester Literary and Philosophical Society, my thanks are due for chapters IV and V on Soils and Climatic Changes. She has also furnished Figs. 6, 7 and 9 for those chapters. The other sketch-maps and diagrams are my own, and in all cases, when possible, acknowledgement is made to the original source from which they are derived. To Mr. Martin A. C. Hinton, F.R.S., of the Natural History Museum my thanks for kind advice.

FLORENCE M. NEWBIGIN

EDINBURGH
June, 1936

v

DR. MARION NEWBIGIN

A TRIBUTE

D R. MARION NEWBIGIN was trained as a biologist in the days before the modern geographical movement, to which she was to contribute such a stimulus, had got under way. She had a vision of the world of life as a sphere of cumulative interactions which she saw modifying not only the structure and functions of the individual plant and animal, but also the assemblages or associations of living things in the various regions of a changing world. A thoughtful traveller, she saw the diversities of plants and animals in the many regions she visited for purposes of study. A careful student, she realized intimately how the plant and animal population of a region changes in the course of time, even if climate remains constant ; while climatic change has wrought vast revolutions again and again, leaving to us relics of a past plant-cover or a former fauna to give that complexity which is the charm and at the same time the difficulty of biogeographical study.

Dr. Newbigin's vivid conversation and her quickness of thought have inspired students of geography for many years, and it has been a privilege for an old friend to attempt to finish a book that unfortunately she was not able to revise before her death. As far as possible her work has been maintained with a minimum of alterations that she would probably have made had she lived. In any case of doubt as to such alterations her statements have been maintained. The sections on Soils and on Climate Changes were left in an earlier stage of development, and Miss Margaret Dunlop has tried to work Dr. Newbigin's material into a more completed statement, which is necessarily short and illustrative rather than exhaustive. It is hoped that all changes and additions in Dr. Newbigin's manuscript have been made in a proper spirit of reverence for the work of a very distinguished geographer, whose contributions to geography as a branch of the humanities have been at least as valuable as those to its biological side which are embodied in this book. It was indeed the combination of scientific and humanist thought, touched with genius and enriched by travel and study, that made Dr. Marion Newbigin so valuable a contributor to the progress of knowledge and still more of understanding.

H. J. F.

CONTENTS

PART I: LIFE AND ITS ENVIRONMENT

PART IV: FACTORS OF PLANT GEOGRAPHY

ILLUSTRATIONS

PART I

LIFE AND ITS ENVIRONMENT

CHAPTER I

INTRODUCTION

THE TERRESTRIAL PLANT COVER AND ITS SIGNIFICANCE

ONE of the outstanding features of land surfaces is the general presence of a plant cover. This varies enormously in density, both vertical and lateral, from place to place. Sometimes, as on mountain-tops, snow and ice-covered surfaces, or other 'desert' areas of varying types, it thins out or seems to disappear; elsewhere it displays extraordinary luxuriance and diversity. In areas of moderate or subdued relief, vegetation contrasts are often the most striking features of the surface, and afford the most obvious means of subdividing it. Further, much of our direct impression of the meaning of accentuated relief is due to the way in which the heights and hollows are picked out by differences in the plant cover. Thus a valley as an actual feature may be invisible from a distance, but the fact of its presence may be deduced from the presence of a belt of trees interrupting the continuity of grass or moorland.

Obviously, then, the geographer must take some account of natural vegetation. We have to note, however, that the almost instinctive conclusions which we all draw when we look at an area of varied natural vegetation are based on what the botanists call the physiognomy or general appearance of the constituent plants. A dense wood suggests at once the presence of a fairly thick and moist layer of soil, a hillside with stunted shrubs and rough grasses a thin soil, exposure to wind, and, seasonally at least, to low temperatures. We assume, that is to say, a certain relation between the look of the plants and the natural conditions under which they are growing, and the wider our experience the better founded this assumption appears to be.

Modern ecological botany, the study of the relation between plants and their habitats or dwelling-places (the Greek *oikos* = house, hence ecology), seeks to give precision to this general conception. The fact has much importance for the geographer.

In the first place the ecologists lay less stress upon the actual species present in particular areas than upon the fact that those present form a community. Within that community certain kinds of plants predominate by virtue of their size and numbers, and the characteristic vegetative form (life-form) of these is regarded as being both an expression and an index of the local habitat factors. For example, in the coniferous forests of northern latitudes or on the greater elevations, certain kinds of needle-leaved trees, such as pines, spruces, larches and so forth, are the largest and most abundant plants present. Their presence shows that the sum total of the physical conditions is such as to impose a method of carrying on the organic functions which finds its expression in the structural features of such conifers. On the other hand, a deciduous forest has as its dominant members trees with larger, softer leaves, shed at the end of each vegetative season. The nature of the leaves indicates a quickened physio-logical *tempo* as compared with the conifers, and points to generally higher temperatures and more abundantly available water.

The geographer is hampered by the fact that reliable con-clusions in regard to average temperatures, rainfall, humidity and the other climatic elements cannot be arrived at in any particular area without long-continued and precise instrumental observa-tions. Further, though the significance of the fact is not always appreciated, such observations even in civilized countries are con-fined to certain stations, often somewhat widely spaced. Even in such areas, therefore, comparatively little is known, from direct instrumental observation, of local climatic variations due to elevation, slope, amount of exposure to or shelter from prevailing winds and so forth. Over large parts of the earth's surface, again, fully-equipped meteorological stations are few and recently established. If the evidence afforded by the plant cover can be interpreted, then the characters of that cover give a means of drawing direct conclusions as to both the normal and the excep-tional sequence of meteorological phenomena. The natural vegetation forms, as it were, a self-recording mechanism register-ing the prevailing conditions. In some cases, as with certain types of trees, the records available cover a longer time-period than the existing accurate instrumental observations, for some trees live for many centuries. The details of the wood of the Californian Sequoias have indeed been used in investigating long-period rainfall fluctuations.

In other ways, also, variability of rainfall from year to year may be registered by the natural vegetation much more precisely than by the meteorologist's method of averaging totals. For example, some deserts, such as the Sahara, show two main types of plants, those adjusted to permanently arid conditions, and the rain plants. The latter can lie dormant, usually in the form of seeds, often for a prolonged period. But these seeds germinate rapidly when rain falls and develop into forms showing little apparent adaptation to drought. The fact that they occur proves that at times rain falls in sufficient amount to ensure that the upper layers of the soil remain moist at least for a certain number of weeks. If temperatures are sufficiently high several generations of such short-lived plants may occur in one season, while, on the other hand, the resistance of seeds or other structures is such that it is possible for them to lie dormant for many seasons. A study of the plants of such arid regions may therefore give us a clearer picture of what actually happens than a series of mean monthly totals based, say, on a ten-years' average. Within such a period certain seasons may be wholly negative so far as the rain plants are concerned, the small precipitation recorded having no significance, while other seasons again may be at least relatively moist and lead to a considerable amount of growth. The fact that rain plants form an integral part of the flora in such areas is in itself a proof that ' wet ' seasons must occur with fair frequency.

Somewhat similar conclusions can be drawn with regard to soil. The scientific study of soil is quite recent and has as yet been carried out only within limited areas, for it is necessarily laborious. But, if conclusions derived from the study of the relation between the soil cover and the type of vegetation are well founded, then the results have a wider application than within the area where they were made.

In both cases, it should be noted, the matter has both theoretical and practical importance. The detailed study of the response of plant communities to the habitat factors gives the geographer a vivid picture of the actual conditions prevailing over the different parts of the earth's surface, and enables him to supplement the limited results of detailed observation and research. It also affords a key to the use which can be made of the land, and helps him to give an intelligible account of the factors influencing man's spread, a subject which must necessarily form a large part of geography. Thus an important part of biogeography must be a general survey of the main plant communities present on the surface, with such detail in special cases as to make clear both methods and results. In contrast to the ecological botanist, however, the geographer must emphasize the natural conditions and he will study the plant response only in so far as this brings

out the nature of the former.   This enables him to discard much
detail on which the ecologist necessarily lays stress.

THE ANIMALS ASSOCIATED WITH THE GREAT PLANT COMMUNITIES

When we turn from land plants to land animals a great contrast
is apparent.   The zoologists, save to a very limited extent, have
not been able to recognize definite animal communities, nor is
their study of adaptive response of the same immediate geographical value.   Some of the reasons for the latter fact are clear
enough.   So far as the more highly differentiated animals are
concerned, their usually considerable power of locomotion and
their (apparently) purposive actions enable them partly to evade
direct environmental control.   Not a few perform migrations on
a scale sufficient to render periodic and non-periodic variations
in weather conditions of minor importance, climatic control of
range is thus less rigid than with plants, and adaptation to
particular climatic conditions less essential.

Apart from such obvious points there is something more
fundamental.   In the general case the zoologist is more aloof
from the geographical standpoint than the botanist, because
habitat for him involves not only the purely physical elements of
relief, climate and the nature of the substratum, but also the
plant cover.   Largely, that is to say, he takes it for granted that
the plant communities present are an environmental response,
and limits himself mainly to the interrelations of organisms,
particularly animals and plants.   This must be so when we
recall that the terminal link of what are called food-chains is in
all cases the green plant.   That is to say, whatever intervening
links or complications may occur, carnivorous animals feed
directly or indirectly on herbivorous ones, and the latter on
chlorophyll-containing plants.   It is only such plants which can,
in sunlight, build up organic matter from its elements ; all other
living things require some pre-existing organic matter as a
starting-point.   Thus, in one way or another, all animals are
linked to plant communities, and the conditions which determine the existence of these control also that of the dependent
animals.

With this is associated the difficulty which the zoologists, as
compared with the botanists, find in recognizing definite communities.   A plant community, large or small, gives us clues to
the environment because its members display as common features
direct responses to physical features of the environment, and

thus it enables us to form some idea of the nature of these. In the general case, animal response is indirect and occurs through the intervention of the plant cover. For example, it is not difficult to show that the essential features of an equatorial forest, such as its dense and luxuriant vegetative growth and the virtual continuity throughout the year of fruit and seed production, are related directly to the temperature and rainfall conditions. The more obvious animal responses, such as the frequent development of special climbing organs (grasping limbs, prehensile tail and so forth), and the use of fruits and seeds as one main food supply, with resultant structural adaptations (' nut-cracker ' beaks in birds, the form of the teeth in mammals and so on) are not related immediately to the climatic conditions but indirectly through the plant response. In the general case, that is to say, there is a dual community, plant plus animal, and the latter element cannot be considered without taking account of the former, and seems on the whole of less geographical importance. It follows that the most successful attempts to define animal communities have been made where living green plants are either absent, as in ocean depths, caves and so forth, or, as in moderately deep water, fresh or salt, are present chiefly as microscopic algae. So far as land surfaces are concerned, the presence of animals is generally linked so closely to that of conspicuous green plants that it is rarely feasible to consider the two separately.

To the ecological botanist the fact is abundantly clear and has a curious consequence. In considering the habitat of plant communities he devotes some attention to what he calls biotic factors, that is, the influence exerted by animals and man. He notes, for example, that the presence or absence of many earthworms in a soil has considerable influence on soil characteristics and therefore on the functioning (or metabolism) of the plants growing in the soil. The persistence of the type of deciduous forest characteristic of middle latitudes is closely related to the fact that the abundant earthworms consume the fallen leaves and help to bring about a ' turn-over ' of the salts which the trees require in large quantities. Again, the way in which the earthworms drag down the leaves to the lower levels and eject their castings at the surface is important in modifying the effect of rainfall on the soil constituents. Similarly, the ecologists point out that under natural conditions a grassland and its herbivorous animals so react on one another as to co-operate with the influences of physical conditions in maintaining both. If the natural animal population be replaced by man's large flocks and herds, the vegetation may change though the climate remains the same.

A similar effect may be produced when a variety of grass-eating animals is replaced by a single type of stock animal.

There is an obvious practical corollary. It is a waste of time and involves needless repetition to separate completely the two sides of biogeography for the geographer's purpose. Plants and animals are closely linked in nature, at least over land surfaces, and they should be linked in our survey. There is a natural and continuous sequence. Physical conditions express themselves in the plant cover which in its turn greatly influences the natural animal population. The animal element is usually less significant than the plant cover.

How far, then, need we take our survey of land animals for geographical purposes? Their limb-bones give some of the great grass-eating ungulates power of swift motion over relatively level surfaces, and they differ notably in size, limbs and teeth from the herbivorous rodents as well as in limbs and teeth from the carnivorous mammals, in both of which the fore-limbs at least serve other functions in addition to the purely locomotor one. It is worth while for the geographer to note such points, for they bring home to him the fact that the type of soil favourable to wide stretches of grassland is developed only over fairly level surfaces. With such plain surfaces the geographer is concerned from many points of view; it is important that both their characteristic plant communities and the animals which show the most perfect adaptation to the total conditions are apparently of geologically late origin, and have evolved side by side.

The African lung-fish (*Protopterus*) makes a nest or case of mud during the dry season, and lies dormant within this, using its lungs the while. The Queensland lung-fish (*Ceratodus*) never leaves the water and uses its lung only when the medium is foul with rotting organic matter. Such facts tell us something of the contrasts between river régimes in the two regions. Cases such as this are what the biogeographer chooses for study; adaptive responses without geographical significance he may leave untreated.

TAXONOMIC DISTRIBUTION OF PLANTS AND ANIMALS; ITS GEOGRAPHICAL ASPECTS

This study of interrelations is but a part of biogeography, and we have to note another aspect in which animals play a more important part. A general survey of the outstanding plant communities of the globe shows us that there is, as indeed one would expect, a certain broad similarity between those present in corresponding climatic regions. Thus British Columbia and southern Chile both display coniferous forests. When we compare the two types as regards the kinds of trees present, however, the differences are outstanding. The same sort of thing occurs elsewhere, but it is particularly noteworthy when areas in the widely separated southern land-masses are compared with those in the north, which are indeed all but continuous across the narrow Bering Strait. The nature and extent of the contrast, however, as, for example, between the trees found in the rain forest of the Amazon Basin and those of the equivalent African forest, can scarcely be appreciated without detailed botanical knowledge and an understanding of the differing topographic control. It is otherwise with the associated animals, especially the larger and more conspicuous forms. Here the contrast between the mammals of similar plant communities in the different land-masses is at once obvious in itself and has important consequences to man. That, for example, South America at the time of its discovery by Europeans had in its wide grasslands and savannas none of those great ungulates which swarm in the similar lands of Africa—no vast herds of antelopes, no buffaloes, no horses, no giraffes—is a fact which can hardly escape notice. Scarcely less remarkable is it that the civilized Indians of Peru should have had peculiar stock animals, unknown in either the wild or domesticated state outside the continent, but yet, as the Spaniards recognized, showing indications of affinity with the domesticated camels of the Old World. Australia, as is well known, shows even more remarkable peculiarities in its indigenous animal life.

Such features of distribution must be interpreted, and we may take into account present physiographical conditions only or endeavour to trace the effects of past ones.

Organisms tend to spread outwards from the known or supposed area of origin in all directions till some check occurs. That check may be of a physical nature, may take the form of a barrier such as a mountain range, a wide belt of water, or a definite change of climate such as that associated with desert areas. It is possible then to recognize biogeographical regions delimited by barriers of this kind. Thus the Atlas Mountains and the Sahara Desert, with its eastern continuation, form a barrier between much of Africa and the lands to the north ; the Himalayas shut off India from the rest of Asia ; Australia is separated from other continents by ocean, and so on.

When we try to investigate in detail the question whether such barriers do in point of fact bound areas with characteristic and contrasted floras and faunas of their own, we find at once that we have to take into account the means of spread of the different types of organisms. Plants, because they reproduce by well-protected seeds or by spores, and because the seeds so often display adaptations to ensure passive dissemination by wind, water or animals, are not as a rule so effectively stopped by purely physiographical barriers as are animals. It is, of course, true that the mere passive dissemination of seeds or spores does not necessarily ensure colonization of new areas, unless these afford habitats suitable for the whole life-cycle, including germination, vegetative growth and reproduction. At the same time, we do find that many families and genera, or even species, of plants have a very wide distribution, and that satisfactory floral regions are not altogether easy to define.

Some kinds of land animals resemble plants in this respect, either because, like migratory birds, they have themselves great powers of locomotion, or because, as happens with minute forms or those reproducing by small, well-protected eggs, passive transmission is possible. Most terrestrial mammals, however, except those such as the bats with considerable powers of flight, have little power of crossing lofty mountain ranges, or wide belts of water, and, if adapted closely to a particular type of habitat, such as dense forest or a desert, can rarely traverse a considerable region displaying quite other characters. We find, therefore, that it is comparatively easy to divide up the globe into zoo-geographical regions, based mainly, though not exclusively, on their mammalian faunas. Such regions are demarcated by barrier belts, oceans, mountains and deserts being the most important of these. The regions show a certain rough correspondence to the existing continental areas recognized by geographers, particularly so far as the two Americas and Australia are concerned. The greatest land-mass of the globe, on the other hand, that made up of the continuous continents of Europe, Asia and Africa, is divided into three parts by the belt, characterized in part by its great aridity and in the east also by its notable elevation, which crosses it in an east-north-east to west-south-west direction. This belt separates a wide northern non-tropical area from the great peninsular area of Africa, stretching far to the south, and from the smaller peninsula of India, with Further India, more limited in latitudinal extension, but still extending southward far beyond the northern tropic.

Some study of these zoogeographical regions must form an integral part of biogeography ; they emphasize features of which the geographer must take cognizance, and they give additional detail to his picture of the surface. They are determined largely by facts concerning the more familiar and conspicuous animals, but less familiar forms often show points of interest.

But the geographer can hardly be expected to stop there. He is well aware that the land-masses have not always had their present shape, extent and relief. Much of his study of physical geography in the wide sense is indeed concerned with the analysis of the various elements present, with the story of their development, and with the proof that all land surfaces are undergoing ceaseless change. The mountain chains which form the main barrier between inter-tropical and extra-tropical Asia are, he knows, not an initial feature of the earth's surface but can be ' dated ', geologically speaking, with considerable definiteness. The aridity of parts of the Sahara, again, is in all probability a characteristic of quite late origin. Here, then, we come to the second aspect of our problem, the influence on organic distribution of past geographical conditions. Before looking at it, however, we must try to define the problem more precisely.

The example already given, that of the distribution of conifers, may once more serve as an illustration. Conifers are all either trees or shrubs, never herbs. They show a certain direct environmental response in that they tend to form definite communities only under certain conditions of climate and soil. But that does not mean that all coniferous forests are strictly comparable from the systematist's point of view. Apart from the very notable contrasts between the species and genera present in the belts found in various parts of the northern hemisphere, we find that no species and few genera are common to the northern and southern hemispheres. That helps to make clear the difference between the systematist's and ecologist's standpoints. The ecologist seeks to show that any recognizable community of organisms, or indeed any individual species, if it is to survive, must needs possess a certain adaptive response to its habitat or dwelling-place. The systematist, or student of taxonomy, seeks to group the organisms he studies in such a fashion as to make clear their natural relationships. Nowadays he does this on the assumption that descent with modification has occurred. This means that he regards all the species included in a genus as having had an immediate common ancestor, while related genera can be traced back to a more remote ancestor, so that they can be grouped into families, families into orders, and so forth. Species he regards as having originated within some definite area of the surface, but as being more or less plastic. Thus a spread to a new area, differing from that of origin, may lead to variation,

with a possible rise of new species. If the separation between
the two areas is sufficiently complete to minimize intermixing,
and if the new area is markedly different from the first, differentiation may go on till new genera, families and larger groups arise.
Such processes, as the record of the rocks shows, take what we
call geological time to work themselves out ; they must also be
associated with those vast changes in the structure and form of
the surface, and in the associated phenomena, which the physical
geologists have proved to have been a feature of earth history.

Note the results. The systematists have catalogued, in pains-
taking detail, the present-day distribution of species, genera,
families and higher groups over the surface. They have shown

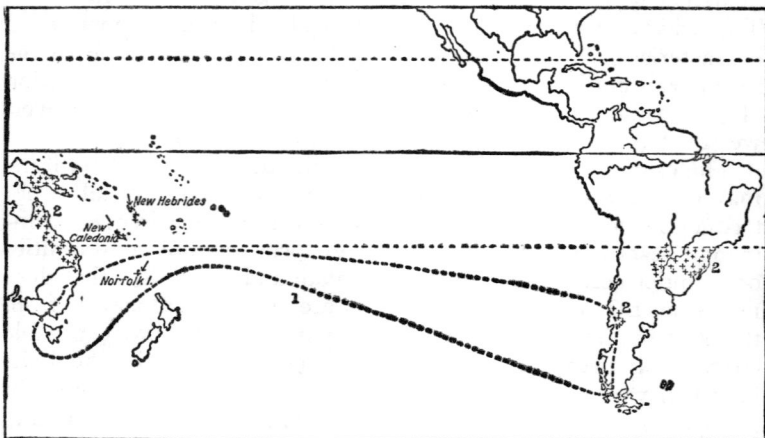

FIG. 1.—1. Distribution of Eucryphia. *After Hutchinson.* 2. Distribution of
species of Araucaria

that, as a convenient means of arranging the mass of detail, it is
possible to recognize certain regions defined both by their physical
features and by their organisms, even if it is not easy to fit all
organisms into precisely the same regional framework. But this
is only a beginning. They are precluded by their own method
from assuming that the different groups were always present in
their existing form in the regions recognized ; in many cases,
indeed, definite evidence is available to the contrary. For
example, the coniferous genus Araucaria, to which the familiar
monkey-puzzle of Chile and the beautiful Norfolk Island pine,
both common in cultivation, belong, is now found native only
in the southern hemisphere. But Araucaria cones occur as
fossils in the London Basin. Thus a monkey-puzzle, derived

from seed, the initial source of which was Chile, may now be growing in a park beneath the soil of which lie traces of its fossil allies.

Such facts, and there are a multitude of them, raise a number of questions. Can we assume, in this particular case, that Araucarias originated in the northern hemisphere ? If so, why did they disappear there, and how did they reach the southern hemisphere ? Can we offer any explanation of the curious way in which the living species are scattered, as if by chance, over the southern land-masses, in Chile, Australia, New Zealand, Polynesia ? Finally, and most important for our immediate purpose, is the geographer concerned with questions of this kind ?

It is difficult to see how he can afford to ignore them entirely. He devotes much attention to the structural elements, geologically ancient or geologically late, of the land-masses. Any serious study of the continents, for example, must begin with a recognition of their oldest element, round which as a nucleus the remainder has been built. It must be so when we remember how much influence, even on human geography, is exerted in North America by that great exposed mass of ancient crystalline rocks which forms the Canadian Shield, and in Europe by the comparable mass which forms the Baltic Shield. Further, no world survey can be systematic if it fails to take account of the virtual continuity of the lands in the northern hemisphere and their wide separation in the southern, or to attempt to consider the causation of the difference. Finally, the geographer, however strictly he strives to limit his field, must needs be greatly concerned with that notable phenomenon, the series of Pleistocene Ice Ages, the evidence for which is spread so widely over the surface.

There can be no doubt that the present distribution of organisms, taken in conjunction with past distribution as shown by fossils, throws much light upon the physical history of the earth. Since the geographer is constrained to take that historical development into account, at least in its broad outlines, he cannot afford to neglect one important line of evidence, that afforded by organic distribution. Some of the facts also are peculiarly stimulating to the imagination. The insignificant little Blue-eyed Grass (*Sisyrinchium*), of the Iris family, is abundant in North America, but occurs naturally elsewhere only in Kerry and Galway in Ireland, the last outpost of Europe. Does its presence mean that we can look back to a geologically late period when the North Atlantic Ocean did not exist, and what are now the continents of Europe and America were one land-mass ?   Similarly, despite the great differences between the plants of equatorial South America and equatorial Africa, there are some minor traces of similarity, rather less outstanding than that offered by the Blue-eyed Grass.   Does this mean that Africa and South America were once connected, but became separated at an earlier date than the northern areas ?   Are we allowing the interest of such facts to tempt us to leave the geographer's own territory ?   Surely not, for the human geography of both South America and most of Africa has been deeply affected and influenced by their isolation from the Eurasian land-mass.

We shall then add to our initial survey of the interrelations between organisms and their environment, as expressed especially in the great plant communities and their animal associates, a broad survey of the taxonomic distribution both of plants and animals.   That survey must both include present conditions, and attempt to offer some explanation of these by taking account of earth history, including the effects of the Pleistocene Ice Ages.

OCEAN LIFE

So far we have been concerned with terrestrial organisms ; we have still to consider the significance of the life of the sea to the biogeographer.   Here animals are more important than plants. Comparatively few kinds of higher plants can tolerate even occasional complete submergence beneath a water surface, fewer still permanent submergence.   Both phenomena also are more marked with salt, i.e. ocean, water than with fresh.   The brown and red marine algae, commonly called seaweeds, are anchored to rocky sites on the ocean margins, and may there form miniature ' sea-forests ' of considerable density ; but their depth range is sharply limited, and in relation to the size of the oceans they occupy little space.   Thus the most important green plants of the oceans are the minute floating algae.   Even these, however, because of the fact that the sun's rays have a very limited power of penetration, are, during life, confined to the upper layers of the water.   The result is that, in the oceans as a whole, animal life is more abundant and much more diverse than are green plants.   Marine animals include highly specialized mammals, such as the whales, a few reptiles, fishes and an enormous number of invertebrates, some of which are not represented on land or in fresh water.   It would seem also that all levels of the ocean from the surface to the great depths contain some animals.

The deduction is fairly obvious.   Whereas over the lands it is the fixed plants, mainly those of complex structure, which afford us the main key to the prevailing physical conditions, in the oceans we are for the most part dependent upon the animals, provided we can zone our captures, to aid us in interpreting these. Offshore, shallow water is kept constantly moving by waves and currents. Shallow-water animals, as a response, tend to show either considerable power of swimming against currents, or by their fixed habit, or power of burrowing, or in other ways, offer passive resistance to the displacing forces. Deep-water bottom animals, on the other hand, do not as a rule possess organs of fixation, and where they are free-swimming seem to possess but slight muscular development. This confirms the inferences from other lines of evidence that the bottom waters are unaffected by waves and little moved by currents, both of which influences are largely due to wind.

On the other hand, because the oceans are much more continuous than the lands, and because, apart from climate, physical barriers between one part of the world ocean and another cannot be recognized in the same fashion as barriers on the lands, the taxonomic distribution of marine animals is of much less importance than that of terrestrial forms. When outstanding contrasts in the kinds of animals present can be recognized between one part of the ocean and another, apart from those directly due to climate, then the adjacent land surfaces are exerting some influence, direct or indirect. It may be, as with seals, and with penguins among flightless marine birds, that part of the organism's life is spent on land and only certain land surfaces are suitable. Again, many purely marine animals are confined to shallow water showing particular conditions influenced by the nature of the substratum. Such forms often give rise to free-swimming larvae, but these must find a suitable habitat within a fixed limit of time, or perish. This necessarily limits their range, so that we should not expect to find precisely the same forms, for example, under similar conditions on both shores of a wide ocean, unless some land surface gives opportunity for a slow spread round its borders. Broadly speaking, however, ocean life offers the geographer comparatively little of value from the point of view of taxonomic distribution, the main facts being adequately brought out by the terrestrial forms.

ECONOMIC BEARINGS OF BIOGEOGRAPHY

The final, and it might be supposed the most important aspect of biogeography, is the economic one. Here, however, we find that at least so far as the chief cultivated and useful wild plants are concerned, much of the material already finds a place in the ordinary text-books, and does not require special consideration. Certain problems, it is true, are inadequately treated there and demand fuller discussion in the light of biological principles. In the main, however, the economic side need be treated only in summary fashion.

SUMMARY

Summing up, then, we have three main topics to discuss in this book :

1. The influence of natural conditions on the distribution and outstanding features of the great terrestrial plant communities and the animals associated with them.

2. The outstanding facts of the taxonomic distribution of organisms over the land surfaces, in so far as this distribution throws light upon the present features of these and on their probable past history.

3. The response made by marine organisms to the ocean habitat in relation to the conditions existing there, and the similar response in the case of the fresh-water habitat.

Before we attempt this threefold survey, however, certain general principles must be laid down. In particular, we must have a clear if generalized notion of the main living kinds of plants and animals, which involves a study of the elements of taxonomy.

NOTE

Up to the present the inclusion of a biogeographical section in text-books of physical geography has been a less marked feature of English books than of continental ones. Thus de Martonne's *Traité de Géographie physique*, 4th Edition, Vol. III, *Biogéographie* (Paris, 1927), written in collaboration with Aug. Chevalier (Plants) and L. Cuénot (Animals) gives a very full survey, a similar one occurring also in the 7th Edition of Supan's *Grundzüge der physischen Erdkunde* in Vol. II, Part 2, *Pflanzen u. Tiergeographie* (Berlin and Leipzig, 1930) where the section on Plants is by Erich Leick and that on Animals by Ferdinand Pax. No corresponding treatment of both subjects within a single volume is available in English. Most general works on Natural History include a section on distribution, while the English translation of Schimper's *Plant Geography on a Physiological Basis* (Oxford, 1903) is indispensable, and there is a new German edition (1935). See also M. E. Hardy, *The Geography of Plants* (Oxford, 1920), and Newbigin, *Animal Geography* (Oxford, 1913), also H. Gaussen, *Géographie des Plantes*, and M. Prenant *Géographie des Animaux* (Paris, 1933), the last two small but comprehensive books included in the Collection Armand Colin, Section de Géographie. Eug. Warming's book, available in translation as *Oecology of Plants* (Oxford, 1909), contains much valuable material, but its utility for most geographical students is diminished by the great number of unfamiliar technical terms used.

CHAPTER II

THE ELEMENTS OF CLASSIFICATION (TAXONOMY)

THE AQUATIC ORIGIN OF ORGANISMS

ALL land organisms show clear indications of an ultimate origin from aquatic ancestors, and progressive adaptation to terrestrial habitats has been accompanied by steadily increasing specialization, so that, in the main, land plants and land animals are more differentiated, that is, are ' higher ' on the tree of life than aquatic ones.

A large number of animals, however, as well as a much smaller number of plants, have returned from the land to the water. When this occurs, as with such mammals as whales, dolphins and porpoises, the organisms display a degree of differentiation, as to both structure and function, which no biologist believes could have been developed if all their ancestors had been aquatic. A porpoise may to the untrained eye look like a fish ; but in its bony structure, its nervous system, its method of reproduction, the way in which the young are nourished and so on, it affords clear proof of descent with modification from land forms. For example, before birth, but not after, it displays remnants of that hairy coat so characteristic of land mammals, and so important for these organisms as a means of retaining the body heat whatever the surrounding variations of temperature.

Both in geological time and in space the physical variety of the land environment has been and is very much greater than that of the ocean one. The latter is characterized by at least relative uniformity. The land surfaces have acquired their present size and shape as the result of a long series of changes, which are still going on, and at the present time they differ enormously from place to place. Earth history seems punctuated by successive ' revolutions ', finding expression in the rise of great mountain chains, and followed by periods of relative quiescence till energy is accumulated for a new outburst. It would appear that the enormous changes in the land surfaces, e.g. the rise of mountain chains and the major associated climatic variations, have given a great stimulus to organic variation. Thus we can connect the appearance and development of new and more highly differentiated terrestrial organisms, both plants and animals, with certain definite periods of earth history. For example, the Tertiary period of mountain-building, followed by the Pleistocene Ice Age, was associated with special differentiation in many of the higher groups, both plants and animals, notably the seed plants called angiosperms, and among vertebrate animals, birds and mammals. Such forms show at once a more perfect adaptation to the diversity of conditions prevailing on the land surfaces, and a more complete freedom from the control of the primeval aquatic environment, than the forms which preceded them.

The latter statement may appear obscure, but its meaning can be simply illustrated. Among land plants we find that the ferns and their allies are less completely fitted for terrestrial life than higher plants of more recent origin, in that the fertilization of their germs can take place only in the presence of water. That is true also of some of the living gymnosperms, the order to which the conifers belong, but not of the conifers themselves. When we examine the angiosperms, or true flowering plants like grasses and oak trees, we find further that their sex-cells are so protected as to be perfectly tolerant of the absence of water without loss of vitality. That is, there is evidence of increased adaptation to an environment where moisture may at times be absent, while the whole mechanism of reproduction in ferns shows greater dependence on the presence of at least a film of water. Put in another way we find that sexual reproduction in the higher plants may be accomplished at a height of 100 or more feet from the surface, in the free air which is liable to constant changes in both humidity and in temperature. But in ferns the process can be carried out only on a substratum far less exposed to change, nearer in its physical aspects to the still more constant medium in which their aquatic ancestors lived.

Again, among animals the common frog may be taken as an example of the vertebrate order of amphibians, the order whose members mark, as it were, a definite stage in the adaptation to terrestrial life. Mating in the frog can take place only in water though the adults live on land ; the eggs are laid in water and the young, delicate, unprotected organisms pass the earlier part of their life there. On the other hand, the higher mammals give birth to living young, though the fact that they had aquatic ancestors is indicated by the presence in the unborn young of clefts at the sides of the throat, comparable to those which in

the frog-tadpole bear the gills with which that animal breathes
during its life in water.

Amphibians appear as fossils in much older rocks than do
mammals, just as ferns and gymnosperms appear in earlier ones
than do the seed plants called angiosperms.   Multitudes of such
cases show that in most groups of living things there is a progress
through geological time from earlier forms that are either aquatic
or not yet very far removed from aquatic ancestors to later more
complex forms adapted for life on land.

THE DIVERSITY OF EXISTING ORGANISMS

This concept of the successive appearance in geological time
of more and more specialized forms of life, increasingly adapted
to a complex terrestrial environment, has to be supplemented
before even an outline classification can be made clear.   Even
the simplest outline brings out the enormous diversity of existing
organisms, and this despite the fossil evidence that many kinds
have disappeared.   Of the latter fact the fossil galleries of the
great world museums afford proof enough ; the meaning and
implications of the existing diversity are not so easily grasped.

Certain broad statements can be made about the outstanding
organisms present at different geological epochs, which are at
once picturesque and, within limits, useful.   Thus towards the
close of the Palaeozoic era the most specialized vertebrates
existing were certain large amphibians, known to us only in the
fossil state.   The Mesozoic or Secondary era is often called the
Age of Reptiles, for during it reptiles attained a size and dominance
not paralleled either before or after.   In Tertiary times, again,
mammals, represented earlier only by small and undifferentiated
forms, seem to have attained their climax.   Land plants show a
parallel development, giant fern-allies and gymnosperms being
characteristic of the later part of the Palaeozoic era, while the
angiosperms, though they appeared during the Mesozoic epoch,
did not become dominant and diverse till Tertiary times.

Such general statements are apt to give rise to serious mis-
conceptions.   They seem to suggest, for example, that living
reptiles are but the dwindling remnants of a class which has had
its day, and is doomed to disappear before the dominant and
victorious mammals.   In point of fact, however, we find that
while there are living forms—the New Zealand lizard (*Hatteria*
or *Sphenodon*) is the outstanding example—which do seem to be
the last survivors of orders that have otherwise disappeared, yet
there are orders of reptiles, such as the snakes, which are appar-

ently of quite late origin and, along their own lines, are highly specialized. That is, reptilian evolution did not stop when mammals began to take the centre of the stage. The mere fact that not a few living reptiles are adapted for preying on mammals is proof enough that great changes have occurred within the reptilian class since mammals appeared on the earth. The same sort of thing occurs with many other groups. Thus, while gymnosperms appear as fossils before angiosperms, and numbers of the early gymnosperms have disappeared, yet many living forms of gymnosperms are apparently of quite late origin, and are products of recent evolution.

Such facts mean that we have to add another concept to our original one that the evolutionary process has to be visualized in terms of progressive adaptation to a changing physical environment. That concept must serve as a starting-point ; it is difficult to suppose that evolution could have occurred in an unchanging and perfectly uniform earth. But if of the beginnings of the process we know nothing directly, yet the earliest fossils definitely recognized show that organisms were already diverse and relatively complex. Thus throughout geological time adaptation has had a double aspect, involving response both to varying physical conditions and to other organisms. What we assume to have happened is that as a result of the great physical changes which accompanied the periods of earth disturbance, new surfaces became available for colonization, and certain plastic forms were able to occupy these and varied rapidly, giving rise to entirely new types. But neither the first known fossil records of such new types, nor the subsequent increases in numbers and sizes of their representatives, imply a complete change in the life of the globe. The same stimuli which caused the appearance of the new types also started fresh courses of evolution among some representatives of the original stocks. This latter evolution, however, was of different type in that it took place within the limits of the pre-existing groups, i.e. it was of more limited scope than the first. Finally, it appears to be generally true that in addition to these two processes a large amount of elimination took place ; forms like the large amphibians, the giant reptiles, many large fern-like plants and so on, being apparently too specialized for adequate fresh variation to take place, were unable to compete with the new forms.

The diagram (Fig. 2) is an attempt to represent this thesis graphically, and, though it is necessarily much simplified, only one group of animals and one of plants being shown instead of a multitude, it may yet prove helpful. It is intended also to emphasize the fact that plant and animal evolution are two parallel and interrelated processes, so that any change in the one set of organisms affects the other. Further, it suggests that we must not take the ' struggle for existence ' too literally as implying that extinction is the inevitable fate of older, less differentiated groups when newer, more differentiated ones arise. If it were so, we could not explain the enormous diversity of life, the diversity which, if it greatly complicates the taxonomist's task, yet gives biology its wealth of content.

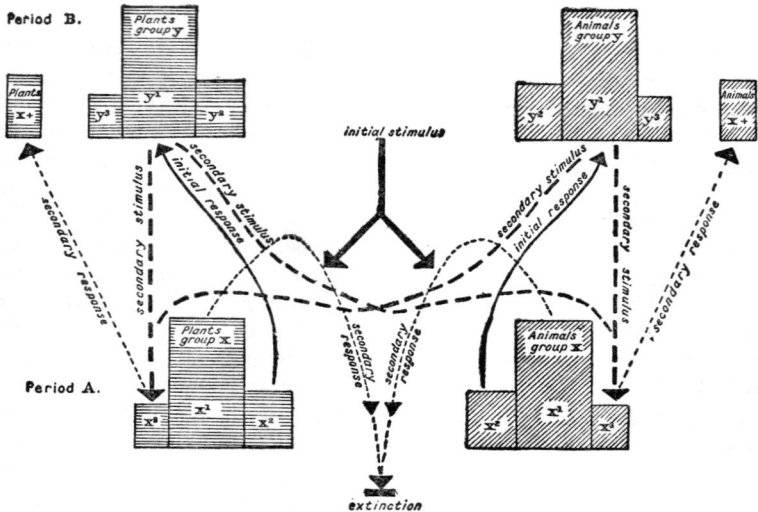

FIG. 2.—Scheme to show effects of interrelated evolution in geological time

During a given epoch (A) some great change in surface conditions is assumed to occur, acting as a primary stimulus upon existing organisms. One group of animals and one of plants is indicated, each being assumed to include three main kinds, X^1 being the large dominant forms, with apparently little power of variation ; X^2 highly plastic, little differentiated forms ; X^3 intermediate types. The first effect of the physical change is to cause rapid evolution in the X^2 groups, which give rise to entirely new groups (Y), so well fitted to the new conditions as to be able to multiply rapidly and vary in many directions. But the appearance of the Y forms, combined with the original stimulus, leads to secondary evolution in the X^3 groups, which give rise to new types (X plus) within the framework of the original group (class, &c.). Thus period B is characterized by a steadily increasing predominance of the new Y groups, but also by the presence of the modified descendants of the X^3 groups. Finally, many of the specialized forms (X^1) of the original groups are unable to persist, both because of their limited power of adapting themselves to the new conditions, and because of the direct competition of the new Y groups. Their disappearance, however, may be slow, so that a certain number may survive into the B period

The rise of new groups has always simultaneously given new opportunity to adapted representatives of the old, in addition to causing extinction of some of the original types. For example, many living kinds of snakes, in addition to preying on birds and mammals, find suitable habitats in forests made of kinds of trees which did not exist during the Mesozoic Age of Reptiles. Thus the appearance of modern birds and mammals, and of the new kinds of plants associated with them, did not mean either the suppression of the whole class of reptiles, or the relegation of a few survivors to isolated and remote areas ; it meant both that an additional variety of habitats and foods were available, and that there appeared new forms capable of taking advantage of them without losing the essential reptilian characteristics. Foresters, dealing with cleared land, habitually use the presence of what they call ' indicator species ', usually grasses and other herbs, which are angiosperms, to decide whether or not the soil is suitable for planting conifers. They assume both that the presence of such angiosperms is evidence that the soil has certain characters, and that, if it is clear that these plants have occupied the ground for a long period, they will have so modified the soil as to leave it suitable for conifers. Many kinds of herbaceous angiosperms accompany the conifers to their limit, both in latitude and in altitude. Thus the appearance on the earth of angiosperms permitted certain plastic gymnosperms to occupy sites previously unavailable. We must not, that is to say, over-estimate the losses which the gymnosperm group underwent as the result of the evolution of the angiosperms. These losses were partly counterbalanced by a gain both of territory and in differentiation.

Though the immediate purpose is to suggest the reason why systems of classification must be complex, and to help to make their basis clear, another point may be mentioned in passing. To the statement already made about the dominant organisms of the different geological epochs it is sometimes added that the present period is that of Man. The corollary is appended that as the result of his want of forethought and of his powerful weapons, he will speedily exterminate most other forms of life save those which are of some use to him or too insignificant to be worthy of attack, and so reduce the wealth of life to relative poverty. There seems no reason to adopt so gloomy a position. We cannot suppose that man as he exists to-day marks the end of the evolutionary process, and the superman who is yet to be may have less of that passion for destruction which is wiping out so many of the larger mammals and the more beautiful birds. But there is more than this. If the developing mammals which, as it would seem, used their superior intelligence and more effective weapons to help to exterminate the giant reptiles of the past, had had sufficient power of reflection they might have triumphed in the thought that all reptiles were doomed to dis-

appear before them.   They would, as we know, have been utterly
wrong, for man, the most specialized of the mammals, still pays
heavy toll to the poisonous snakes ; the new reptiles avenge the
defeat of the old ; the type remains, if in changed form ; what
seem to be purely destructive forces are creative in addition.
So far as past conditions offer a basis for drawing conclusions,
then, the Victorian poet's knowledge of taxonomy was defective
when he said :

> So careful of the type ? but no.
> From scarped cliff and quarried stone
> She cries, ' A thousand types are gone.
> I care for nothing, all shall go ! '

Life to-day, despite the process of elimination, is not poorer but
richer and more varied than in any previous epoch.   To take
account of known extinct forms in our outline taxonomic system
would mean certain additions, but in the main these would be
of minor units within the broad framework shown.

THE CLASSIFICATION OF ANIMALS

This discussion helps to make clear what is meant by saying
that modern systems of classification are based on genetic
principles, and involve the grouping together, in successive
major and minor divisions, of forms more and more nearly
related.   We have seen that within the class of reptiles great
changes have taken place in geological time.   The giant dinosaurs
of the past have disappeared, but there are modern forms like
snakes with but little apparent resemblance to their predecessors,
as well as modern lizards resembling the old types at least in
retaining the two pairs of limbs which the snakes have lost completely.   The curious New Zealand lizard, on the other hand,
already mentioned as the last survivor of an order otherwise
extinct, is nearer modern types of lizards than most of these
are to the snakes, so far as external appearance goes.   This
means that, behind the characters which catch the eye, there are
certain fundamental features which point back to a common
ancestry for all the different kinds of reptiles, but that upon
these are superimposed other characters differentiating orders of
reptiles within the class.   The members of a reptilian order have
a more proximate ancestor as compared with the more remote
one from which all reptiles are conceived to have been derived.
Some at least of the reptilian features are fairly obvious.   All
reptiles have a scaly skin, which distinguishes them from the
smooth-skinned amphibians no less than from the feathered

birds and the hair-covered mammals ; all reptiles lay eggs which hatch into miniature adults (the fossil eggs of dinosaurs have been found with the young within), and when limbs are present the digits bear claws, both distinctions from the amphibians, such as newts and salamanders ; the teeth when present are simple and similar, differing notably from those of most mammals ; the skeletons show a number of very marked differences from those both of birds and mammals, as well as of amphibians.

It is true that in particular cases one or more of these criteria may fail us. Limbs may be turned into paddles, as in the turtles, and then display no external resemblance to the ordinary reptilian limb, but not a little to those of marine mammals. They may be absent or, as in some extinct forms, be turned into ' wings '. Teeth may be absent, as in both turtles and tortoises, or may be modified as in the fangs of poisonous snakes. The scales may be curiously modified, as into ' tortoiseshell '. In other words, both living and extinct forms display a wide range of variation in appearance, in habitat and in modes of life, and generally in their adaptive response to a correspondingly wide range of environmental difference. But behind the variations there is a definite stamp, inherited from the reptilian ancestor, which marks the reptile as distinct from other kinds of vertebrate animals.

We may think of reptiles, or of any other group of animals, as oscillating round a fixed pivot. The oscillations are the variations in type which may occur within the limit of the group. But if they reach a magnitude that renders stability impossible, then what corresponds to a toppling-over occurs, and a new group arises with an equilibrium of its own. It may not be possible for us to trace the relation, e.g. in the case of reptiles, between the different characters ; the external scales, the simple five-toed limbs, each toe with its similar claw, the undifferentiated teeth, the arrangement of the bones, the small, relatively simple brain, the peculiar circulatory and respiratory mechanisms, the method of reproduction and the structure of the reproductive organs ; but there does seem to be a linking element, so that any outstanding change in one set of features involves changes in others. Conversely, however wide the range of variation within a group may seem to be, it has very definite limits ; inherited organs or structures, apparently quite useless in forms adapted to particular habitats may be retained, often in a vestigial state. In the case of the embryonic hairs of the whales and dolphins already mentioned, we can but say that it is an essential feature of the mammal that the skin gives rise to hairs, and, while in the whale order the hair coat has lost its original function and has disappeared in the adults, yet during the course of development the skin conforms to the mammalian type. The original print goes too deep to be erased by adaptive response.

This notion that the members of any group, large or small, do not possess a mere collection of characters, but have some fundamental unity which finds expression in the sum-total of the characters, has an important result. It means that in the minor units, particularly the species, the smallest of all, some apparently quite accidental and trifling feature may be diagnostic. Entomologists, for instance, sometimes define species of insects mainly on such minute points as a spine, a group of hairs, a particular process of an organ, and so on. This is not so fantastic as it seems, for they find not only that the feature is constant ; not only that it is often associated with some small differences in mode of life between closely related species ; but that there is something more. When breeding experiments are carried out they find that forms with the diagnostic feature are perfectly fertile when interbred, which is not necessarily the case when the attempt is made to cross them with nearly related forms in which it is absent.

We are, however, concerned with the major groups recognized, and the features upon which emphasis is laid. Within the animal kingdom the largest unit is the phylum, and all members of a phylum are supposed to have a common, if geologically remote, ancestor. All vertebrates, from fish and fish-like forms to mammals, including man, fall into a single phylum, the outstanding feature being the presence of a backbone or vertebral column ; or of its predecessor the dorsal rod called the notochord, which is always present in the young, whether they are embryos or free-swimming larvae, and in a few primitive forms persists intact throughout life, not being replaced by a vertebral column. The fact that such primitive forms exist, and the features which they display, lead to the assumption that vertebrates arose, at a very early period of earth history, from some simple creature, without either notochord or vertebral column, that is, from an invertebrate ancestor.

Apart from the vertebrates there are a large number of phyla of invertebrates of varied sizes and complexity. But invertebrates are never so complex, nor do they attain the size reached by vertebrates, both living and extinct ; with exceptions also, of which the insects are the most noteworthy, they are more closely tied than are the higher vertebrates to the primitive aquatic habitat. Again we assume that all the animals included in the different phyla, simple or relatively complex, minute or fairly large, like some of the giant cuttlefish, have had a far-back common origin in very early forms of life ; but again it is largely a matter of hypothesis, for the stages can be but dimly traced.

Phyla are divided into classes, classes into orders, orders into families, families into genera, genera into species, and so far as the vertebrate phylum is concerned the major classes are fairly easily distinguished.   Confusion between the scaly reptiles whose eggs laid on land hatch into forms like the parents, and the smooth-skinned amphibians whose eggs hatch into aquatic, gill-bearing larvae, is common in everyday speech ; but this is largely because we have no common word for the amphibia. Probably few people fail to recognize that there is a real distinction between a toad or a salamander on the one hand and a lizard on the other.

It is much more difficult, for those without special training, to distinguish between the phyla and classes of invertebrates, but fortunately comparatively few of the classes are of much importance to the biogeographer.

OUTLINE CLASSIFICATION OF ANIMALS

PHYLUM VERTEBRATA

CLASS MAMMALIA (see also Chap. X)

Sub-class I.   Placentals ; development occurs within the mother's womb with nutrition through an attachment called the placenta.   Young born with the form of the adult and fed at first from mother's mammary glands, usually a definite succession of milk teeth and adult teeth or vestiges of such a succession ; world-wide in distribution and divided into many orders.

Sub-class II.   Marsupials ; young born incompletely developed, only vestiges of tooth succession ; numerous and diverse in the Australian area, elsewhere a few occur only in the Americas.

Sub-class III.   Monotremes or egg-laying mammals, represented by three living forms only, confined to the Australian region.

CLASS AVES OR BIRDS

Those with a keeled breast-bone for the attachment of the muscles of flight are universally distributed, but the Running (i.e. flightless) Birds, with reduced fore-limbs and a flat breast-bone, are now restricted mainly to the Southern Hemisphere.

CLASS REPTILIA

Universally distributed but most abundant and varied in warmer latitudes as sun-heat is required for the hatching of the eggs. Five living orders occur : (1) Crocodiles ; (2) Turtles and Tortoises ; (3) Snakes ; (4) Lizards ; (5) Beaked Lizards including among living forms only the New Zealand lizard.

CLASS AMPHIBIA

Eggs fertilized and laid in water in which early life is passed. Adult form usually attained by metamorphosis. The class includes Frogs, Toads, Newts, Salamanders and Blindworms, and is also practically universally distributed, but in New Zealand there is only one native species—a frog.

CLASS FISHES

Widely distributed in both fresh and salt water and including a number of diverse groups. As with most aquatic animals, those found in fresh water appear to have been derived from marine ancestors.

PHYLA OF INVERTEBRATES

These are numerous, among the most important being the following : Mollusca or shellfish, slugs and cuttlefish, including marine, freshwater and terrestrial forms ; Arthropoda, including as chief classes the Crustacea (crabs, shrimps, barnacles), mainly aquatic, the Insects, mainly terrestrial, the Arachnids, including the terrestrial spiders and scorpions as well as the marine Limulus or King-crab and several extinct groups ; Echinoderms, wholly marine and including starfish, sea-urchins, brittle-stars, and so on ; many kinds of worms, especially the Annelids or Ringed Worms (earthworms and sea-worms) ; Coelentera, mainly marine, including corals, sea anemones, jellyfish, and so forth ; Sponges, some fresh-water but mostly marine ; Protozoa or one-celled animals.

CLASSIFICATION OF PLANTS

A number of interesting points arises when we turn to the vegetable kingdom. There is in the first place a certain measure of correspondence between plants and animal groups. Just as the simplest animals, the Protozoa, consist of single cells carrying on all the physiological functions, and are dependent on the presence of at least a film of water or other fluid, so we have parallel series of simple unicellular plants, green and non-green. In some cases, indeed, differentiation is so slight that the same organisms may be claimed by the zoologists as animals and by the botanists as plants.

Starting from such simple forms there has also been a certain parallelism in the evolutionary process in the two cases. Just as the terrestrial vertebrates are the most specialized animals of the lands, so the highest of the terrestrial plants are the seed-bearers, and the two groups have shown a corresponding development in time, the double process having been responsible for giving the land surfaces, considered as the home of life, their existing features. In plants and animals, as already stated, the major lines of development have been accompanied by secondary and subsidiary ones. Thus, although primitive members of the fern alliance are assumed to have given rise to the seed plants, and many early fern types have disappeared, yet there are many living ferns which are obviously products of more recent evolution.

Plants are much more restricted than animals in the matter of the possible range of differentiation. The green plant needs sunlight and so is excluded from deep water and concealed sites on land, both of which can be occupied by various animals. Soils may harbour protozoa, many kinds of worms and insects and burrowing amphibians and mammals. Green plants, or the green parts of plants are excluded except at the actual surface, and competition among them is largely a struggle for a certain amount of light, with death as the inevitable fate of the conquered. Animals can often evade some of the intensity of the struggle by acquisition of adaptive responses such as concealment.

Moreover, the fact that the environment of the plant is in a sense more limited and more uniform than that of the animal suggests that there is a more limited range of variation among plants. If we presuppose a primitive organism, not yet definitely plant or animal, but possessing the potentiality of evolution in the two directions under the influence of a changing environment, then the results in the case of animal evolution will bring into action more varied stimuli giving a greater range of adaptive response, and as a consequence a more varied occupation of the earth.

It naturally follows that there are fewer great groups of widely different type among plants than among animals, and that the external differences between members of a large plant group are less marked than between members of a large animal group.

In the simplest green plants, the one-celled algae, the whole surface of the cell absorbs water with salts in solution, and also, thanks to its green substance, builds up new organic substance from absorbed carbon dioxide by means of energy derived from the sun's rays. This latter process is called photosynthesis. Some forms, such as the widespread diatoms, float freely in water, fresh or salt ; others may find a film of moisture sufficient for their purpose on a variety of exposed surfaces, such as rocks and stones, trunks of trees and the uppermost layer of the soil. More conspicuous are the long filaments, or strands, or fern-like masses, or encrustations, which form the larger marine and fresh-water algae. In the ocean these larger forms (seaweeds) are mainly fixed to a substratum, as is well illustrated by the common bladder wrack (*Fucus*) or the oarweed (*Laminaria*). But the organs of fixation do not obtain anything from the substratum ; they are merely a means of ensuring that the plant is retained under the particular conditions to which it is fitted. The thallus, or little-differentiated plant body, consists of cells of broadly similar nature, with scarcely any division of function among them, and the whole must be bathed with water which is sufficiently shallow to allow the necessary light to penetrate, and also contains the salts required.   Surfaces at once sufficiently firm to support a thallus of any size, and not liable to excessive erosion or deposition as a result of the movements which occur in shallow water, are somewhat infrequent.   Thus the area which can be occupied by the larger seaweeds is strictly limited.   Further, the necessary salts are ultimately derived from the lands, and tend to sink downwards in seawater below the limit at which green

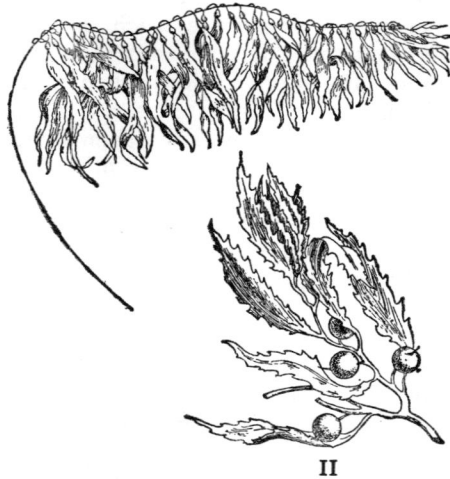

II

FIG. 3.—I. Sea-wrack (*Macrocystis pyrifera*).   II. Gulf-weed (*Sargassum bacciferum*)
After F. Höck

plants can live.   Even floating unicellular marine algae, therefore, tend to diminish in numbers in certain areas and during certain periods of the year.   Thus the parts of the ocean which can be occupied by plants are limited vertically by the need for sunlight, and to some extent at least horizontally by the demand for mineral salts.   Since also the two processes of photosynthesis and salt absorption in algae are carried on by the same cell, or by virtually all the cells near the surface of the multicellular thallus, the possible range of structural differentiation is small.   It is not difficult, then, to understand why the multitude of animal phyla represented in the ocean has little parallel among plants.   The green plants of the ocean indeed may be said to consist of algae, fixed or free, plus, in shallow water, a comparatively small number of higher forms which have made the return journey from the land to the sea.

Apart from the minute unicellular algae which lodge on damp surfaces, and the algae, large and small, of fresh-water bodies, green land plants must obtain from the substratum to which they are attached water and the mineral elements of their food. These mineral elements are absorbed in a weak solution by cells specialized for the purpose, as in mosses and their allies, or by the organs we call roots, which are of more complicated structure but bear absorbing cells called root-hairs. Increasing adaptation to the terrestrial habitat, as already explained, shows itself particularly in the fact that in the higher forms the process of fertilization, or union of the sex cells, can be accomplished independent of the presence of water. In all algae, in mosses, in ferns and in the lowest of the gymnosperms, at least a film of water is essential for the process. All plants higher on the tree of life than algae, however, show at least this degree of differentiation that the cells or organs which penetrate the substratum and absorb from it dissolved salts have different functions and characters from those cells which carry on the function of photosynthesis.

Now the fact that the truly terrestrial plant, during its period of vegetative growth, must possess at least two sets of organs each with well-marked characteristics, sets a definite limit to possible variation in external form. The roots must react negatively to light and positively to gravity and moisture, for their function is to grow downwards into the substratum and there to absorb water containing salts across the thin cell-walls of the root-hairs. The green organs must react negatively to gravity and positively to light, for their special functions can be discharged only with free exposure to sun and air. Some land plants, such as the liverworts in the moss alliance and the prothallus or sexual mechanism of the fern, appear to differ little from some seaweeds, for the green parts resemble the algal thallus. Even here, however, we have the essential difference that the simple root-like structures (rhizoids) are absorbing organs and not purely a means of fixation. Except in these few cases, land plants tend always to have a definite and characteristic make-up, the absorbing roots being usually linked to the flattened leaves or leaf-like organs of photosynthesis by some form of stem, which serves as a transmitting organ or link between the two.

One consequence is that while the appearance of an animal, at least in the general sense, gives us usually some hint of its systematic position, plants offer far more difficulty because of their greater uniformity. A moss may recall a fern and some members of the fern alliance are habitually called ' mosses '. Tree-ferns recall cycads, which are survivors of ancient gymnosperms, and cycads are constantly confused with palms, which are angiosperms. The real distinctions between the different kinds of plants lie only in part, sometimes only in minor part, in their vegetative organs ; taxonomic position is actually fixed mainly by their methods of reproduction, and by the details of the process and its results. The higher forms as compared with the lower tend to show greater rapidity and certainty of reproduc-

FIG. 4.—Cycad (*Cycas revoluta*)

tion and a fuller measure of protection for the germs from variations in the environmental conditions. The green land plant is bound to the ground by its need for dissolved products of rock decomposition and to the sunlight by its need for solar energy. The nature of the double bond limits the possible variations in the life-forms. Differentiation finds its chief expression in the more or less complete liberation of the fertilized egg-cell from these bonds, and reaches its maximum in the angiosperm. There the well-protected seed within its coverings encloses a miniature plant, supplied with sufficient reserves to enable it to make a start, but capable of tolerating a very wide range of environmental variations in the resting state, and requiring to absorb neither sunlight nor water with mineral salts to maintain its vitality.

This brief survey of plant physiology helps to make clearer the reason why plants, much more than animals, reflect the varying conditions which prevail over land surfaces, and thus affords a key to the interpretation of these. Tree-like forms occur in many families of plants widely separated by descent, and the same fact is noteworthy also among herbaceous plants. One may even find analogies of form and mode of growth in trees or herbs of very diverse families in response to special environmental conditions. The study of plant-forms in this ecological sense, that is, in relation to edaphic (ground) and climatic conditions, differs therefore very considerably from the study of plant taxonomy, the analysis of relationships of species, genera and families.

The response of animals to environmental conditions varies more according to the innate characters, and the genetic relationships of the animal. A chameleon and a monkey may be found on the same tree in a tropical forest, but though both have grasping digits there are vast differences between the two. The fact that one is a reptile and the other a mammal affects the matter very deeply.

The statement that all animals in the long run are dependent on green plants may seem incompatible with the fact that plants have a more limited range than animals. On the lands the upward vertical limit of plants and animals is approximately the same. But whether we consider the concealed animal habitats on land or the deeper levels of ocean water we have to remember that, while living green plants are excluded, gravity, often with moving water as agent, carries their dead bodies or parts, or those of animals which consumed them, downwards to form the basal food supply. The food-chain is lengthened but not broken, and the mud-eating animal on the sea-floor, or the cave fish or insect, is as completely dependent on the green plant's power of building up organic substance from its elements with the help of sunlight as is a caterpillar on a cabbage. In life the range of green plants is strictly limited ; none the less it is upon them that all other living forms depend.

CHIEF KINDS OF PLANTS

PHYLUM 1

THALLOPHYTA.   *Algae and Fungi*

Plants not showing differentiation into root, stem and leaves ; varied but always simple methods of reproduction. In theory they can be divided into the green algae and the non-green fungi, but the distinction is not always so sharp as it seems. Thus the blue-green algae, reproducing by the splitting of the cell-body (fission), show many analogies

3

with the non-green bacteria, the agents which effect organic decay, and are the causes of many diseases in other organisms. Again, the lichens, often very conspicuous, consist of fungi living in partnership (symbiosis) with small algae.

Fungi are of many kinds and either depend on decaying organic substances or are parasites. There are, however, various forms of partnership with other organisms, apart from lichens. Thus various higher plants, especially moorland trees and shrubs, have fungoid threads (mycorrhiza) on their roots which seem to aid in the absorption of mineral food.

The larger algae of the ocean fall into three groups, successively more and more tolerant of less intense light, these being the green, brown and red algae. Unicellular forms, in addition to the diatoms, include the Peridinians, with brownish-green colouring matter, often regarded as Protozoa, i.e. as belonging to the animal series.

PHYLUM II
BRYOPHYTA. *Mosses and Liverworts*

Plants showing the beginnings of differentiation into root, stem and leaves, but without true roots. Methods of reproduction are complex, but capsules containing a multitude of minute spores are characteristic. There are no vascular bundles in the simple stems. Some are aquatic and a damp habitat is essential to all. Mosses form a more conspicuous element in the vegetation in northern latitudes (moors, the tundra, &c.) than in warmer areas.

PHYLUM III
PTERIDOPHYTA. *Ferns, Horsetails, Club-mosses*

In these plants roots, stem and leaves are present, as in all higher forms, and definite vascular bundles, that is, strands of conducting and strengthening tissue, occur. Regeneration is by spores which give rise to a prothallus on which the sex-cells are formed.

These three phyla are often grouped as *Cryptogams*, because the sexual process, when it occurs, is concealed, the light and minute unicellular spores formed in another phase of the life-cycle furnishing the most obvious method of multiplication. As contrasted with them the *Phanerogams*, the higher forms, bear ovules which after fertilization become complex seeds and include an embryo plant.

PHYLUM IV
GYMNOSPERMS. *Cone-bearing Plants*

Here the ovules are ' naked ', that is, not enclosed within an ovary ; the leaves are usually needle-like or scale-shaped ; the plants are always trees or shrubs, never herbs, and mostly evergreen. Four classes are included :

    (*a*) Cycads.
    (*b*) Gingkoales.
    (*c*) Conifers.
    (*d*) Gnetales.

(*a*) Cycads include only some nine living genera, confined to tropical and sub-tropical latitudes, and rather more common in southern than in northern inter-tropical areas. They were once much more numerous than at present and show certain definite affinities with ferns ; thus we are led to conclude that they constitute the scanty persistent remnants of an ancient stock.

(*b*) A special class has been erected to include the Maidenhair tree (Gingko) formerly regarded as a conifer, but displaying certain fern-like features in its reproductive process. It is the only living representative of the class to which it belongs, and is geologically old. Probably originally native to western China, it appears now to be known only in cultivation.

(*c*) Conifers, like Cycads, were once more numerous than at present, but they form a far more specialized and larger group, with over 40 genera and a much larger number of species. They are most abundant in the cooler parts of the globe and can there compete successfully with angiosperms ; they may form almost pure forests in which certain species are represented by vast numbers of individuals. There is a marked contrast between the genera of northern and those of southern latitudes, the latter appearing to be more primitive.

FIG. 5.—Maidenhair Tree (*Gingko biloba*)
After Warming

(*d*) Gnetales include only three living genera and are warm-temperate or tropical. The living forms are highly specialized and the ovules show what looks like the beginning of a covering, recalling the ovary of Angiosperms. It is believed, however, that the latter more probably arose from cycad-like forms.

The Gymnosperms have a twofold interest. The conifers, because of their social habit, their quick growth and soft, easily-worked timber, are of considerable economic importance, while the fact that nearly pure coniferous forests occur only under certain conditions of climate and soil makes these forests a valuable index of the habitat factors. The other hree classes are far less numerously represented, whether as species or as individuals, and have little economic importance. Since, as compared with the conifers, their distribution is limited and often highly localized, they have no great significance as a means of characterizing particular types of habitat. On the other hand, their distribution, both past and present, like that of many of the conifers, is of great value in any discussion of the physical history of the land surfaces. Thus the

Maidenhair tree, like the coniferous genus Sequoia (now limited to California), was widespread before the onset of the Ice Age, and in both cases the reduction in range can be regarded as a result of changes during that difficult period.

PHYLUM V

ANGIOSPERMS

These are the true flowering plants and have the ovules enclosed in an ovary. There are two classes, each with a large number of orders :
  (a) Monocotyledons.
  (b) Dicotyledons.
Monocotyledons have one seed-leaf, parallel-veined leaves, and the parts of the flowers usually in threes. They are predominantly herbs save that the palms and some trees and shrubs of the large lily-family occur almost exclusively in the warmer latitudes. The grasses, with 4,000 species, are almost all herbs, though the larger bamboos, again in warm latitudes, may grow very high and have woody stems.

Dicotyledons have two seed-leaves, net-veined leaves, and the parts of the flower typically arranged in fours or fives. Herbs, shrubs and trees occur within the limits of a single order, the Leguminosae or Pea order, hardly less important than the grasses, affording one familiar example, and the Rose order another. But Dicotyledonous trees can tolerate a greater range of climate than Monocotyledonous ones, and some arborescent orders such as that of the Fagaceae, to which oak, beech and chestnut belong, have a wide distribution in latitude. It is characteristic that the forest trees of cool latitudes include only Dicotyledons and Conifers.

The largest Dicotyledonous order, that of the Compositae or Daisy family, which includes some 900 genera with over 13,000 species, and is regarded as the most specialized order of plants, has a very small proportion of trees and shrubs. Further, arborescent types within the order are particularly marked in the Australian region, the Daisy Bushes (Olearia) of gardens, mostly introduced from New Zealand, being examples. Since the herbaceous habit is believed to be of recent origin, this is another illustration of the tendency for ' old fashioned ' forms to occur in the southern hemisphere.

NOTE

J. C. Willis, *A Dictionary of the Flowering Plants and Ferns* (Cambridge Biological Series) is invaluable for reference. The 4th edition in one volume is remarkably complete so far as living genera are concerned, but omits some general material found in the earlier editions in two small volumes. In studying the classification of the major animal groups, the value of museum visits should not be overlooked, and the *Guides* to the different groups issued by the British Museum (Natural History) are useful. Of the numerous Natural Histories that edited by R. Lydekker as the *Royal Natural History* (London, 1893–6) may be mentioned. The ten (much more costly) volumes of the *Cambridge Natural History* vary greatly in scope, but Vol. IX, *Birds*, by A. H. Evans (1899), and Vol. VIII, *Amphibia and Reptiles*, by Gadow (1901), may be specially noted.

The topics dealt with in this chapter form part of plant ecology.

See especially *Types of British Vegetation*, by A. G. Tansley (Cambridge, 1911), *The British Islands and their Vegetation*, by A. G. Tansley (Cambridge, 1939), *Aims and Methods in the Study of Vegetation*, edited by A. G. Tansley and T. F. Chipp (London, 1926), and *Practical Plant Ecology*, by A. G. Tansley (London, 1923), both with copious references ; also W. Leach, *Plant Ecology* (London, 1933).

CHAPTER III

PLANT RESPONSE TO ENVIRONMENT

MANY parts of the surface of the land are clothed with forest of different types ; in others trees are absent and the natural vegetation is of the herbaceous kind. In some regions, again, the plants are closely packed together, leaving no bare surface visible ; in others they are widely spaced with intervening barren areas. Can such contrasts be linked up with those differences in relief, in the nature of the underlying rocks and surface deposits, in climate and so forth which it is the business of the physical geographer to study ? So far we have assumed that the answer is in the affirmative ; it remains to be shown that the problem of the actual relation is exceedingly complex.

If we compare a heather moor with a coniferous forest the outstanding feature is the presence in the former of a multitude of dwarfed, shrubby plants, and in the latter of tall trees. A deciduous or hardwood forest would equally show tall trees, but the nature of the leaves, the method of branching and so on makes it easy to distinguish between the two. If, then, it is true that the characteristics of the communities are in some way a response to environmental differences we see that this response finds its most obvious expression in the morphology or form of the most conspicuous plants. The last qualification is important. A deciduous forest may include some conifers ; the transition between heather moor and coniferous forest is often quite gradual, so that, as the trees diminish in size and numbers, more space is available for the multiplication of the low shrubs, which may be relatively abundant even within the forest proper. As regards even the broadest distinctions between types of plant communities the most that can be said is, therefore, that conditions may favour one type without excluding others. Thus it is generally true that certain climatic conditions favour those communities of herbaceous plants which we call the grassland cover, and others some type of woodland cover. But herbaceous plants can thrive perfectly in areas which carry natural forest, and their absence, or small numbers, or appearance only at certain seasons in such areas is due not to the physical conditions but to the fact that the trees when in full foliage may kill them by over-shading or in other ways prevent them from thriving. That is, the plant response is complicated by the element of competition and the adjustments produced during the struggle for existence.

The next point to notice is the significance to the plant of the morphological differences expressed broadly in the contrast between tree, shrub and herb, and more precisely in the minor differences between kinds of woody and herbaceous plants. A tree requires a more continuous supply of soil moisture than does a herbaceous plant, so any study of dominant forms of a plant community demands some general knowledge of plant physiology, and also of the effects on plants of external conditions. It seems easy to say that for their vital processes green plants demand a certain intensity of light, heat and moisture, and that therefore in most climates there is a spring awakening stimulated by all these factors in combination. Actual examination of plants at once raises a doubt whether matters can be so simple. The same factors which stimulate deciduous trees to clothe themselves in new leaves and begin active growth may simultaneously cause certain herbaceous plants to die down. The increasing sunshine and warm spring rains which awaken oak and beech cause the snowdrop to fall back into quiescence. Similarly, particularly in the Mediterranean Lands, those seasonal changes which lead many shrubs and trees into the resting stage awaken other herbs to a period of activity. The chemist is convinced that if two substances are brought together under definable conditions a particular reaction is inevitable. The plant physiologist can only say that there is a general tendency for certain conditions to produce particular responses ; he cannot assume that the response will inevitably occur.

It may be expressed in the plants' morphological features, and these in their turn owe their significance to their connexion with function. The response, however, is not simple and direct, but is a result of adaptation, and competition, both between kinds of plants and between kinds of communities, plays a large part. A particular type of community may be excluded from an area not because the conditions are necessarily unsuitable, but because it is unable there to compete with another type. Two kinds of plants may grow under what seem to be to the geographer identical conditions, and yet show a marked difference of response.

Such facts mean two things. We are justified in saying that, broadly speaking, the distribution of the great types of communities over the surface represents a response to the sum-total of the conditions existing in the different parts, so that different combinations of factors find their organic response in the presence of forest or grassland or of a desert community. But the response is organic, is the result of a continuously acting process of adaptation, and is not analogous to physical and chemical reactions.

THE HABITAT FACTORS

The ecologist calls the influences exerted by the environment habitat factors, and the most obvious of these are due to climate and soil. The meaning he assigns to the word habitat must be made clear. In general use it signifies the place or kind of place in which a plant or a community lives, so that we speak of aquatic, marsh or dry habitats, and so on. More precisely it means the sum-total of the effective conditions to which organisms are exposed within their dwelling-places. In theory, if not always in practice, the various controls can be regarded as exerting quasi-independent influences, forming the habitat factors distinguished as climatic, edaphic (p. 33) and so on.

Climatic factors, of course, vary in character both from place to place and from season to season within the same place, and have the most direct influence in determining the distribution of the great plant communities. Broadly speaking, indeed, the major communities recognized are the organic response to those periodical changes in the duration and intensity of sunlight, temperature and rainfall conditions, which are themselves determined by the movements of the earth and modified by the distribution of land and water and the relief of the land surfaces.

It might seem, in view of the fact that the majority of land plants are rooted in a substratum derived from the alteration of pre-existing rocks and minerals, that the distribution of the major types of rocks over the surface would exert as great an influence as climate. In other words, we might suppose that edaphic factors are as important as climatic ones. Such a supposition is negatived by the broader facts of distribution. We can be sure that the great change from, e.g., woodland to grassland is associated with some difference in climate between the two areas. It is not necessarily true that there is simultaneously a change in the geological characters and composition of the underlying rocks or even in the characters of the surface deposits. Such a change may occur, and in an area which is climatically transitional may determine which community prevails. An example familiar to most geographical students occurs in the state of Texas, where an outcrop of limestone covered by close-textured clay determines the appearance of the ' Black Waxy ' prairie or grassland, while adjacent areas, where the soil is of a sandy nature, are timbered. On the other hand, the general limits between grassland, and forest in the interior plains of North America are a result of climatic factors and not of any notable differences either in the nature of the underlying rocks or of the surface deposits.

Moreover, those variations in the character of the soil from place to place which affect plants most, are largely independent of the rocks from which its mineral elements were derived, and on the other hand are greatly influenced by climate. Soil, indeed, in the sense of the part of the substratum occupied by plant roots, is something much more complex than a collection of mineral particles or products of mineral decomposition. Its characters are influenced by the way in which it was formed, whether *in situ* or as a result of transport from a distance ; by the length of time during which the formative processes have acted ; by the climate conditions influencing those formative processes ; by the existing vegetation and so on. Any plant or any community at any part of the earth's surface must show a certain direct adjustment to the climatic factors ; their control cannot be evaded by even the humblest member of the community. Part of this control is exerted through the soil ; for soil temperatures, the moisture content, the reaction of the soil water, even the relative proportion of fine and coarse particles in the upper layers, are all affected by climatic factors. Further, the features of the soil are notably influenced by the activities of the various soil organisms, and the presence of the different kinds of these and their relative numbers is itself an indirect climatic response. The recognition of the major types of soil and the study of their distribution are by no means unimportant to the biogeographer, but climatic factors are more important because they influence both the organisms and the physical processes upon which soil formation depends.

One result has some interest. The ecologists lay great stress upon edaphic factors largely because their field work as a rule includes the study and mapping of minor communities found within areas sufficiently small to exclude any great variation in climatic factors. Thus, what the geographer would sum up as a ' grassland ' would by the ecologist be regarded as consisting of perhaps a large number of small communities. In such cases some edaphic factor, as for example the question whether the

soil water is acid, neutral or alkaline, may be the determining
cause of the detailed distribution. Emphasizing minor edaphic
factors some ecologists are apt to take comparatively little interest
in the distribution of the great soil types, the investigation of
which has been mainly carried on by other specialists, often
showing an agricultural bias. Much of this material has not as
yet found its way either into ecological or geographical text-
books ; the subject must be treated in some detail here. The
main facts in regard to climate, on the other hand, may be assumed
to be known to the geographer ; plant response will be the subject
chosen for emphasis.

Before passing on to this topic we have to note that in addition
to the climatic and edaphic factors the ecologist recognizes two
other kinds. With one of these, the biotic (p. 7), we are not
at the moment concerned, as we are dealing here with the plant
response to physical conditions. The other is constituted by
what are called physiographic factors, which include the effect
on plant communities of position in relation to local topography.
It is clear that these factors exert their effect by producing local
modification in climatic and edaphic conditions. Thus in east
to west valleys in mountain regions there is a considerable difference in temperature conditions between the sunny and the
shaded side owing to the contrasted aspect. As a result of
increased evaporation the slope facing the sun will tend to be
drier as well as warmer than the other, and, if the total rainfall
of the area is moderate, the natural vegetation cover may be
denser and even forest-like on the shaded side, whereas the other
may suffer from seasonal or general aridity. A dense cover of
vegetation has a marked effect in checking erosion and stabilizing
stream flow, this being especially true of forest because of the
large roots and the heavy canopy. If forest on the dry and
sunny side is maintaining itself with difficulty, then a comparatively minor cause, such as a great hurricane, a fire due to natural
agents or human action, or ill-regulated cutting, may have far-
reaching effects. The destruction of the trees will increase
erosion and cause ravining, landslips may occur, burying the
surface deposits below and exposing new rock surfaces above to
accelerated weathering. Thus the edaphic conditions may change
so completely that natural regeneration of forest is impossible,
and the effects of erosion become cumulative. The resultant
vegetation contrasts may thus be due less to strictly physiographic
factors than to climatic and edaphic influences. Even where the
run of the valley is such that no notable contrasts in temperature
or moisture conditions occur between the two sides, rock structure

may be such as to produce great differences in degree of slope, and this will influence the edaphic conditions on the two sides, both through water action and owing to the differing effects of gravity.

In studying large-scale maps also the geographer is always striving to correlate the multiplicity of distributions shown. Topographical maps, for instance, in the general case indicate the distribution of woodland in relation to contours, that is, to relief, and it is as much a part of the geographer's task to find some explanation of this distribution as to relate the number and size of the glaciers on either side of a lofty mountain chain to the prevailing climatic conditions in each case, and so on. Generally, it is constantly being driven home to him that broad statements about climatic conditions or the nature of the surface deposits within an area have to be accepted with caution, for there may be great local variation in detail.

PLANTS AND THE CLIMATIC FACTORS

The geographer has often been primarily interested in crop-plants. Now, many crop-plants are literally ' man-made ' in that they are the result of crossing and artificial selection and would be unable to maintain themselves in the areas where they flourish best were it not for man's aid. That aid is given both in the form of protection from competition in the fullest possible sense, and in ensuring special conditions. Those conditions, it may be said, are rather a matter of edaphic than of climatic factors. But we have already seen how close is the connexion between the two. Many of the farmer's operations also, such as draining, ploughing, surface cultivation and so on, modify the moisture content of the soil and thus are in effect equivalent to modifying rainfall. Irrigation again implies the possibility of rendering the plants independent of rainfall. Further, if means of directly increasing temperature have little importance in farming practice as against the small-scale production of luxury crops, yet the farmer has a number of possible methods of minimizing exposure to dangerously low temperatures which again affect the incidence of climatic factors.

There is another point which is apt to be overlooked. We have reason to believe that wild seed-bearing plants can continue to exist only where the climate permits them—it may be only at considerable intervals of time—to run through the whole life-history from seed to seed again. Flowering and seed-setting are responses to particular meteorological stimuli, and the adjustment

may be very precise. As with the parallel process of reproduction in animals, what appear to be quite minor changes in natural
conditions, whether local or due to transference to a new habitat,
may throw the mechanism out of gear so that sterility results.
The most usual stimulus to seed formation is a decrease in available moisture without notable change in temperature. The
exhausting nature of the process and the reserves necessary to
carry it through mean as a rule that its onset occurs at the close
of a period of active vegetative growth, while the same causes
normally lead to its being followed by a definite pause. Therefore
one of the major responses of wild plants to climate is an accurate
timing of the sequence of events in their life-history with the
average meteorological sequence within the habitat. This organic
rhythm is so disturbed in the case of many cultivated plants
that its enormous significance in the case of wild plants is difficult
to realize. Note that not a few cultivated plants are habitually
multiplied without seed formation, i.e. by a vegetative process—
bananas, sugar-cane, potatoes, sisal are a few conspicuous
examples. In not a few cases again the economic product
obtained does not necessitate the completion of the life-history,
as witness tobacco, rubber, root-crops, &c. Even where, as
with cereals, it is the seeds which are utilized, it is not essential
that next year's crop should depend on locally produced seed ;
most farmers indeed appreciate the need for at least an occasional
' change of seed '.

Finally, and perhaps not least important, we have to note that
the inevitable emphasis on economic plants means that the conception of the plant community is largely alien to the geographer.
Crop plants are for the most part grown in cultures as nearly
pure as farming methods permit. The idea that there is in
nature an inter-communal struggle and adjustment, involving a
differing response to the same meteorological sequence on the
part of the various members, is not easily realized. That an
explanation of the differing response must be sought is an even
more subtle point apt to escape notice.

Let us turn next to the geographer's aims and methods in
studying climate. His primary aim is to grasp the physical
causes which determine the variation in the climate elements
from place to place and from season to season within the same
place. This enables him to draw up such a regional classification
of climatic types as will serve his particular purpose. That
purpose again is mainly to relate the distribution of the various
types to other distributions, particularly those of forms of human
activity, including agriculture in the widest sense. As his criteria

in distinguishing between the different types of climate he lays special stress upon the mean annual range of temperature, obtained by taking the difference between the means of the hottest and coldest months, and on mean total rainfall and mean monthly or at least mean seasonal rainfall.   It is unusual to find much emphasis laid upon the lengths of the longest and shortest days in a special treatment of climate, the essential points being supposed to be known from the discussion elsewhere of the principles of mathematical geography.   Actual average hours of sunshine are however sometimes noted, particularly in contrasting areas showing, respectively, much and little cloudiness without outstanding differences in total rainfall.

To such figures it is becoming more and more the custom, particularly in the case of the crop-lands of North America, to add some further details on the factors determining the distribution of outstanding economic plants.   Thus the average length in days of the period free from frost or from ' killing frost ' is often noted, as well as such points as the contrasts between day and night temperatures and the reliability or otherwise of rainfall during certain critical periods.   The general value of such material is, however, reduced by its limited application.   A ' killing ' frost has no meaning except in terms of the particular plant, or plants, unable to survive it.   In point of fact its meaning is often even more restricted, for it may signify only that the plant referred to, if subjected to a particular temperature at a certain stage of growth, will not continue its development to the point at which it yields the product required.   The fact may be of enormous importance to the farmer concerned ; its significance to the student of plant geography may be negative unless he can prove that the limit named, when plotted on a vegetation map, corresponds to some change in the character of the natural communities.   If the plant has been introduced from another area, or if, though of native origin, it has been greatly altered in cultivation, the probability of such a correspondence is small.

The emphasis on mean figures is due to the convenience of this method of summarizing the enormous mass of available data. It is probable that even for the geographer's purpose their value has been overestimated.   The frequency and amount of considerable deviations from the mean are additional factors of great importance for the plant geographer.

Temperature, for example, may be looked at from two standpoints.   On the one hand, we have the question of tolerance of exceptionally low temperatures without serious and permanent damage.   The amount of tolerance varies enormously both from plant to plant and from stage to stage in the case of a particular plant, and for our purpose actual figures have little value.   What is important, however, is to realize that at all stages wild plants must be adapted not only to average meteorological conditions but to the probable oscillations round the means at each period. This has an important bearing on the physiognomy of a natural plant community.   It is, indeed, one part of the reason why we can recognize physiognomy as an element in the characterization of a natural community.   Artificial groupings of plants such as occur in parks and gardens do not display this general similarity of appearance, just because the plants included have been derived from a variety of sources.

Again, the delicate adjustment of certain functions to particular temperatures or ranges of temperature may give the occasional occurrence of unusually high temperatures much greater significance than their numerical effect on long-period means would suggest.   This is especially true of seed maturation.   We are a little apt to think of seed-setting as necessarily an annual process. In a balanced community, however, where space available for new colonists is normally very limited, it may be said to have two purposes, that of replacing natural wastage, and of allowing for the possibility of spread to a new area.   Natural wastage in many areas is slow, the plants being either long lived as individuals or having considerable power of vegetative spread, and seed-setting may be a long-period phenomenon, occurring at irregular intervals.   In that case it may be a response to those exceptional temperature conditions which are obscured by smoothed-out means.   In such cases it may be said that it is not the mean but the occasional high temperatures which are the really important matter in reproduction.

There are other ways also in which the ordinary treatment of climate is insufficient for the needs of the plant geographer. As a rule, for example, little emphasis is laid on the amount of the precipitation which falls as snow.   When figures are given, also, they indicate, necessarily, averages obtained from a few stations.   To the ecologist, however, not only is the general question of great importance, but he finds that, especially within upland areas, snow accumulation or snow dispersal due to shelter or exposure may notably affect details of distribution.   This again makes clear the reason why he is forced to recognize special physiographic factors, for the climatological data of easy access are insufficient.

Mean figures again not only obscure the variations which occur from year to year and from season to season, but their apparent precision is apt to give rise to wrong ideas. In itself rainfall has only a limited importance to plants ; what matters most is the amount of moisture obtainable from the soil. That depends not only on the average total rainfall ; not only on the relation between rainfall and temperature, which affects both evaporation from the ground and the plant's loss of water, as well as its power of absorbing water ; but on a number of other factors in addition. For example, the degree of penetration into the soil is important. This is influenced on the physical side by the nature of the soil, and from the organic standpoint by the level occupied by the roots of the plants. Frequent light showers may stimulate shallow-rooted plants to activity by bringing water within reach of their roots, but fail to have much effect on deeper-rooted ones because much of the water does not reach the stratum occupied. Thus a particular mean seasonal or monthly rainfall figure may imply extreme ' aridity ' for one set of plants and adequate moisture for others. Generally, both the effective, as compared with the apparent climatic condition as shown by mean figures, and the adaptive response of plants to these are highly complex and relatively unfamiliar.

PLANT COMMUNITIES AND THE PHYSIOLOGICAL RESPONSE TO CLIMATIC FACTORS

So far the discussion has had as its aim the bringing out of two sets of facts. The one is that the geographer's conception of climate has definite limitations. The other is that his notions of plant response, if derived particularly from a survey of the world distribution of crop-plants, lose much of their validity when naturally growing plant communities have to be considered.

The geographer finds that over by far the larger part of the earth's surface either temperature or rainfall falls seasonally below the needs of cultivated plants, either in the sense that they cannot then be grown at all, or when, as in the case of woody plants, they occupy the ground permanently, at least they fail to yield the product desired. Thus he is apt to conclude that the most obvious climatic effect is to produce a kind of stop-and-go mechanism, periods of activity alternating with quiescence.

His world survey may lead him to the further conclusion that so far as crop production is concerned the most suitable conditions are a high concentration of favourable factors during one period, associated with a very definite check at another. It is at least true that the lands within which such types of climate prevail are responsible for the major part of the world's yield, even if the effective causes are recognized as complex.

Again, the fact that the cereals are the most important crop-plants and are ' annuals ', running through their whole life-history within a period which may be much shorter than that required for the earth to make a complete revolution, leads to much emphasis being laid on the sequence of events during the period of growth and the apparent climatic control of this sequence. In other words, the geographer is aware that plant activity normally includes three processes, usually conditioned by rather different factors. The start, whether represented by germination or the simpler unfolding of resting buds, requires in the most general case as stimulus an increase in the intensity of light and in the temperature both of air and soil and/or an increased supply of moisture. Subsequent vegetative growth can tolerate much variation of conditions so long as a certain limit is not passed. Some new stimulus, especially, as already noted, a decrease in the water supply involving something in the nature of a drying-out, or ripening, process in the vegetative organs tends to stimulate flowering and seed formation. The three processes are, of course, not necessarily concentrated within one season of activity, nor is the response to the major climatic factors regarded as always simple and direct, since even within the same area harvesting is not simultaneous with all kinds of crops.

Again, the geographer tends to group the major types of climate to correspond with this general conception of plant response. Thus within the somewhat limited area where the typical equatorial climate prevails he relates the absence of marked seasonal variation in light intensity, temperature, and rainfall, to the absence of periodicity in plant function. There is no definite resting period, growth and reproduction are virtually continuous, so that the cereals are largely excluded. As the equator is quitted rainfall becomes more and more concentrated within the warmer season though temperatures remain high throughout. Thus with many plants a resting period tends to occur, becoming longer and longer as total rainfall diminishes and its concentration in time is more marked. The coincidence of the rainy season with that when high temperatures prevail gives rise to the assumption that this tropical belt is one of high productivity, an assumption not always borne out by the facts. At the same time the drought check favours the ripening and harvesting of some cereals.

As latitude increases we pass into the so-called temperate belt where the total rainfall and its seasonal distribution vary greatly from place to place, giving rise to a number of climatic types. The essential point, however, is the marked functional periodicity associated especially with the low winter temperatures, though there may be a drought check at some other season. Finally, with a further increase in latitude the unfavourable season is so prolonged that all or practically all cultivated crops are excluded by the shortness and uncertainty of the growing season.

The matter has only to be put thus for it to become clear that the geographer's preoccupation with certain types of plants, considered as individuals and not as members of a complex community, leads to over-simplification. What actually occurs is much more complex. Thus if a temperature or drought check were in itself the sole and sufficient cause for the passage of plants into the resting stage, this stage should be more marked the more severe is the check. Obviously that is not the case. In temperate latitudes the resting stage is more marked with deciduous (hardwood or broad-leaved) trees than with conifers ; yet the latter tend to occur in areas with lower winter temperatures. Arctic plants would be expected to have a very definite resting stage. In point of fact they are often evergreen, showing little external change from one season to another. More than this, some show the remarkable feature that their flower buds have as high a degree of resistance to low temperatures as their other buds. It is true generally with plants of temperate latitudes that once the flowering process has started it must be carried through, a check at this stage being fatal to the formation of viable seeds. But the flower buds of some Arctic plants form during one growing season, persist throughout the extremely low temperatures of an Arctic winter, and yet open and set fertile seed the following season.

Again, most plants do not display a simple and direct response to the onset of favourable conditions. It is only over-emphasis on mean figures, and neglect of the oscillations these figures conceal that could suggest such a possibility. Thus in climates like that of the British Isles ' false springs ', i.e. a notable rise of temperature followed by a cold spell, are not infrequent. Such 'unseasonable ' conditions may do great damage to introduced plants in parks and gardens owing to the way they lead to premature growth ; native plants for the most part make no response. The wariness, as it were, of native plants as compared with the apparent reckless abandon of introduced ones is indeed an outstanding feature in many areas. In our own country it is only familiarity which makes us oblivious of the extraordinary spectacle of native oak and ash standing bare and gaunt in mild spring

4

weather while the introduced sycamore and horse-chestnut spread their leaves in the sunshine.

Facts of this kind show that neither the alternation of resting and active stages, nor the timing of the three major processes included within the latter is a direct response to external stimuli. Rather are they both the result of intimate adaptations of the plant to its habitat and to its associates and competitors there. But competition, like the phrase ' struggle for existence ', has to be interpreted in a special sense.   It is much more than a crude struggle for space, light and moisture, and must be regarded as part of nature's method of ensuring diversity of life.   We may note in illustration some outstanding cases.

In the equatorial forest there is no dominance in the ecologist's sense, that is, no species, no group of species, stands out as regards either size or number of individuals.   Species are very numerous and those present may change from place to place without the character of the forest being altered.   On the other hand one kind of life-form, the tall tree with large, evergreen leaves, prevails overwhelmingly.   This type of tree is the structural response to a habitat where light, temperature and moisture conditions are uniformly favourable, just as the functional response is seen in the absence of a resting stage and the continuity of all the organic functions throughout the year.

Note how the temperate deciduous forest contrasts with this. Here a period when the conditions are particularly favourable alternates with one when temperatures may be almost uniformly low and intensity of sunlight is greatly diminished.   We must not, however, say merely that these factors check plant activity during the winter season.   The point is rather that those structural adaptations which permit the dominant plants to take fullest advantage of the favourable season involve a method of functioning too specialized to be carried on during the less favourable one. Thus the trees are characteristically broad-leaved, or, in other words, the leaves are relatively large, they have but a thin cuticle, and their arrangement on the tree facilitates the fullest possible exposure to light and air.   That means two things.   On the one hand, considered as starch-making organs they reach a high degree of efficiency.   On the other, the adaptations which give them their efficiency mean that they can function only within a limited range of temperature conditions.   Their shape and arrangement mean that they give off a large amount of water ; the roots therefore must be exceedingly active and soil moisture must be both abundant and readily available.   The delicacy of leaf structure also implies extreme sensitiveness to high wind and low temperatures and is associated with a need for much heat-energy for effective functioning. Any sudden check to an organism functioning in this fashion has potential dangers so great that survival within the habitat is conditioned by a precise adaptation not only to the average climatic factors but to the probable range and frequency of serious deviations from the mean. Thus we cannot say that the trees unfold their leaves when temperatures reach a particular height, or lose them when it drops below a given limit. Unfolding occurs when there is a reasonable probability that during a continuous period they will be able to function freely ; shedding means that the whole tree is in the act of adjusting itself to an entirely different set of conditions, it is only a symptom of an internal physiological change.

This means that the major elements within the community, those which give it its characteristic appearance, are those most perfectly fitted to take continuous advantage of the most favourable period. Where, as in the equatorial forest, all periods are equally favourable, the vast majority of the plants present are tall trees and all are simultaneously active. In the deciduous forest trees, shrubs and herbs in variety are present, but one or a few species of trees, numerously represented, form the dominants. This dominance, however, brings in its train such limitations that ample space and opportunity are left for subsidiary plants which may at certain seasons be both abundant and conspicuous— witness the spring wealth of anemones and bluebells in many open woods. Such subsidiary plants can as it were carry on their activities at a lower level building up less complex and massive tissues, having as a rule a much longer resting stage than the dominants and evading their competition by resting when they are most active.

In endeavouring to explain this difference of response to the same climatic factors on the part of the two sets of plants we have to add that the trees are adapted during their active period to a particular range of temperature, and that temperature affects both air and soil and thus two kinds of functions. Organs adapted to carry on photosynthesis under fairly high temperatures are by these adaptations unfitted to withstand low air temperatures, and also give off water rapidly. That loss must be compensated by rapid root absorption ; but this may be impossible till the penetration of warm spring rains to the deeper levels of the soil has raised soil temperatures there. Thus early in the season, though there is abundant water in the soil, it may not be available to the roots of a warm-weather organism like the summer-green tree. Many of the herbaceous plants, on the other hand, are both more tolerant and have their roots at a different soil level. Thus they can start into activity sooner, taking advantage of what is a ' dead ' season for the trees. Once the latter have awakened, however, the shade they cast and the changes in the moisture content of the soil due both to their demands and to a possible drying of the surface layers, produce a kind of physiological winter for the lowlier forms, which fall back into quiescence.

In a sense, and despite the obvious differences, we may regard the coniferous forest as the physiological equivalent of the tolerant plants of the deciduous forest, freed from the competition of the summer-green trees. Under summer conditions the conifers are physiologically less efficient than broad-leaved trees ; but they can function under a much wider range of temperature. They are, as it were, always ready to take advantage of any temporarily favourable period, without any physiological or structural change-over, and can equally well withstand intercalated unfavourable periods. Thus, whether in a particular area of moist temperate climate the characteristic community is the deciduous or the coniferous forest will depend, other things being equal, upon the length of the favourable period and on its nature. If it is long and more or less uniformly warm, the broad-leaved trees will gain because of the complete way in which they utilize the favourable factors. If it is short, cool and marked by considerable fluctuations, then the tolerance of the conifers will more than counterbalance their inability to take such full advantage of the periods when temperature is relatively high.

By a parity of reasoning it is easy to show that, where summer moisture is not sufficient throughout to meet the needs of broad-leaved trees, the herbaceous plants, because their requirements are less, may gain the upper hand so that deciduous forest passes into temperate grassland. In this case the fact that temperate forests have been so largely cleared by man gives us an opportunity of noting another point. The subsidiary plants of deciduous forests under natural conditions suffer from a summer deficiency of light and moisture because of the presence of the trees. When the trees are removed these checks cease to act. But, though the herbs respond by increased growth and by a prolongation of the growing period, their adaptive characters seem to set a limit, growth slackening before the actual conditions make the pause inevitable. Once again, then, we see that plant response depends on the innate features of the organisms developed as a result of adaptation to particular factors rather than on the factors themselves.

In these cases the major control is exerted by temperature even if rainfall affects the result. In areas where temperatures do not fall continuously below a fairly high level, but where there is a seasonal deficiency of moisture the adaptive response is rather different. In essence, however, it has the same basal features. That is, the most numerous and most conspicuous kinds of plants in any area are those which can make the fullest use of sun-energy in the manufacture of organic compounds under the given range of other climatic factors. When the climatic range is great the adaptations necessary to achieve this end may limit the period during which the process can be carried on. Provided that during their inactive period conditions are not such as to inhibit any kind of plant from functioning, and this is rare, other kinds of plants become active then.

The various types of tropical and semi-tropical climate afford examples of a drought check without a notable temperature one. In monsoon climates a heavy total rainfall may be more or less sharply limited to one season. Again the total may be low and there is then usually much variation from year to year though the seasonal limitation remains. As aridity increases so also does the variability till we reach the desert condition where rainfall is both low and irregular.

Applying once again the principles already laid down, it is clear that the physiognomy of the communities present will depend on the amount and reliability of the rainfall. Where the total fall is great the predominating types will be able to take the fullest advantage of high temperatures plus abundant moisture. Tall trees may thus be characteristic and, at least during the rainy season, these show some of the characteristics of those of the equatorial forest, e.g. large leaves adapted rather to promote transpiration than to resist drought. This in its turn may involve the deciduous habit and a definite resting period. But this is not necessarily the case. The drenching monsoon downpours not only feed great rivers but come with such intensity as to make it impossible for the ordinary channels of the rivers to carry off the water. The resultant flooding may moisten large tracts in such a fashion that water remains available during the ensuing dry season. In such moistened areas monsoonal forests may display almost the luxuriance of equatorial rain forest, and, as in the latter, one kind of life-form, the tall evergreen tree, may predominate. As a rule there is a kind of gradation, trees which retain their leaves throughout alternating with others which show a longer or shorter resting period.

Where the total rainfall is moderate or small and the dry

period long, two major adaptive possibilities present themselves. The predominating forms may be those which can carry on their functions quasi-continuously because their water demands are low. Structurally this means that the leaves are reduced or absent, their starch-making function in the latter case being discharged by more resistant stems or leaf-stalks ; the succulent habit is frequent, i.e. water when available is stored within the plant instead of being used in the course of a rapid metabolism involving much transpiration. Minor adaptations, such as a scrambling habit, a covering of wax or hairs, the presence of spines and so on, occur which further diminish water loss. The stunting of the aerial organs diminishes ground shading, while wide spacing is apparently often essential because of the extensive root-run necessary for each plant to collect the water required.

Clearly here again there is opportunity for another kind of plant, for during the rainfall periods, whether these are seasonal or irregular, water is temporarily abundant. Thus plants without definite drought-resisting adaptations, and therefore with a greater capacity for rapid transpiration and for the active metabolism associated with this, can take advantage of the combination of warmth and moisture. Not only that but—while it lasts— they can take more advantage of the combination than the former type. On the other hand, the cessation of the rains and the drying out of the soil impose not only a sharp check upon their activities but necessitate a highly resistant resting stage. Seeds seem to attain the highest degree of resistance, but many forms of subterranean bud, such as bulbs, are very resistant to drought.

Thus in such areas we tend to find two main kinds of plants, the markedly drought-resistant and the rain-plants, often, but not always, annuals. The one set show a marked alternation of active and possibly long quiescent stages. The other set, at least so far as their vegetative organs are concerned, show little apparent response to rainfall, preserving their stunted appearance while their neighbours flaunt green leaves, and conversely may show no obvious resting stage. Which set predominates depends on the total amount and frequency of the rains, and the appearance of the community alters in correspondence. But this does not vitiate the basal conclusion that the conspicuous members of any community—dominant in size, in complexity of structure and in persistence above ground—are those able to make the fullest use of the period when the climatic factors are most conducive to active metabolism, and that in the general case their adaptations give opportunity to subordinates, usually of lowlier habit and with a longer resting stage, to run through a period of activity.

When conditions are uniformly favourable throughout the year such subordinates find but little opportunity, and this is largely true of very unfavourable ones. Any sharp and regular seasonal contrast, however, involving as it must some kind of readjustment on the part of the major elements, gives the subordinates their chance.

Thus we see that while it is true that the natural vegetation of any area does give information that supplements usefully the ordinary statistical treatment of climate, yet the evidence it affords is highly complex and requires careful interpretation. Plant response to climatic factors is not direct but a result of adaptations both to the habitat and to the other plants occupying the same habitat, and both aspects must be taken into account in drawing conclusions.

CHAPTER IV *

SOILS AND SOIL STUDY

WE are concerned mainly in this chapter with a discussion of the major soil types in the latitudinal belts of the world. This involves us in a study of the conditions for soil formation in these broad divisions, and requires a brief preliminary consideration of the soil-forming processes, and some mention of their relation to plant nutrition.

The bringing into cultivation of soils either 'virgin' or previously imperfectly utilized revealed a whole series of new problems, for in the new countries there was little or no past experience and the method of trial and error proved costly and wasteful. Areas with such kinds of soil are especially widespread in North America and in eastern Europe and its Asiatic borderlands. It was natural, then, that American and Russian investigators should have played a large part in laying the foundation of a new type of soil study, based on natural rather than on cultivated soils. The material introduced into books on general geography with a view to bringing out the influence of soil on the distribution of cultivated plants is based mainly on that found in the older English pedological studies. We find it frequently suggested by implication, if not by direct statement, that the major differences between soil types depend upon differences in the rocks from which their mineral constituents were derived. The Russian investigators especially, on the other hand, lay stress upon climate as determining the distribution of soil types.

In Britain and especially in England the characters of the crustal rocks vary greatly from place to place within limited areas ; the soil is not sedentary, i.e. derived from the underlying crust, but forms the upper layer of transported glacial deposits or consists of alluvium. Within Britain climatic range from a world standpoint is small. It is thus easy to account for the overwhelming importance formerly attached to the correspondence between the variations in the size of the particles constituting a soil, and the character of the underlying rock.

* By Miss Margaret Dunlop, B.A.

Russian and American pedologists begin from a different starting-point, and not unnaturally a discrepancy between the two points of view has developed. The beginnings of vegetal soil are found either in the direct weathering of the solid rocks or in similar processes in the upper layers of the regolith defined as soil and subsoil. *Weathering depends on the local climate*, which does not cease to exert its effect after soil has been formed. Climatic effects become more complex when this soil becomes capable of supporting plant life. So long as the vegetation cover remains intact the growing plants themselves exert a notable influence. The presence of humus resulting from organic decay affects soil texture, and this is but one effect. The particular type of plant community present also is dependent mainly on climatic factors, so that climate has a double effect on vegetal soil.

Climate, therefore, influences the mechanical and chemical changes which occur in the mineral particles, it determines the nature of the plant cover, and this in its turn exerts much influence on soil character.

The problem for the pedologists is, then, the investigation of the influence of the climatic factors on the complex formed by the soil plus its natural plant cover. Here at once a new point arises. Time must elapse before the climatic factors can exert their full effect : this means both that the soil studied must have occupied its present position for a prolonged period, and that it is not liable to receive additions from an external source or to lose matter by horizontal displacement or erosion. Many soils do not satisfy these conditions. Thus alluvial soils are largely of recent origin and may be still receiving periodic additions of new matter carried in suspension by flood water, and deposited later. On slopes soils are constantly tending to lose material by erosion. Less obvious is the fact that ground water may carry dissolved substances from one area down a slope to a soil at a lower level, which may thus receive constantly renewed supplies of salts that would otherwise be washed out by rain.

This led observers at the outset to make a distinction between mature and immature soils, and to a concentration of study upon the former type. These lie in such a position as to minimize externally caused loss or gain, and have so lain for a time long enough to allow the soil-forming processes to exert their full effect. Mature soils are most likely to occur on wide, generally uniform plains showing a level or gently rolling surface. The presence of such plains in Russia and parts of North America is one of the reasons why these countries have been the seat of so much detailed study of the soil-forming processes.

The work of observers there, partly as a result of the reaction from the older over-emphasis on the importance of the parent material, has led them to lay great stress upon the influence of climate as the determining cause of the major differences between soil types.   At one time they made the extreme statement that ultimately the parent material would exert little or no influence, the characters of the fully mature soil being a result of the climatically controlled processes.   Fully mature soils in this sense are probably hypothetical rather than actual.   It may be sufficient to say that two sets of conditions are present, those resulting from the nature of the original mineral particles and those depending on mechanical and chemical weathering as controlled by climate. Which exerts most influence in any particular case depends both upon the time factor and upon the nature and the degree of resistance of the mineral particles.

We must next consider the presence of soluble salts in the soil, the variations in water content and circulation, in the biological influences at work in the soil, and in the amount of organic matter present.   The effects of these variations as manifest in the vegetation cover are seen in a study of individual soil types.

The finer roots of plants absorb a large number of elements in the form of salts from the soil, but four of these—calcium, potassium, phosphorus, and nitrogen—are of special importance because under continuous cropping it may be essential to renew the supplies from an external source.   Iron is also of great importance but of such universal occurrence that problems of renewal are not raised.

Compounds of calcium are widespread in rocks ; many lime-stones consist of almost pure carbonate of lime while a number of minerals, such as some felspars, contain lime in combination with alumina and silica.   On the plant itself the effect of calcium seems to be largely indirect, its main importance lying in its influence on soil texture and soil conditions generally, and in rendering other salts available.   This explains the utilization of great quantities of lime in regions where the soils are largely stiff clays.   The contribution of lime to the growth of bone in animals is important in connexion with the size of the animals.

Potassium affects both leaf development and the process of carbon assimilation which takes place within the leaves and, with absorption and transpiration, is the chief process in plant nutrition. Most salts of potassium are exceedingly soluble in water.   Thus regions where potash felspars are found in abundance in the under-lying rocks, and where the rainfall is moderate, but not excessive, may be expected to be favourable for this aspect of plant growth.

Phosphorus seems to influence root and seed development particularly. Phosphorus compounds accumulate in the green parts of plants, a fact which has much bearing on the stock-raising industry, for calcium phosphate is an important constituent of bone. Highly fossiliferous rocks such as chalk quite naturally have a notable phosphate content.

Iron dissolves out from many rock and soil constituents and gives a reddish tinge to soil water, a colour sometimes accentuated by iron-using bacteria. In regions of heavy rainfall and low evaporation a yellow or reddish tint is imparted to the deeper soil-layers, in some cases even an iron crust (hard pan) may develop between soil and subsoil. When evaporation is greater and rainfall less, the yellowish or reddish tinge is developed in the surface layers of the soil or even an iron crust may be formed over the soil. Iron in the soil thus gives great help in assessing the relation of soils to climate.

From these ' mineral ' plant-foods nitrogenous compounds differ greatly, for plants as a rule obtain their nitrogen supply in the form of nitrates, as these nitrates are produced within the soil mainly as a result of the decomposition of pre-existing organic matter by minute soil organisms, and its conversion into simpler substance more readily available to the root-hairs. Most of the organic matter is derived from the residues of higher plants, animal remains playing a smaller part. In the case of roots, underground stems and subterranean organs generally, the living structure penetrates the soil, and thus after death decays within it. The aerial parts fall to the surface after death, and it may thus seem that their organic matter is on the surface rather than within it. The most important micro-organisms concerned are aerobic, that is, function only in the presence of free oxygen. Thus an excessive rainfall or a high water-table produces water-logging and, by driving out air, checks their activities. Under such conditions organic matter decays with extreme slowness. Further, like other living things, the micro-organisms require a certain minimum temperature and the presence of water ; thus warmth and moisture, not in such excess as to drive out air, promote bacterial activity ; cold, complete drought and excessive moisture check it. Where the climate is cold and wet, and lime is deficient, the paucity of bacteria therefore leads to an accumulation of little altered organic matter, in which some of the structure of the original plants can be recognized. This is peat, sometimes called raw or acid humus, though it is not humus in the pedological sense of the word. Thinner layers of peat may form under comparatively dry conditions where calcium is deficient, as over soil formed from highly acid rocks, that is, those with a high silica content. Here the lime deficiency checks bacterial activity. Again, water-logging with ground-water containing calcium salts in solution may check bacterial activity by reducing the air supply. In this case what is called fen-peat is formed, and this gives the soils of the lower basins of the Wash rivers a non-acid character, which helps to explain the contrasts in the vegetation of fens and peat bogs. Such soils are readily reclaimed by draining, while acid peaty soils are less readily improved and require in addition neutralization of their acid content before some measure of fertility can be obtained.

Thus we have one extreme where, because the nitrate-forming micro-organisms are virtually excluded, organic matter tends to accumulate in a little-altered state and few kinds of plants can thrive. The absence of the aerobic bacteria may be a result of unfavourable climate, especially an oversufficiency of rain for the temperatures and possibilities of evaporation concerned, or may be due to local causes such as absence of lime, or insufficient aeration due to water-logging. At the other extreme we may have rainfall and temperature both almost continuously favourable to bacterial activity. Here decomposition of organic matter is direct, running through to the simple end-products, so that it seems to disappear completely. But so long as the natural plant cover exists the chain is unbroken. Leaves and other dead parts fall to the ground and are acted upon at once by the micro-organisms, carbon dioxide and nitrates appearing as by-products of their activity. The nitrates are washed into the soil and taken up by the roots of the higher plants from the colloidal matter which holds them. The carbon dioxide, again, increases the solvent power of soil water so that calcium is carried down within reach of the roots, to be returned again to the surface in the falling leaves. Once the plant cover is removed, as by the wasteful method of burning forest for cultivation, and subsequently taking crops without adding fertilizers, loss of fertility supervenes rapidly, for the soil has no reserves of organic matter from which fresh nitrates can be generated.

Regions of good drainage in temperate climates illustrate conditions intermediate between these two extremes. Here conditions are only seasonally favourable to plant life, whether macroscopic or microscopic, and the awakening of the higher plants has a reflection in that of the micro-organisms. Decomposition of organic matter is neither permanently checked, nor allowed to run a rapid and direct course. The material destroyed by the bacteria during their period of activity is compensated for by new material added, so that there is a certain carry-over from one season to another. Further, decomposition is indirect, humus being found as an intermediate stage. This can, and in due course will, be further decomposed to yield nitrate, but as it is constantly renewed from the dead matter added, it may be thought of as a permanent constituent of the soil. It is acted upon by the soil water and by the dissolved substances which that water contains, part of it acting as an acid in relation to the soil bases.

Even the worms which play a large part in mixing the surface organic matter with the soil, are specially favoured in the wetter soils of the temperate countries. Their work of drawing down leaves into their burrows, and of ejecting their castings at the surface helps to mingle the organic and inorganic constituents and has given them the epithet, ' ploughers before the plough '.

The immensely fertile Black Earths of Russia are, as we shall see, the example of a perfect combination of the factors affecting soil formation. The summer drought checks the rapidity of decomposition, while the winter cold prohibits continuous bacterial activity, and frosts break up the (rather heavy) soil. In contrast to this we have the soils of Mediterranean regions where decomposition, favoured by sub-tropical conditions, is checked only during the summer drought, and humus is rarely available for any length of time. The richest areas here are without exception alluvial or volcanic.

AN OUTLINE CLASSIFICATION OF THE MAIN SOIL TYPES

Figure 6 represents an attempt at a diagrammatic representation of some of the main soil types. Rainfall and latitudinal features have been emphasized and the variations of evaporation with latitude and seasonal rhythm have been accounted for along the periphery of the zone concerned.

Transported soils are dealt with later, so the diagram must be understood to be one dealing only with soils formed *in situ.*

I. THE SOILS OF POLAR AND HIGH LATITUDES

The southern limit for this study of the soils of polar and high latitudes has been fixed in a purely arbitrary fashion at 60° N. The choice of the Arctic Circle would convey a better impression of the conditions under which the soils are formed, but important areas of tundra would be excluded. In Labrador the tundra extends well to the south of this line, and in eastern

Siberia a northern example of the arid soils of high deserts on the upper slopes of the Stanovoi mountains is omitted, though much of the great longitudinal extent of the Eurasian podsols, which are clothed in their northern portions with a continuous though poorly developed timber cover, is within the line of 60° N.

The division into arid and non-arid types which is maintained throughout Fig. 6, is here made at 10 inches of rainfall. An arid soil tends to preserve organic remains in addition to the soluble products of rock disintegration, in the absence of the

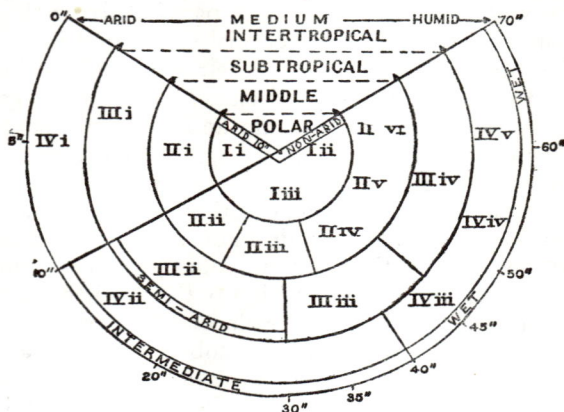

FIG. 6.

I. The Soils of Polar and High Latitudes

I. i. The High Deserts of the Interior
I. ii. The Tesselated Soils
I. iii. The Peaty Soils of Arctic Latitudes

II. The Soils of Middle Latitudes

II. i. The Saline Soils of Desert Basins
II. ii. Chestnut-Brown Earths
II. iii. The Black Earths
II. iv. The Brown Earths
II. v. The Podsols
II. vi. Peaty Soils

III. Sub-tropical Latitudes

III. i. Saline and Alkaline Soils
III. ii. The Red Earths
III. iii. The Yellow Earths
III. iv. Humus Soils

IV. Inter-tropical Soils

IV. i. Saline and Alkaline Soils
IV. ii. Red Earths
IV. iii. Laterite
IV. iv. The Tropical Black Earths
IV. v. The Tropical Humus Soils

microscopic organisms responsible for breaking them down. This, together with the fact that there is a negligible circulation of water, is as true of cold as of hot arid soils. Even with only 10 inches rainfall, slight evaporation and low temperatures combine to give the soils an almost humid character. We must also bear in mind the fact that most of the precipitation of these northern regions is in the form of snow and that this moist blanket, of which 100 inches are required to reach our limit, lies in contact with the frozen soil for long periods, and during the long spring this moistens the ground to considerable depths.

I. i. *The High Deserts of the Interior.* The intense winter cold here produces very coarse soils. The smaller particles, the product of wind-erosion on the rock fragments, form a very friable soil which can support only the more highly specialized plants. Tree-growth is impossible on it, quite apart from the difficulty of altitude. There is insufficient moisture and soil-stability to support the varied mosses of the humid tundra soils, and there is not even temporary human settlement upon such a terrain.

Examples. The soils of the mountains of Alaska, the upper margins of the Greenland ice sheet and of small rain shadow areas in the east of the Scandinavian massif and the mountains of south-east Siberia are of this type.

I. ii. *The Tesselated Soils.* For descriptions of these soils we are indebted to Nordenskjöld, who has studied them along the margins of the Arctic Ocean where they are chiefly developed. They are easily recognized by their polygonal structure which is caused by protracted drying. Drainage is confined to the cracks, which have an effect upon the growth of plants of considerable size similar to that noticeable on treeless loess. The population of the Arctic littorals is dependent for its existence on hunting on sea and land, and is not therefore directly affected by the soil types over which it moves.

Examples. Tesselated soils are found in the extreme north of Siberia and Canada, and in the Arctic American archipelago.

I. iii. *The Peaty Soils of Arctic Latitudes.* These are the soils of the tundra proper, where decomposition is slow, and a high organic content and water-logging are common. There is a more definite division into surface soil and subsoil than in the other circumpolar types already discussed. The subsoil here consists of the frozen soil rendered darker and more compact by the presence of a layer which in Siberia has an average depth of 32 inches. This horizon is subject to modification where hummocky formations due to seepage occur, and in very special cases on the slopes of interior Greenland and Spitzbergen where flowing earths are found.

The plant remains which form the tundra soils include certain hardy grasses, sedges and a number of mosses and lichens. The less water-logged and ungrazed areas support clumps of dwarf birch (*Betula nana*) and dwarf willow (*Salix herbacea*), whilst the acid water has a relatively rich flora. The brightly coloured summer flowers of the tundra are annuals which complete their life-cycle very rapidly whilst the surface of the soil is at its driest. Few herbaceous plants would withstand the winter temperatures, snows and soil conditions. The insectivorous Butterworts and Sundews are a well-known instance of more or less complete independence of the acid and badly aerated soils with their deficiency of nitrogen. Many large rivers discharge into the Arctic Ocean and, within the wide limits of their floods, alluvium supplements the tundra soil, but normally the peat is less thickly developed in northern than in temperate latitudes, by reason of the slow deposition of organic matter.

The interior peoples of Arctic lands are hunters and herders of the reindeer which feed chiefly on lichens, and of the large flocks of migratory birds which come north in the short summer, to feed on the freshwater fish and aquatic vegetation. Cultivation is almost absent.

Examples. The best developments of tundra soils are in northern Siberia and in the north-west territories of Canada.

II. THE SOILS OF MIDDLE LATITUDES

In the broad belt of land between 60° and 40° Latitude north and south of the Equator we may expect temperate conditions to influence soil formation and character. In the southern hemisphere only the southern portion of Chile and the southern half of Patagonia, together with the Falkland Islands, are included. North of the Equator, on the other hand, the British Isles, France, the whole of Central Europe, the Russian plains and their Siberian continuation, where coniferous and farther south deciduous forest is the natural vegetation, and the economic half of Canada are areas in which the six types chosen may be studied.

II. i. *The Saline Soils of Desert Basins.* Here again 10 inches rainfall is the limit for arid soils, for, although higher temperatures and strong westerly winds tend to increase evaporation, humidity is relatively high in middle latitudes at any rate when rainfall is well spread throughout the year. In the regions with less than 10 inches of rain, ill-defined and usually inland drainage and the occurrence of sodium salts in the underlying rock are also required to produce saline soils. In sub-tropical latitudes they may represent former lake basins as in the case of the old Lake Bonneville in Utah. Evaporation of the saline solution drawn up to the surface to replace water already lost in this way is usually responsible for their formation.

A saline soil arises over limited areas in middle latitudes in the following way. An excess of carbon dioxide produces sodium bicarbonate in the lower layers of the soil. The rain comes mostly in late summer and autumn in certain areas and takes the form of heavy showers. The cold winds of winter and the hot dry summers in such cases give rise to longitudinal air spaces which render the soil even more friable, and, with the saline character as an added disadvantage, inhibit the growth of all but halophytic plants.

Examples.   Local developments of these soils in temperate latitudes are found in the stony desert of south-western Patagonia, south-east of the foothills of the Canadian Rockies and around the lower Volga.

II. ii.   *Chestnut-Brown Earths.*   As in the case of the saline soils we must look for the chestnut-brown earths of the semi-arid temperate regions in interior continental situations.   They result from a definite seasonal climatic rhythm which combines winter cold and spring rains with summer drought and great heat. The type occurs east of the Russian tschernozems of which it is a type modified by the lower rainfall and consequent decrease of vegetation, and therefore of humus.   The reaction of the organic content to the more extreme climate is probably responsible for the difference of colour.   The upper soil partakes somewhat of the texture of the saline soils, being friable and rich in carbonates. A considerable humus content and the absence of a saline crust differentiate them from this last type.

The natural vegetation of the chestnut-brown earths consists of sage bush and grass of varying, though never of luxuriant, growth. Under irrigation and dry farming a certain amount of cultivation has spread recently to these hitherto virgin soils and, by removal of the natural grass and bush cover, has in some places promoted undue evaporation.

Examples.   The chief areas of distribution are in eastern Europe and western Asia, viz. the Hungarian basin, Wallachia, south Russia and south-west Siberia on the fringes of the black earth. A small area in south-west Canada must also be included.

II. iii.   *The Black Earths.*   The rainfall limits within which this type is formed have been fixed at approximately 20 to 35 inches. There is still a definite seasonal rhythm, especially with regard to differences of temperature, and another feature is extensive evaporation while the ground is free from snow.   The example which has been most frequently investigated and which was the first soil type to be seriously studied is the tschernozem of south-eastern Europe.   The Russian is merely the west central section of a distribution which extends with breaks eastward to Manchuria, and westward to the foothills of the Carpathians, where, as in Asia, higher land and greater rainfall totals cause a change.   Outliers are found in Hungary and southern Germany.   There is no question here of dependence for distinctive characteristics on the

5

underlying rock, as the formation covers rocks of very varying period and composition. The large organic content is uniformly distributed throughout a large thickness of the upper layer of the soil. Plant remains are not easily recognized as the humus has suffered great disintegration and is very finely divided. The soil is relatively loose in view of the intense desiccating effects of winds and sun over the centre of the Eurasian land-mass, for the soils are free of snow for the greater part of the year. Concretions of carbonates, though less conspicuous than among the tropical black earths, occur at considerable depths below the surface.

These soils, which are exceedingly fertile by reason of their high organic content, support a natural vegetation of a steppe type which produces spring and early summer flowering species dependent upon the melting snows and rainfall maxima of these seasons. The introduction to this chapter contained a reference to the climatic cycle under which the tschernozems are formed and its effect on bacteriological activity must again be emphasized here. It is the summer drought following upon this early maximum, and to a lesser degree the low winter temperatures, which check the decomposition of the remains of the early flowering herbaceous plants, and thus give the anomalous high humus content that one would expect to find only in a wooded situation. The hot summers and rain-free harvest periods render these rich soils ideal for cereal and above all wheat cultivation. In the last hundred years large populations have come to be concentrated on the areas where the black earths occur—this is especially true of the European tschernozems and will be applicable no doubt in the future to the Asiatic and North American areas. The absence of rain in late summer may become a great handicap in these circumstances. Harvests may fail and terrible calamities may occur as we have seen in recent years in the Ukraine. The ideal climatic conditions for the formation of a fertile soil may unfortunately be as harmful to human as to microbiological life.

Examples. In addition to the Eurasian examples already cited, black earths are well developed in the prairie provinces of Canada and in the north of the middle west of U.S.A.

II. iv. *The Brown Earths.* We now come to the areas within middle latitudes, where soils are formed under humid conditions and continuous cultivation can be practised without irrigation. In middle latitudes the rainfall, if it reaches 35 inches, is usually well distributed throughout the year ; there is rarely, for example, a regular drought period compensated for by continuous torrential rain as in some monsoonal areas where much greater totals result from a month's continuous fall. The soils of this group are all leached types, that is, they are distinct from some previously mentioned groups in that excessive evaporation is replaced by a downward current of moisture which dissolves the carbonates that were precipitated in the saline soils and carries them downwards, so that there is left in the upper layers an acid soil with a high humus content.

The colour of the brown earths is due to this humus, as the formation is developed under deciduous forests.   They are less acid and crumble more easily than the podsols, which they resemble, nevertheless, in a complete lack of carbonates from their most characteristic layers.   The difference in acidity is probably due to the fact that coniferous forests, in which the earthworm fauna is at least greatly restricted, are common on the podsols.   These important animal agents in soil-transformation prevent stagnation, and the acid peaty layer immediately below coniferous timber is replaced in brown-earth areas by a humus layer upon which, unless the trees are beeches, a considerable undergrowth may develop.   This, by its encouragement of birds and rodents, makes for deposition of excretion and for burrowing, and, with the destruction of living and dead organisms, for readjustments and uniform distribution of humus, beneficial, for the most part, in the upper 18 inches of the soil.

Brown earths are not formed on sandy areas, but otherwise the parent rocks are very varied.   If drainage is impeded over any considerable area, peaty soils form under the climatic conditions which, given a steady run-off, would produce brown earths. This feature has encouraged utilization of brown earths for the mixed agriculture so characteristic of western Europe, parts of eastern Canada and north-eastern U.S.A.   Above more acid rocks, podsols occur.

Examples.   Brown earths occur over large areas of average height in western Europe, and along the Appalachian foreland as far south as the state of North Carolina.   The more densely populated regions of rural settlement in both continents are dependent on brown earths, greatly improved by intensive cultivation and hence no longer typical.

II. v. *The Podsols.*   These soils are best developed above sandy rocks and are sharply divided into an upper layer, often peaty, which results from prolonged leaching consequent on excessive rainfall ; a second layer with a greater humus content due to the addition of most of the humus of the upper layer to its own better-conserved organic remains, and a third layer of subsoil, which is markedly sandy in true podsols.   There may be iron stain in the lower layers or even a ' hard pan ' or iron crust beneath

the soil.   If clayey substances are formed in the second layer,
a certain amount of interference in the constant downflow of
water is effected, and conifers give place to heaths.   This occurs
if there is a considerable slope.   This humid type is in its best
development unsuitable for the cultivation of all but the hardier
cereals such as oats and rye, and in addition potatoes.   Grazing
animals may be found upon it in fair numbers and dairy farming
may develop.   Lumbering is important where the action of
grazing animals is negligible.

Examples.   Podsols are well developed on Tertiary sands and
older sandstones in the British Isles, on the north European
plain outside the drift areas and river basins, in central Russia
and throughout the latitudinal belt between 60° and 45° N. in
the North American continent.   Western Patagonia and south
Chile have limited regions of podsols.

II. vi. *Peaty Soils*.   Peats, more than any other soil types, are
influenced by climatic changes in that they are entirely dependent
for their substance on the remains of the vegetation which they
support.   This is proved by the occurrence within a bog of
distinct layers representing fen peat—a non-acid type—forest peat
or carr, and acid moorland peat, clearly indicating climatic changes.
These features, combined with the ability of bog acid to preserve
artefacts and human remains, make peat the ideal medium for
archaeological and palaeobotanical investigation.   A brief mention
of this aspect will be found in Chapter V.   Moss or moorland
peats, the more common types, are best developed on high or low
peneplanes and in upland regions of ill-defined drainage, to
which Central European scientists have given the name of
' Hochmoor '.   They are subject to the highest rainfalls of all
peats and therefore of all soils of middle latitudes and have an
immense water content.   Away from the peripheral regions of
a bog, where exposure causes some drying, the upper crust of
solid peat varies in thickness with the rapidity of growth and
decay of grasses such as *Molinia coerulea* and, among sedges,
Rhynchospora alba and the Eriophorums (cotton grasses) and, in
the drier parts, of ericaceous vegetation and moss.   This more
solid upper crust may be floating upon a liquid peat formation.
This unstable condition, assisted by underlying lines of weakness
in the solid rock and unwise turf-cutting, results from time to
time in the disastrous bog bursts peculiar to Ireland and the
Falkland Islands (single examples are known from the Oldenburg
heaths and Solway Moss) in which large volumes of this liquid
peat are released from breaks in the crust.   The more solid
layers are composed of compacted acid remains of mosses and

the Angiosperm species already instanced, and they result from the preservation as opposed to the breaking down of humus. Fen peats, a lowland soil, preserve the remains of seeds and trees such as the alder and willow, and modification by contact with alluvium and the composition of the vegetation which they support make them far less acid than the moss peats. When drained they provide a fertile though rather heavy medium for cultivation. Bog peat is utilized for fuel, and, when levelled or drained, supports only a widely scattered population in inland areas. Fen peats develop in areas of relatively low rainfall and, in eastern England, may be outside our rainfall minimum for this type. Topographic controls produce the equivalent of a high rainfall here. Forest peats develop where, on thin drier acid soils, coniferous trees assist drainage. A change of climate or of drainage may cause peat to form and overwhelm these trees, but they leave in the peat a record of their former existence. On podsols, for example, thin layers of forest peat are visible in many instances to-day.

Examples. Peats occur throughout middle latitudes in the northern and southern hemisphere, where rainfall and relief permit formation. The Central Plain of Ireland is one of the most characteristic developments, and fen (in Armagh) and forest peats—especially of prehistoric types—are also well developed in this heavily glaciated island.

III. SUB-TROPICAL LATITUDES

We must now turn to the results of soil formation under conditions of greater heat, and to latitudes where an evenly distributed rainfall is rare. It follows that soils here, as in inter-tropical latitudes, may often be saline or brightly coloured, giving a warmth to the landscape, especially in the absence of a continuous vegetation cover for some months of the year, to which the peoples of temperate latitudes are unaccustomed. The bright colours are due to iron or other stains in the upper layers and a deficiency of organic matter. In agricultural countries in sub-tropical latitudes, i.e. roughly from 45° N. and S. to the Tropics, this deficiency and the scarcity of water for irrigation are obvious in the larger acreage left fallow each year under the primitive rotation systems which are often practised. Alluvial and volcanic soils are among the most profitable sources of agricultural wealth.

III. i. *Saline and Alkaline Soils.* The method of formation of saline and alkaline soils here is similar to that of temperate latitudes, although greater evaporation and heat, combined with the presence of most of the great inland drainage basins of the world, accentuate the results and greatly magnify the areas of distribution. Upward currents of water bring to the surface soil a solution containing sodium bicarbonate. The carbon dioxide content here is low and sodium carbonate is formed, giving the surface soil a very friable nature. The small humus content derived from the plant and animal remains of the less saline surroundings is washed through this loose cover by the next torrential rain, together with a certain amount of clay and dissolved sodium carbonate, and, in the case of alkaline soils, potash compounds. This, under the action of the greater carbon dioxide content of the subsoil, becomes more or less impervious and, when dry, cracks, as does pure clay, into columnar forms. The upper soil meanwhile dries very quickly and precipitates a portion of its salts at the surface. These are being constantly added to as evaporation increases. The effect of the constant upward current of water and gases evolved is to create large air spaces and a very crystalline soil. The efficiency of saline and alkaline soil formation in the horse latitudes is proved by the deposition of a crystalline crust following the evaporation of irrigation water in these areas. In the western United States and in South Africa this unwelcome development is rendering sterile thousands of acres of rich alluvial deposits where summer heat would otherwise give excellent fruit crops. The decrease in the volume of existing lakes which may be traced to former earth movements is very often responsible for the formation of large stretches of saline soils.

Rough grass and wormwood scrub and a few specialized plants will grow on all but the purest incrustations, and very often flocks of sheep can be sustained on the better areas. The climatic conditions under which saline and alkaline soils are found will never permit of any considerable settlement. Only mining and commercial enterprises based on the salts preserved by the aridity can be expected to show profits under such conditions.

Examples. The Great Salt Lake is the final stage of the reduction of Lake Bonneville. Western U.S.A. has many smaller areas of saline soil. Most of the nitrates of Chile lie within sub-tropical latitudes. The Caspian is also within our zone, as are the soils of the Dead Sea rift, of western Argentina, of the desert of Thar, and of the Australian rift.

III. ii. *The Red Earths* (*Terra Rossa*). these soils are developed under semi-arid conditions above calcareous rocks, and are common in the Mediterranean, particularly on the European side, and, in the West Indies, the north of Cuba counts among the regions of this type. The reddish colour varies in intensity and may be partly masked by a slight organic content. The soil is relatively thin, without any well-marked horizons, and this and other characteristics are more or less constant throughout. The colour is due to a large proportion of ferric hydroxide dissolved, in ferrous form, from the parent rock and precipitated as water evaporates, and, in addition, to a lack of humus. Cracks in the limestone and the least steep faces of crags are often filled with and masked by the deposition of red earth. Normally the soil is rather heavy, though the modified continental climate which develops in the interiors of the Mediterranean peninsulas may render the surface layers abnormally friable. The clayey consistency is derived from residual products of the parent rock. All acid is neutralized by the lime carbonate, and the soil may be marly because of an excess of lime. The reason for the development of a soil of this consistency under semi-arid conditions lies in the heavy winter rainfall and the conservation of the soil during the summer under a ground vegetation composed of annuals, deep-rooted evergreens, and succulents. The humus is derived mostly from the spring and autumn growth and, except in the interiors of the south European peninsulas where winter frosts check bacteriological activity, is being constantly removed ; very little accumulates, and so the soil is greatly impoverished. Subsistence agriculture is practised on this soil ; a rather high nitrogen content compensates for the lack of humus, and its evolution on well-drained slopes causes vineyards to be extensively developed on it.

Examples. The soil is developed at its best in south central Cuba, in southern Italy, in Spain and in Greece.

III. iii. *The Yellow Earths.* Here, again, a very distinctive soil colouring is caused by a lack of dark humus. The ferric oxide present in the red earths has suffered hydration in the yellow earths by an average addition of 15 inches of rain. Thus yellow earths may originate in the ' podsolization ' of red earths along their margins. An increase of ground-water in an arid region by a change of stream flow would have this effect. The yellow earths in their natural state are merely the result of mechanical erosion under hot dry summers and cooler and wetter winters. The humus of the brown and black earths and iron, the coloration of the red earths, are absent, and the soils are rather barren.

Examples. This type is very much more restricted, in view of the transitional total of rain which it seems to require, than the associated sub-tropical red earths, and, as far as its distribution is at present known, seems to be confined to south central France, the central states of the Atlantic seaboard of U.S.A., the Moroccan Atlas, and the main Japanese islands.

III. iv. *Humus Soils.* Soils with a high organic content vary in sub-tropical latitudes between climatic types formed as the result of a seasonal rhythm, and the peats of Florida where, although the rainfall is heavy, irregular drainage is mainly responsible for peat formation. The limit of 45 inches of rain has been taken to complete the grading in these latitudes, but some of the more important humus soils are formed under lower rainfalls. It is accumulating ground water which permits of their formation. This is true of the sub-tropical soil occurring in basins subject to merely seasonal wetness in South Africa and the south-west of the United States. The black soils of south central U.S.A., of the Barbary States, of central China, and of Manchuria, which we may include within the area selected for an examination of some sub-tropical types, are modified tschernozems, modified in that, owing to a smaller but still considerable humus content, they are dark grey rather than black and rarely so well drained. Calcium carbonate solidifies into similar distinctive nodules and rarer traces of iron coloration may be detected. The natural vegetation of these soils is a thin forest with a great development of undergrowth, but no considerable stands of timber. In cultivation they require an artificial stimulus, if continuous cropping is to be successful.

Examples. This type is developed around the north of the Gulf of Mexico and for some distance inland, in the northern and western Barbary States, in limited non-alluvial areas in the centre of South America and in south-west Manchuria. Humus soils in upland basins and, in Florida, lowland peats are a local development. Owing to greater desiccation and evaporation they are far less widely developed than analogous local areas in temperate latitudes.

IV. INTER-TROPICAL SOILS

This designation is self-explanatory as regards latitudinal extent. Here seasonal fluctuations of rainfall originate in the movement of the sun, or, in Asiatic Monsoon Lands and along the Guinea Coast, may be traced to local overheating. Temperatures, unless modified by elevation, are high on the average and considerable diurnal ranges may be recorded in the great deserts. Some of the greatest expanses of alluvium result from the high rainfalls and considerable longitudinal extent of the land-masses in inter-tropical regions. Very diverse and distinctive types may develop *in situ* over areas of similar magnitude.

IV. i. *Saline and Alkaline Soils.* Large areas of the Sahara, Arabian, Atacama and Great Victorian deserts are extra-tropical, but because they are extreme developments with sharply defined limits they may be considered as a whole under this regional heading. Atacama in the pre-war years of greatest exploitation depended entirely on food supplies from outside and caused the Trans-Andean trackways of the colonial period to be used again for the import of herds of Argentine cattle. This gives a clue to the extreme aridity under which the nitrate deposits have been formed and preserved. The weathering agents which are continuously active are winds and frost, and not water, as rain is rare and of the thunderstorm type. Heavy night dews are frozen and serve by expansion to loosen the rock fragments. In the absence of wind-breaks strong winds gather sand and use it to grind away existing rocks. (This is dealt with under the heading Aeolian Deposits.) There is no vegetation of a type that might contribute a leaf fall to the soil, which thus depends for its colour on the parent rock. The soils, owing to strong insolation and a high proportion of salt and quartz crystals, which are its most resistant and its largest grains, are among the highest types to be found on the surface of the earth. Only the Saharan oases and, in recently opened-up countries, mining camps have any permanent settlement.

Examples. The best inter-tropical developments of saline and alluvial soils have already been instanced. To these may be added those of the Thar desert and of inland drainage areas of Mexico.

IV. ii. *Red Earths.* Alternating wet and dry conditions produce these soils of the savanna lands which are the most variable of inter-tropical forms. There is rarely any cessation of bacterial activity, humus is never found in any quantity and the soil is rarely acid. Mineral remains, left after evaporation under direct sunlight, give the soils their colour, which varies from red to red-brown. The nitrate content is high so long as the savanna vegetation is retained. When it is removed by burning and tree-felling and when continuous cropping uses up the available salts, the soils very soon lose their fertility. The rapidity of oxidation of the humus substances assists aeration of the soil and renders it a favourable medium for a few years' primitive hoe-cultivation. The substances most vital to plant nutrition, and chief among them nitrogen and phosphoric acid, very soon need replacement in these red earths. Their vegetation varies, with their richness and water content, from well-developed parkland to dry grass steppe.

Examples. Red earths are common on the tropical plateaux

of South America, Africa, Monsoon Asia, in the Yemen and in
north Australia outside the areas of laterites and tropical tschernozems.   They support tobacco and sugar-cane cultivation under
European supervision in East Africa and north-east Australia,
and native hoe-cultivation throughout Central Africa.

IV. iii. *Laterite.* This much-discussed form, together with
non-humus black soils of which regur is typical, was originally
studied in India, and, like regur, suffers alternating drought and
great humidity.   Some think that high-level laterites were formed
during the ancient peneplanation of Gondwanaland, and they
seem to have developed under conditions of impeded drainage
and at a low level ; they have subsequently undergone uplift.
The occurrence of the process of laterization at the present day
is still controversial.   Laterite is a climatic soil type and is
uninfluenced by the character of the underlying rock, though the
typical weathering of granite is not conducive to its formation.
Three horizons may be distinguished above the parent rock.
The upper layer consists of a friable soil of varying hardness
with frequent air spaces, sandy if the quartz content of the underlying rock is high, but more often resembling lumps of clay.
Iron concretions are often mingled with this layer and, if present
in large quantities, give the surface soil a clay-like appearance,
and prohibit the growth of vegetation.   The second layer consists
of laterite proper, and is in its best development brick-red in
colour, although it may be yellow or even purple.   Small groups
of particles have a considerable clay matrix, but the penetration
of the soil by pores does not permit of the formation of an
impervious clay-mass.   For this reason the soil is not sticky
when moist and it breaks easily, to harden and become com-
pressed as it loses its water and gaseous content.   It was this
quality which caused Buchanan to name it laterite (*later* : a
brick).   It is used widely for building purposes, especially in
southern India.   Considerable pockets of carbon dioxide have
been found in the West African laterites.   The third layer is
the coarser product of weathering of the parent rock and is again
friable, lacking the argillaceous character of the second layer or
true laterite, and lighter, as the iron-content decreases downwards.   A high aluminium-content in the second layer will
probably be a source of commercial wealth in the future.

Laterite is not naturally fertile and occurs in many regions
subject to drought, but its Old World distribution in regions of
dense agricultural populations means that modified types, often
without iron concretions, are brought into use for subsistence
agriculture.

Examples. Laterites are developed in British Guiana and on the Brazilian highlands, in the Guinea coast lands of West Africa, in east Central Africa and Madagascar, on the Deccan and in west Australia.

IV. iv. *The Tropical Black Earths.* As with the temperate tschernozem, the natural vegetation of these soils is steppe. The organic content, although preserved from continuous decomposition by drought, is assumed by most investigators to be due to finely divided titaniferous magnetite, although it is doubtful whether this would apply to all tropical black earths, or to even that portion of the Indian regur which is developed away from the basaltic Deccan trap. A high carbon content in the humus may be partly responsible. The soil is not so deep on the average as in the case of the last-mentioned soil type. It is again a clay soil, and cracks on drying, with beneficial effects. The upper layer is subject to desiccation during the dry season, and becomes very friable. Under the action of wind it falls into the deep cracks, and the surface is therefore being constantly renewed. Evaporation is great, although a high gaseous content helps to imprison some of the soil water. Tree-growth is impossible under these conditions, and grasses are dominant. The mineral and humus remains favour cotton-growing, often under irrigation. The hardier short staple types which resist dry atmospheric conditions are most common. Cereals are also grown and tea and coffee plantations are developed on these soils.

Examples. The regur of the Bombay Deccan and Central Provinces is the best example. Other black cotton soils occur in Kenya, in northern Argentina and in northern Morocco, and small developments are recorded from the West Indies.

IV. v. *The Tropical Humus Soils.* Here, with an equatorial rainfall giving enormous totals, we have great areas of humus soils. The luxuriant growth of inter-tropical forests (it must be remembered, however, that the richest growths are developed on alluvium) produces great quantities of organic matter (for oxidation) that can be rapidly disposed of under climatic conditions which are extremely favourable for bacterial activity. In the absence of light, which is necessary for the life-processes of the normal plant, saprophytic and parasitic plants develop on this dead material and upon other plants which they eventually kill and add to the soil substance. Even in equatorial latitudes peat may develop, as between mangrove roots on the western coasts of Africa. This extreme acid type is not, however, common in inter-tropical latitudes.

Immense depths of such soils are registered, as might be

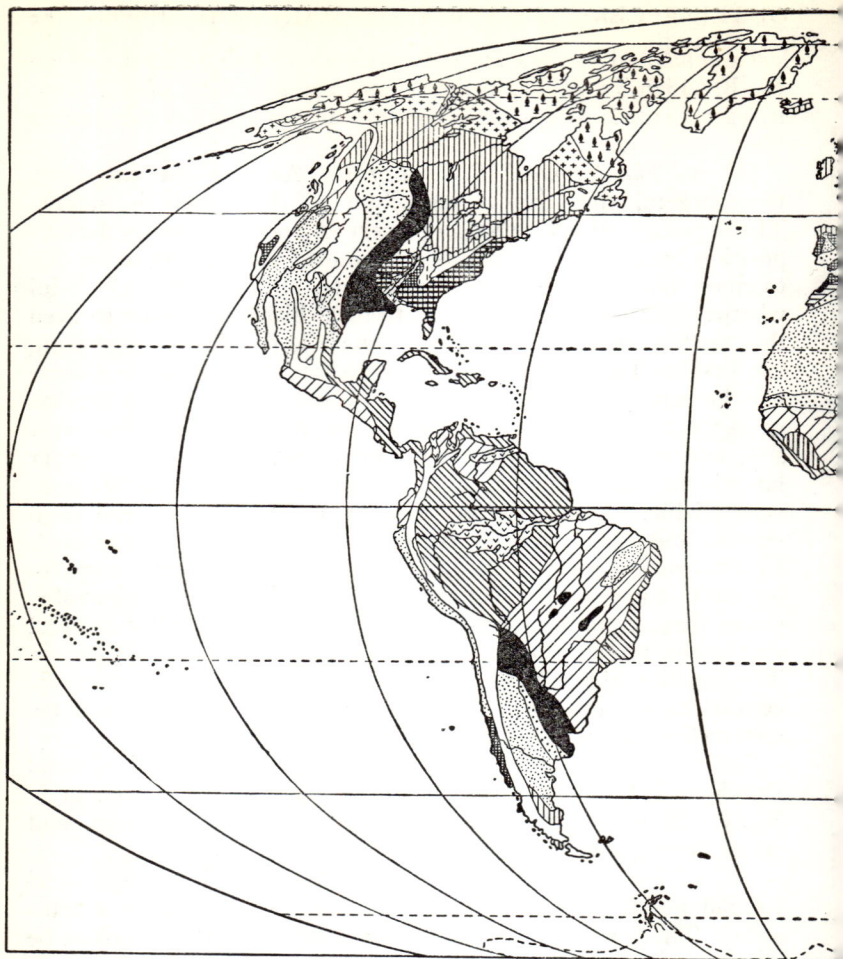

1. Soils of the high deserts of the interior
2. Peaty soils
3. Red earths (Sub-tropical latitudes)
4. Red earths (Inter-tropical latitudes)
5. Tesselated and peaty soils
6. Podsols
7. Yellow earths

FIG. 7.—A Generalized Wor

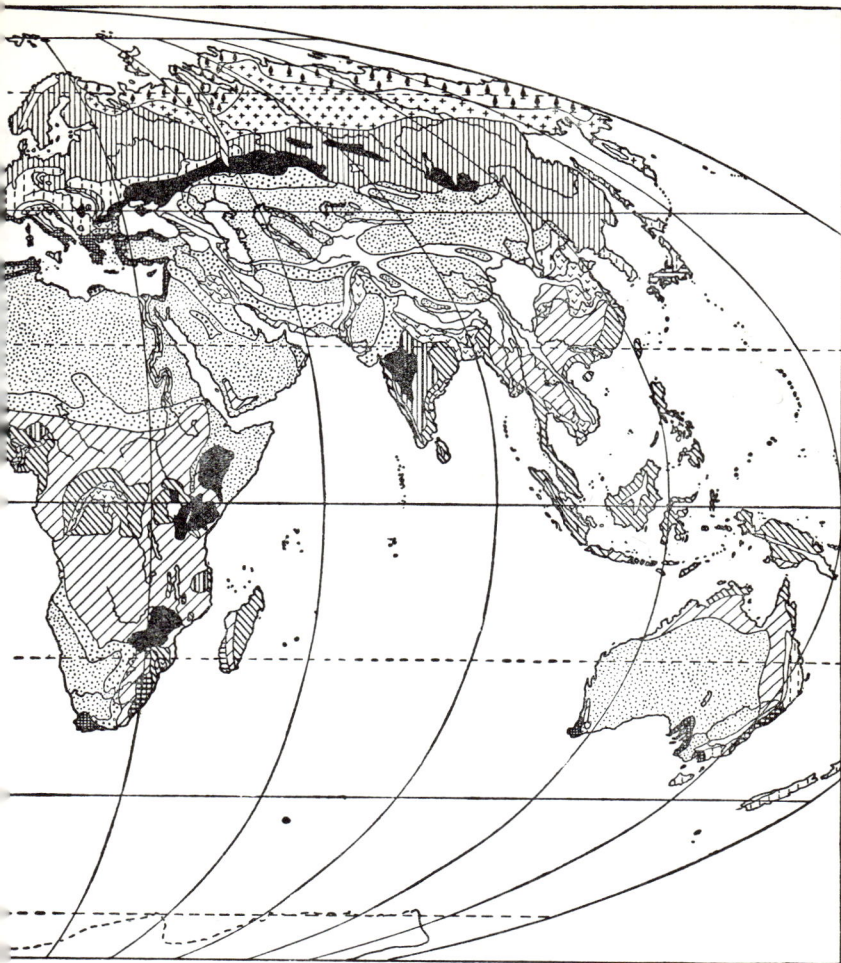

8. Laterite
9. Brown earths
10. Humus soils
11. Black earths
12. Humus soils
13. Alluvium
14. Chestnut-Brown earths
15. Saline and alkaline soils

p of the Main Soil Types

expected in view of the uninterrupted weathering, though heavy erosion originating from tropical downpours may remove much of this soil on slopes.   The best developments of humus soils are therefore in areas of impeded drainage, or in inter-riverine country outside flood-limits.   Climatic conditions do not permit European settlement in these areas and, except in the Dutch East Indies, they are still mainly in the hands of lowly hunting and collecting tribes.   Conditions are ideal for plant growth, but plantation crops must be carefully tended because of the phenomenal growth of weeds on these soils.   They support dense forest naturally, though areas such as the selvas proper are developed, as already stated, on alluvium.   Here, again, we have a climatic type independent of the parent rock.

Examples.   These soils are found everywhere, especially in low-lying areas, in inter-tropical and monsoonal countries which experience continuous humidity.   They are developed in their best expression in equatorial countries proper.

V. TRANSPORTED SOILS

Detrital or transported soils, the products of rock weathering and associated remains, have undergone movement from the area in which they were originally formed and have been redistributed and re-sorted.   The agency may be wind, in which case the re-deposited soils form aeolian deposits, or water, when they become alluvium, or ice in the case of glacial soils (water may, of course, be a secondary factor in this last process).   Ice acts to-day only in upland or polar regions and the majority of the existing glacial deposits date from Pleistocene times.   Volcanic soils are produced by the action of the usual forces of erosion upon volcanic ash and consolidated lava conveyed to the slopes of volcanoes by the force of an explosion.

VI. AEOLIAN DEPOSITS

VI. i. *Dune Sand*.   The grains which go to form this soil are very much coarser than loess particles, the components of the other chief wind-borne deposit, and they do not consolidate in the same way when stopped by obstacles.   There are two distinct types of grains : (*a*) those of humid regions where the resistant quartz grains are dominant and where mineral fragments do not adhere to the grains, and (*b*) the less regular desert sand grains which are covered with decomposed minerals in the form of small particles.   The sand grains of humid regions, which are confined to coastal districts, are usually rounded by the action of sea and rain-water and are raised up behind the seashore where the wind, not having encountered anything to break its force, is at its maximum velocity. The deformation of shrubs in coastal districts bears witness to the power of the prevailing onshore winds. Even if salt incrustations remain on the sand particles they are very soon washed through the dunes into the subsoil. Thin deposits of blown sands may be found for many miles inland in temperate latitudes, but the core of the dunes is rendered stable by its moisture content, and there is never any tendency to definite movement of the dunes as in deserts. The modifications of the natural vegetation are similar, though much accentuated in arid regions.

Sands of coastal areas cast up by the sea are often the finest grade of the load of rivers flowing off the surrounding country. The nature of the particles is influenced by the character of the local rock or reefs offshore to a marked degree. Considerable diurnal ranges of temperature in desertic country produce rapid disintegration of rock surfaces, and particles are swept away in the wind which becomes an active erosive force by reason of the fine material which it carries. Rain is rare and the particles remain encrusted with the products of their own decomposition or that of surrounding particles. They are therefore equal in productivity, when irrigated, to the finer clays and silts of alluvial deposits where the transported products of decomposition of dune sand and of rocks of every type are concentrated. In the oases the virgin sands produce excellent crops under careful cultivation, but sand-dunes proper are useless for this purpose. Dune sand further inland may be planted with tamarisk or with conifers, whose timber and resin are valuable in industry.

Examples. Dune sands are best developed on the coasts of south-eastern U.S.A., where, especially in the south, they are distinctly calcareous, on the coast of north-west and north central Europe (the Landes area of France is the classic European example), in Australia and elsewhere. The distribution of desert soils has already been outlined (page 73).

VI. ii. *Loess.* This widely distributed type is a dust rather than a sandy soil. The particles are therefore borne for much greater distances, given wind velocities similar to those of deserts. In north China, the chief area of present-day formation, the minute grains originate under desert conditions. We must distinguish at the outset between loess deposition by the wind in accumulations of very great thickness, and re-deposited loess, which has undergone a second journey to its present station by means of stream action. This latter is a stratified and thinner deposit. No definite horizons can be detected in the original soil. Loess soils are exceedingly porous, as the minute particles offer little resistance to water, and longitudinal air spaces, formed by the decay of grass stems as the loess accumulates over it, assist percolation. Few large stones are found and the equality of size among the grains makes for stability. Thus, in spite of the friability of this non-argillaceous deposit, people may dig caves into the loess where it is dissected by streams, and live there in safety in the absence of earthquakes. Re-sorted loess and the more mature types of the great European area are capable of great fertility under favourable climatic conditions. Continued deposition in parts of north China tends to restrict cultivation. Loess does not permit much growth of forests, and for this reason the relatively narrow strip which flanks the Carpathians and Bohemian mountains and stretches into western Germany was an early route of primitive hunters and peasants into northern and western Europe and, with the loess of the Danube basin, the cradle of cultivation and civilization in central Europe.

Examples. In addition to the upper Hwang-Ho basin, the southern pampa of Argentina is also accumulating loess at the present day. The Austrian and Hungarian areas along the Danube, and the south German, Polish, Roumanian and Russian areas are well known.

VI. iii. *Alluvium.* This is the soil of present-day and former courses of streams, of flood-plains, of estuaries and of lake shores. Alluvia are differentiated on the basis of texture into gravels, silts and clays. The finer deposits reach the lowest levels and are found farthest from the stream in its flood-plain. The gradation is well marked in any considerable stream. Hanging valleys among the higher glaciated mountain ranges of the world have alluvial cones at their point of entry into the main valley where there is little sorting of material. The stream remains turbid as it carries the finest material of its load into the main stream. Mature alluvial soils may be said to exist in old river terraces, where they are often greatly dissected, and over former lake areas. In humid climates alluvium is usually immature and may even be covered by water for parts of the year, and then the ordinary agents of weathering cannot attack it.

Alluvial soils are immensely rich as is shown by the existence of ' warp ' soils in eastern England : here an attempt at artificial reproduction of the alluvial clays typical in Lincolnshire and adjacent counties. Monsoon Asia has the greatest development of alluvium for its area and on it is centred a very large proportion of the world's population.

Examples. Other great developments are in the Amazon basin, the Congo basin (although plateau conditions do not favour the development of a flood-plain comparable to that of the Amazon), the Nile, the Mississippi, whose lower course is higher than the alluvium which it deposits because the coarser particles are dropped and piled up on either bank, and in the basins of the great rivers of North America and Eurasia which discharge into the Arctic Ocean.

VI. iv. *Glacial Deposits.* These may be differentiated into boulder clay, esker gravel and outwashed sand. All have been transported over considerable distances and re-sorted in the process, and, although the influence of the rock of the surrounding country is often apparent in the colour of the boulder clay, they may contain, in addition to boulders of the local rock, large erratics and boulders of all sizes from a long distance. Boulder clay varies in fertility and, unless it is very heavy, or contains too much detritus, has usually become a centre of intensive cultivation under average climatic conditions.

The esker gravels are often very coarse, hence their preservation in elongated mounds of considerable length and height. They are used for road metal, and for pasture, as they are often grass-covered and may have a fair development of woodland. Out-washed sands form heath country which is often planted with coniferous forest. In the absence of lime in the sand, its rich ericaceous vegetation differentiates it from the more acid moorland with its inferior drainage and its large proportion of coarse grasses and sedges.

Examples. Boulder clay is developed over large areas on lower land or in pockets in heavily glaciated country over central Canada and north central U.S.A., and in northern and north-western Europe, within the limits of the largest Pleistocene Ice Sheet, i.e. roughly north of lat. 50° N.

Central Ireland has some of the best eskers in existence, and north Germany some very infertile stretches of outwashed sand ; and, generally speaking, both these types tend to be limited to the southern limits and earlier lines of retreat of the ice. The formation of all three glacial deposits may be seen to-day in Greenland, Alaska, and the Rockies, in the Alps and along the Himalayas.

VI. v. *Volcanic Soils.* These are found in all unstable areas from the ice-free peripheries of the craters of Antarctic volcanoes to the Mediterranean and Japan, long the scene of recurrent vulcanicity. The minerals necessary for plant nutrition are often present in the soils of volcanic slopes, and this, in addition to their natural warmth, renders them very productive, giving

6

adequate compensation for the absence of humus, at least immediately after formation. Some lavas, and pumice and volcanic ash
in particular, weather extremely easily and are partly re-deposited
at lower levels. Rapid plant growth and decay quickly modify
the original friable and often rather coarse soils in this way.

Examples. The Mediterranean, Japanese, and East African
volcanoes have very rich soils on their flanks. The slopes of
Etna and Vesuvius are notorious cases of man's defiance of natural
forces in the exploitation of a favourable terrain.

NOTE

The great work of reference on this subject is the series : *Handbuch
der Bodenlehre*, edited by E. Blanck. Band 1–10 (1929–32). An effective
pedological summary is readily available in G. W. Robinson's *Soils,
their Origin, Constitution and Classification*, 2nd Edition, 1936. An
older volume which stresses the economic significance of the study is
E. W. Hilgard's *Soils, and their Relation to Climate and Plant Growth*
(1907). *The Evolution and Classification of Soils*, by E. Ramann (1928),
has an instructive classification of soil types.

CHAPTER V

CLIMATIC CHANGES AND THEIR EFFECT ON THE PLANT COVER

WITHIN the lifetime of a particular plant climatic factors do not often change appreciably, though edaphic factors generally do. None the less, climatic change does occur and such changes have been of very great importance in causing gradual, but fundamental, alterations in the vegetative cover of many localities. We know that there has been a complex alternation of glacial and interglacial climatic phases within the days of mankind, and that research is establishing the occurrence of quite notable, if less extreme, climatic changes in Europe since the retreat of the Pleistocene Ice Sheet.

The dynamic aspects of the vegetation cover of the north will be seen to be much more important than a mere description of its static aspect at any given moment.

Coincident with these climatic changes, and like them essentially a cyclic phenomenon, we have changes in the level of land and sea, caused by the melting of ice and consequent increase in the volume of circulating water, and by earth movements. Earth movements affect the vegetation cover by exposing land bridges and facilitating plant migration, or by limiting the spread of progressive species, and isolating others in relict areas, in the case of an increase in the proportion of water on the surface of the globe.

The more extreme manifestations of climatic fluctuations are seen in the Ice Ages. In Canada, Coleman has found boulder clay, greatly changed, in the lower Huronian deposits, i.e. in rocks laid down in Archæan times. Evidence is widespread for the existence of an ice sheet in immediately pre-Cambrian times. In Devonian times South Africa suffered glaciation, while, in the early Permian, sub-tropical latitudes generally, in both eastern and western hemispheres, seem to have come under the influence of an extensive ice sheet.

The Quaternary Ice Age, the most recent great catastrophe of

* By Miss Margaret Dunlop, B.A.

this type, has been divided, so far as the Alps are concerned, into four periods, the Gunz, Mindel, Riss, and Würm Ice Ages, with corresponding interglacial phases, and is thus in itself, particularly in central Europe where all these stages are represented, an example of the rhythmic alternation of climate which now concerns us.

On both sides of the North Atlantic we learn from the nature of the Quaternary deposits that there were four culminating stages in the growth of the Ice Sheet, and that some intermediate climatic phases were at least as warm as that of the present day in middle latitudes in Europe, and may even have been sub-tropical. That the Ice Age was not a simple thing was proved by Morel seventy years ago from remains of a warm temperate plant association found between two layers of glacial clay. It is upon this and subsequent evidence that our knowledge of the Ice Ages is based. No general idea of plant distributions can be gathered from isolated borings. Very often the layers bearing plant remains have been destroyed by the advancing ice. Clays with a relatively high grit content are in any case a poor medium for preserving plant remains. The record for the glacial and interglacial vegetational sequence is by no means so complete nor so readily investigated over large areas as it is in the case of the post-glacial sequence, where less extreme conditions provided greater continuity of more normal floral types. The plant remains have been studied here in a medium which lends itself more easily to investigation than the interglacial beds, viz. the acid bog and alkaline fen peats discussed in Chapter IV.

Investigations into post-glacial climatic changes by modern methods, based on the preservation of seeds, fruits, leaves, twigs and wood, show directly the response of the vegetative cover to climatic changes. The most direct indices to former climatic conditions are trees and shrubs, which dominate by their life-form the other components of the plant cover. They produce woody stems which preserve well in bog acid, and vast quantities of pollen grains which are larger than those of most herbaceous plants. Being anemophilous their pollen is adapted to withstand wind transport over long distances. A consideration of two extreme cases, the substantial acorn or beech mast, and the minute and ephemeral seeds of any orchid, e.g. Lady's Tresses (*Spiranthes autumnalis*), will serve to indicate the possibilities for the preservation of the seeds of trees as opposed to herbaceous plants.

We shall discuss the possibilities for survival of a very limited vegetation during the Ice Ages at a later stage of our study of plant migrations. Borings into the lowest layers of post-glacial peat prove that the initial stages of the Transitional, i.e. immediately post-glacial, period were, like the previous interglacial phases, times of unequalled plant migration. By reason of the numerous transitory displacements outside the immediate limit of the ice, and the adjustments in pressure distribution, climatic and vegetational conditions fluctuated enormously. The two major vegetational changes, i.e. the gradual but widespread replacement of tundra by steppe, and of steppe by woodland, initiated modifications which gave rise to innumerable intermediate types.

Nor was the spread of vegetation uniformly south to north following the retreating ice margin. Phenomena such as the breaking of the Gulf Stream across the Wyville Thomson ridge, resulted in an inflow of relatively warm water against the western flanks of the Ice Sheet which, in addition to accelerating its dissolution here, allowed vegetation to develop on the *nunataks* of Norway at an earlier date than on the ice-free areas of Scania.

The interglacial layers usually show an overwhelming proportion of hazel pollen, with birch, aspen and pine common in the earlier phases. The fir and elm come in in the course of the interglacial phases—the oak and lime also are characteristic of the interglacial phases at their best. Towards the end of each interglacial period there was a gradual diminution of tree forms, and deciduous species in their best expression decreased, pine and birch becoming all important. The Dryas flora, the stunted vegetation common to-day around the margins of the Greenland Ice Sheet, then came southwards. *Dryas octopetala* (Mountain Avens), a herbaceous plant of the present-day sub-arctic or cool alpine regions (on Ben Loaigh it is found to-day around the 2,000-feet level, though it reaches sea-level in the anomalous County Clare and Galway areas), had associated with it the Arctic willow (*Salix polaris*) and the Dwarf birch (*Betula nana*).

In the deposits left by the retreating ice, there are associated with the Dryas flora skeletons of the banded lemming and other Arctic animals at present confined to the tundra or northern steppes of Russia and Siberia. Immediately above the Dryas layers, and closely associated with them, were traces of several aquatic and marsh plants such as Potamogeton (pondweed), Typha (reedmace), Myriophyllum (water milfoil) and Sphagnum (bog moss), and other genera, some of which, though usually regarded as temperate in range, are common in Greenland in close proximity to localities occupied by Dryas and its associates.

The two sets of plants, the terrestrial and the aquatic, enable one to visualize in the late interglacial and early post-glacial periods, a treeless tract, as in the present-day Arctic, with a few prostrate willows profusely sprinkled with woolly catkins, clumps of white-flowered Dryas, and many other flowering plants.   In the marshy hollows would be occasional lakes or tarns tenanted by Potamogeton and other aquatics able to endure an Arctic climate tempered by the concentrated rays of the summer sun.

In the present age, which is post-glacial or possibly interglacial, the cycle began in a similar way with a Dryas flora.   The pine then appeared and extended its area, and this was paralleled by a corresponding northward advance of the birch.   The temperature rose, probably together with an increasing rainfall, and warmth-loving deciduous types such as the oak, elm, and lime came northwards, and in the ensuing years of maximal warmth attained their widest distribution.   This last-named phase is known as the Atlantic period, and was naturally a time of establishment, adjustment and unequalled plant migration in Europe. This may be seen from the table opposite. At the end of the Atlantic period, or post-glacial maximum, there was once more climatic deterioration.   The Sub-Atlantic phase of cold, wet weather with great frequency of cyclones and consequent storms forms a contrast with the Atlantic period or climatic optimum.   The period 1800 to c. 800 B.C. including the western European Bronze Age and the beginning of the Iron Age witnessed considerable changes not all in the same direction.   Adjustments of the vegetation cover proceeded parallel to the changes of rainfall and temperature.   In the late Atlantic phase the beech (*Fagus sylvatica*) and associated hornbeam (*Carpinus betula*) spread gradually from their south European stations and, in the Sub-Atlantic, because of their ability to withstand cold wet weather, ousted the oak and corresponding deciduous species, and became important constituents of the vegetation cover of north-western Europe.   The components of mixed oak and coniferous forest maintained themselves in a subsidiary position, and later with some amelioration of climate tended to advance once more.   Conifers in particular have tended to return to their former dominance in the north-west.

An attempt at a diagrammatic representation of the correspondence between climatic and vegetational changes in post-glacial time is included for reference.

The pine period proper, the Boreal phase of the pollen analysts, and upper Palaeolithic stage of the archaeologists, was characterized throughout Europe by a continental climate, as is evidenced

Climatic Periods	Development of the Vegetation of Western Europe	Principal Earth Movements	Climatic Variations
VI. MODERN CLIMATE	Maintenance of beech and spruce fir.		Merging into present-day conditions. A little less humid; possibly a little warmer. Amelioration *c.* 300 B.C.
	Hornbeam comes in.		
V. SUB-ATLANTIC Damp and cold, especially in the first centuries. 800–400 B.C.	Beech and fir dominant with increasing cold and humidity. Upper Peat Bog Period in British Isles.		
IV. SUB-BOREAL Desiccation and warmth, grading to V. 2000–800 B.C.	Upper Forest Period in Great Britain. Pine still common only on fringes. Cotton grass, not moss peat, formed.	Elevation in north Europe. Depression of land in central Europe. (English submerged forests.) Slight rise of land. Contraction of Öresund and Straits to North.	Great increase of humidity. Heat diminishes. Conditions give maximum extension of Atlantic species towards the East. Desiccation, especially in north central Europe. Warmer.
III. ATLANTIC Maritime — warm, moist climate. *c.* 3000–2200 B.C.	Immigration and rapid spread of alder. Oak, elm and lime; mixed oak woods. Lower Peat Phase in British Isles.	Formation of 25 feet beach in Scotland. 50 feet sinking of Fenland. Relative sinking in South Baltic lands.	Maximum heat. Probably wetter.
II. BOREAL Desiccation. Continental.	Forest peat. Hazel and birch common. Scottish submerged forests show a predominance of pine.	Baltic and North Seas become connected.	Still dry and continental, but warmer.
I. TRANSITION PERIOD Sub-arctic and Arctic climate.	Incoming of willows and myriophyllum.	Widespread elevation in Fenno-Scandia. Tilting N. to S. Severance of external connexions of Baltic. Raised beaches formed.	Post-arctic dry (Steppe) climate. Gradually becoming less rigorous. Very cold still.

by the desiccation of the peat layers. At a date which has been fixed provisionally at 3000 B.C. but may be earlier, moist conditions set in, giving the warm maritime climate of the Atlantic phase. This climatic optimum produced a mixed forest cover in which both the oaks (*Quercus pedunculata* and *Q. sessiliflora*) and the elm and alder dominated the associated vegetation. Then about 2100 B.C. began the transitional period in which the beech among deciduous and the spruce among coniferous trees were the principal colonizers under a climatic régime which whilst still warm was considerably drier than the Atlantic period, especially round about 1200 B.C. This period ended in the late Bronze Age, at a date which may be fixed with some measure of accuracy for

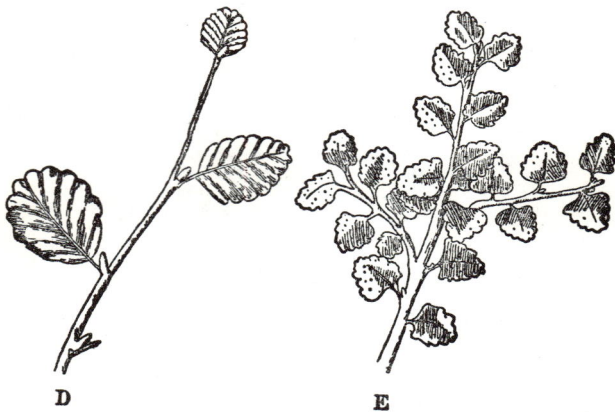

D   **E**

FIG. 8.—D, Deciduous Beech (*Fagus Gunnii*). E, Myrtle or Evergreen Beech (*Fagus Cunninghamii*)

After Geoffrey Smith

most parts of Europe at 700 B.C. The later part of the warm moist Atlantic phase witnessed the spread of agriculture through central Europe. A little before 2000 B.C. the early megaliths were being built on the western shores of the continent while in the warm phase towards 1200 B.C. came the rich civilization of the late Bronze Age in Scandinavia.

Northern Europe then experienced the catastrophic change of climate which is typified in German and Norse mythology as the Fimbul Winter or the Twilight of the Gods. The cooler and wetter conditions with more rapid circulation of air made for improved conditions in Mediterranean Europe, and although the fine Bronze Age civilization of north central Europe shows markedly retrogressive tendencies, in Spain there is a renewal of energy at this stage. The beech and spruce became dominant, the beech in north central, and the spruce in south central Europe, while peat spread in many previously forested areas. The peat of the first two centuries of the period, i.e. *c.* 700 to 500 B.C., consists largely of the remains of Sphagnum moss and the common reed (*Phragmites communis*), and is greatly decomposed as a result of interaction of wind and rain on the surface layers, and the difficult conditions under which deposition proceeded. That formed in historic times, and above all since the early medieval period, is more compact, and the plant and animal remains gave evidence of general readjustment, consolidation and further colonization and replacement, and the influence of man upon the vegetation cover becomes increasingly apparent.

The varying rates of dissemination of plants give rise to stimulating discussion when their present-day isolation in relict areas comes up for consideration.

The British islands and in particular Ireland are to-day separated from the continental portion of Europe. The flora of the British Isles is largely derived from the continent, and questions of date of establishment involve us in an estimate of the changes in the levels of land and sea, and in an examination of the possibilities of dissemination of the seeds and to a lesser degree of the vegetative portions of plants, by animals, water or wind. We must take into account, in addition, the climate of the period in which we have assumed that migration took place.

A group of plants which is of special interest in this respect is the Hiberno-Lusitanian flora which is based on species limited for the most part to western and southern Ireland and western and northern Spain. Single species occur in Devon, Cornwall and Dorset and western France. Fig. 9 is an attempt at a purely diagrammatic representation of the contacts between the species concerned. The numbers are placed in the chief centres of distribution. It will be seen that the main trend of relationship is direct between Ireland and northern Spain and the south-western England and western France play a very subsidiary part in defining the main line. Most of the species are not therefore derived from those parts of Europe immediately adjoining the Irish stations.

The distribution of the Hiberno-Lusitanian species which we must now discuss is a littoral Atlantic type in the fullest sense of the word. To central European botanists 'Atlantic' signifies western European in much the same application as the term

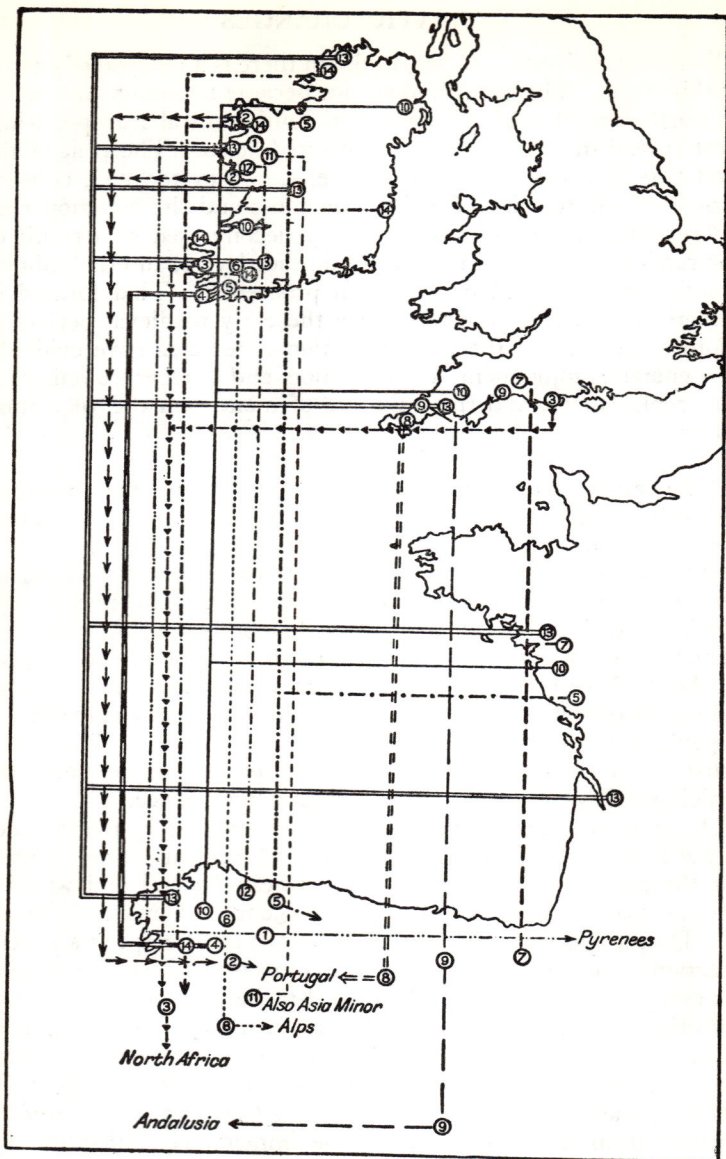

FIG. 9.—Hiberno-Lusitanian Contacts

1. Dabeocia polifolia. 2. Erica mediterranea. 3. Simethis bicolor. 4. Saxifraga Geum.
5. Arbutus Unedo. 6. Pinguicula grandiflora. 7. Erica ciliaris. 8. Erica vagans. 9. Lobelia
urens. 10. Glyceria Foucaudii. 11. Neotinea intacta. 12. Erica Mackaii. 13. Euphorbia
hiberna. 14. Saxifraga umbrosa

Note.—Arbutus (5) is important in Killarney. Glyceria (10) is centred in Clare. Euphorbia
(13): widely distributed and very abundant in Cork and Kerry

' western maritime ' in connexion with climate. The use of ' Atlantic ' would be judged permissible in the case of the Hiberno-Lusitanian flora by even the most exacting schools of botanical thought.

The Irish counties with which we are concerned are Tirconnail, Sligo, Mayo, Galway, Clare, Limerick, Kerry, and Cork, with, in the case of single species, Down and Wicklow in addition. At what is for most of the species concerned the southern termination of our series of contacts, we have the ' Lusitania ', which includes Galicia and Asturias, Spanish provinces where most of the species occur together, and northern Portugal. Our ' Lusitania ' largely lies north of the Roman province of that name.

The heaths are perhaps the most representative section of the group. The beautiful large-belled St. Dabeoc's Heath (1) *Dabeocia polifolia*, occurs on the heaths of Connemara and the country immediately north of it, and on the pastures of western France, of Asturias, and northern Galicia. *Erica Mackaii* (12) (Mackay's Heath) has a similar, though more restricted, distribution. Its only British stations are in south-western Connemara and in certain localities in Mayo. In north-west Spain it is confined to north-east Galicia and northern Asturias. *Erica mediterranea* (2) (Mediterranean Heath) has a wider distribution in southern Europe, but in Ireland is found only in two upland areas, i.e. Mayo, where it attains a height of 6 feet, the average for a mature plant in its Spanish stations, and in south-western Connemara, where on the northern slope of the Roundstone, at the 700-feet level, it is from two to three feet high. It is also found on the borders of the Bay of Biscay. The two other heaths which we must mention are *Erica ciliaris* (7) (Fine-leaved Heath) and *Erica vagans* (8) (Cornish Heath). They are restricted to south-western England, the former to Dorset and the latter to Cornwall. *Erica ciliaris* is developed locally over much of pluviose Spain, and *Erica vagans* is scattered sparingly over Lusitania, as defined above.

The two saxifrages, *Saxifraga umbrosa* (14) (London Pride) and *S. Geum* (4) (Kidney Saxifrage) and especially the former, are more frequently found in western Ireland, and *S. umbrosa* occurs in an additional station in the Wicklow mountains. *S. Geum* is confined to the mountains of south Kerry and Cork, where *S. umbrosa* is common. Similarly in the Iberian peninsula they are often found together, although Kidney Saxifrage colonizes lower altitudes on the whole, on damp rocks in Portugal, north-west Spain, and the upper Pyrenean slopes.

Arbutus Unedo (5), the Strawberry Tree, the only woody plant of our series which reaches a fair height, attains its finest European development among the Killarney Lakes. It also grows well in Sligo, and a study of Irish place names indicates a much wider distribution in historic times in western Ireland, before its utilization for charcoal began. In south-western Europe the Strawberry Tree is confined to the southern coasts of the Bay of Biscay, and is sparingly developed in northern Spain. It is found all around the Mediterranean shores.

Variegated Simethis (3) (*Simethis bicolor*), a small liliaceous flower, is confined to Kerry in Ireland, and southward across the eastern Atlantic it occurs in north-western Spain and in the northern Barbary States, whence its transport with the seeds of *Pinus Pinaster* to Bournemouth was thought to be responsible for the former occurrence of Simethis in the pine woods of that resort.

Pinguicula grandiflora (6), the large flowered Butterwort, loveliest of Irish blossoms, flowers in spring in Kerry, and less abundantly in western Cork. It is more widely developed in suitably watered areas of pluviose Iberia, i.e. northern and north-western Spain and Portugal. *Lobelia urens* (9) (Acrid Lobelia) is found on moist heaths in Dorset and Cornwall in Britain, and in the wetter parts of Andalusia (i.e. the coastal regions) and northern Spain, and in western France. *Glyceria Foucaudii* (10), a monocotyledon allied to our lawn grasses, is found around the Shannon estuary and Strangford Lough. In Great Britain it is found only on the western half of the Channel coast. It occurs along the south-eastern margins of the Bay of Biscay and south into the Mediterranean. Next we have *Neotinea intacta* (11) (Dense-spiked Orchis), found on the limestones of Clare, and on the wind-blown calcareous sands of the rocky pastures of Connemara and Mayo and here only near the transition between lake-strewn land and island-studded bay ; it is matched in northern Spain and on the limestones of the Mediterranean as far east as Asia Minor, but never in Britain. Lastly we must note the distribution of *Euphorbia hiberna* (13) (Irish Spurge). It will be seen from Fig. 9 that the Irish centres are in Donegal, in west Mayo and south-east Galway (small colonies), and in Cork and Kerry (more abundant) ; a few British areas are to be found in Devon and Cornwall. In Spain Irish Spurge is confined to eastern Galicia and to the Pyrenees, except in the case of isolated examples, and in France to much the same area, but not the same habitat, as *Lobelia urens*.

The invertebrate animals with a similar distribution have been tabulated by Praeger in the following way (*Proc. Royal Irish Acad.*, XLI, Section B, No. 8, 1932) :

	Ireland	Britain	Continent	Remarks
Helix pisana . . .	E.	S.W.	S. France, Mediterranean	Also Atlantic Islands.
Geomalacus maculosus .	S.W.		Spain, Portugal	
Otiorrhynchus auropunctatus	E. to N.		Pyrenees, Auvergne	
Tegenaria hibernica. .	E.W.S.		Pyrenees	A nearly related species.
Eluma purpurascens. .	E.	Cornwall	Mediterranean	Also Atlantic Islands.
Metaponorthus melanurus	E.		Mediterranean	Also Atlantic Islands.
Metaponorthus cingendus	S.W.E.	Devon	France, Spain	
Philoscia couchii . .	E.		Mediterranean	Also Atlantic Islands.
Trichoniscus vividus .	S.E.		France, Spain	

Although these snails, woodlice, spiders and beetles are for the most part less conspicuous than their floral counterparts, their striking distribution at the present day is no less instructive. The occurrence of these floral and faunal groups is no mere coincidence, and we must now outline the theories which have been formed on their origin and isolation.

The question is either one of relatively recent, or one of pre-glacial or interglacial, dispersal, and we must now consider the possibilities for dissemination in these widely differing epochs.

The theory that the grouping is due to Hiberno-Spanish trade and exchange of fishermen and products does not bear investigation. If human agencies have been at work, the present distribution, which is by no means coastal or confined to low-lying harbour sites and their hinterland, could be better explained in terms of megalithic cultural rather than medieval trading contacts. A megalithic type, the unsegmented gallery, is common to the western Irish, French and Iberian areas of the above flora. Outliers of tombs and flora occur too, e.g. in Co. Wicklow. That seeds were brought with food plants cannot be proved until Lusitanian remains are found in peat contemporary with, but not earlier than, *c.* 2000 B.C.

We must remember that the advance of the ice in the Ice Ages was extremely slow, and did not proceed with the rapidity and violence one might easily assume to have been features. Adaptation and retreat of plants could proceed.

As south-west Ireland was probably ice free throughout the Ice Ages plants would retreat thither and might survive, but we unfortunately lack evidence concerning the plants of those early days in that region. The difficulty of preservation of the seeds of the plants concerned, some of them of a very ephemeral type, and of their pollen and leaves (except in the case of the Ericas) in the disturbed interglacial beds complicates investigation.

In north-western Spain conditions were less rigorous—western Lusitania, at least, was not in the same proximity to the Cantabro-Pyrenean Sheet as was Kerry to the Irish ice.   Yet adaptation for survival, if this indeed did occur, proceeded to the same degree. This rather makes for a return to the theory of survival from pre-glacial times in the original form.

Galway and Mayo were centres of local ice sheets, and at the period of maximum glaciation, early in the Quaternary Ice Age, these must have been joined to the main British Ice Sheet. Evidence of a post-glacial spread of the Lusitanian species from the Kerry area is necessary to explain their presence there to-day, as extermination was presumably their fate during the Ice Ages. This spread from Kerry may possibly have occurred in the rela-tively varied period of post-glacial time.   There have undoubtedly been more favourable climatic phases than that of the present day as we have already seen. (See Fig. 9.)

The assumption that extermination was bound to follow the establishment of the rigorous conditions of the Ice Age, has been challenged by Forbes, in a paper which does not deal solely with the group with which we are concerned, ' On the connexion between the distribution of the existing fauna and flora of the British Isles and the geological changes which have affected their areas especially during the epoch of the Northern Drift ' (*Mem. Geol. Survey of Great Britain*, 1, 336–432, 1846).   It has been argued that the present-day area of Lusitanian plants represents a retreat rather than an advance since the Glacial Period.   In view of the post-glacial fluctuations of climate, an early post-glacial establishment, say in the warm dry Boreal, would be adversely affected by climatic deterioration in subsequent pre-historic times, and, with the progress of pollen analysis and peat investigation generally, this argument becomes less convincing.

The late Clement Reid has argued for a wholesale dispersal of the Lusitanian plants in the post-glacial period by purely chance introductions, whereas we now look back to a succession of climatic and orographical changes complicating dispersal due to wind, water, or animal agencies.   His arguments attempt to surmount the obstacle of the present peculiar distribution by the shortness of the period in which spread has taken place.   It is admitted that the post-glacial period of approximately 25,000 years does not compare with any former major geological division as regards duration.   It might also be argued that the rather

difficult country in which the species are found in Britain limits
an outward spread. But immigration usually proceeds from east
to west in the British Isles, and if the species were present in the
ice-free area of south-eastern England and spread westwards to
such an extent that in early post-glacial times they were universal
in the south of our islands, why are they to-day absent from what
was formerly the nucleus of their spread?

Thus we must return to the theory of survival. We are obtaining increasing evidence of the presence of ice-free areas throughout
the northern hemisphere, and of the association with them of
relict floras. Scandinavian investigations into the flora of Greenland show us a very much more extensive and more varied flora
than one would consider possible, in close proximity to the
immense Ice Cap which is second only to that of the Antarctic
at the present day. Fernald, for example, sends from the Gaspé
peninsula on the southern bank of the St. Lawrence estuary, a
record of survivals in an extra-glacial environment. Teesdale
has a curiously anomalous flora which has been explained in
terms of a survival through the Ice Age. If within the influence
of the Greenland Ice Sheet four hundred and sixteen vascular
cryptogams have already been listed, one begins to expect and to
justify statements of corresponding survivals in southern Britain
and Ireland. Some of the common British wayside flowers have
colonized considerable areas in Greenland. Many of the heaths
with which we are dealing extend to considerable heights in both
Ireland and Spain, and may be covered with snow for a considerable time in winter. In the case of most members of the group
wind force and not low temperatures limit the distribution of the
plants concerned in the Atlantic coastlands in which they occur.
Therefore, assuming that lower temperatures confined our group
to the Atlantic littoral, we may argue that in the absence of too
strong wind they were able to maintain themselves there throughout the Ice Ages. The Hiberno-Lusitanian species are distributed along the flanks of two of the greatest cyclone tracks
affecting present-day Europe. It is widely believed that the
presence of the Quaternary Ice Sheet was responsible for the
development of an anticyclone of enormous size and stability.
We may thus assume that the almost continuous force of the
westerlies, which blow to-day directly on to Kerry and north-
western Spain, then the ice-free portions on the periphery of the
Irish and Cantabro-Pyrenean sheets, would be replaced by a long
period of calms more favourable to growth.

The claim for survival of highly resistant seeds in the case of
the devastated surface of the island of Krakatoa, postulated soon

after the eruption by Praeger, has since been substantiated by Backer's investigations. The events of the volcanic catastrophe and complete burial of the surface beneath lava and ash failed to render the seeds concerned inert.

The general argument in this problem of the Lusitanian flora, one of many centres of discussion on relict species, is for the existence of a migratory route in pre-glacial times, possibly when oscillation of the earth's crust, and its effect on the distribution of land and sea, facilitated movement between the chief centres of occurrence of these plants. Isolation came with the growth of the Ice Sheet and with widening of the intermediate area, and it has been maintained ever since.

NOTE

The best summary of the pollen analyst's method available to British readers is Godwin's paper in the *New Phytologist*, 33, 4–5, 1934 : ' Pollen Analysis. An outline of the problems and potentialities of the method.' A further paper which summarises much of this author's work is : ' Pollen Analysis and the Forest History of England and Wales ', *New Phytologist*, 39, pp. 370–400, 1940. G. Erdtmann's *An Introduction to Pollen Analysis*, 1943, is a comprehensive study by one of the leading Scandinavian authorities. An account of the cultural and vegetational changes following upon climatic fluctuations will be found in Cyril Fox's *Personality of Britain*, 4th Edition (1943). W. B. Wright's *Quaternary Ice Age*, 2nd Edition (1936), is the classic study of that phase.

In connexion with the Hiberno-Lusitanian flora R. Ll. Praeger's *Botanist in Ireland*, 1934, and summary of recent theories cited on page 92 should be studied.

PART II

THE MAJOR PLANT COMMUNITIES AND THEIR ANIMAL ASSOCIATES

CHAPTER VI

TYPES OF PLANT COMMUNITIES

PLANT ASSOCIATIONS

A BARE surface of land becomes covered with plants which succeed one another until eventually a sort of equilibrium is reached and certain kinds of plants, some, it may be, large and dominant and others smaller growing in their shade, take permanent hold. Such a durable climax plant community is called an Association. It may be under the protection of some dominants that smaller subordinate plants spread into the area, but the removal of the dominants, for example by man, need not involve disappearance of subordinates, some indeed may grow the more freely. Alterations of plant associations may thus be highly complex. In Britain, thanks partly to impoverishment of the natural flora, we may have on uplands a plant community dominated by Scots Pine (*Pinus sylvestris*), or ling (*Calluna vulgaris*) and bell-heather (*Erica cinerea*). In the equatorial rain forest on the other hand there is rarely a dominant plant, and two areas of forest that look very much alike may yet yield very diverse species of tall trees, climbing plants or lianes and epiphytes or plants growing on others. Again, Pines (*Pinus*) and Larch (*Larix*) cover vast areas of coniferous forest or taiga, but the species in Asia, Europe and North America differ greatly. This concerns the botanical ecologist far more than the biogeographer.

The geographer is, however, interested to reflect that the complex diversity of the equatorial rain forest is partly due to the fact that it is a very ancient feature of the vegetative covering of the earth. The wealth of species of pines, larches and so on in North America is again related to the antiquity of the forests concerned, for in North America during the Pleistocene Ice Ages the forests retreated southwards and afterwards returned. In Europe on the other hand the earlier forests of the north found themselves pinched out between the northern and the alpine ice sheets and many species were extinguished in the resulting crises. To the geographer, then, the species making up plant associations are less important than the prevalence of life-forms such as in ordinary

99

speech are called herbs, shrubs, trees, climbing plants, epiphytes and so on.

Raunkiaer has attempted to classify plants according to life-forms and he lays stress especially on the positions of buds, i.e. on the arrangements for future growth.   Such a system is bound to have limitations as its author fully recognized.

(1) Phanerophytes.   Stems rise more than 10 inches above the soil and bear exposed buds.   This group includes almost all trees and shrubs unless they are specially stunted ; it is thus the group of woody plants but excludes some low scrambling plants that may be almost woody.

(2) Chamaephytes.   Buds at or near surface of soil, e.g. many heath plants, dwarfed birch, arctic willow, a large number of herbaceous plants such as saxifrages (e.g. London Pride), thyme on rocky pastures, sea-thrift, moss-campion (*Silene acaulis*), the last a sub-alpine type found on rocky marine littorals.

(3) Hemicryptophytes. Resting buds in surface-soil, e.g. many grasses, rushes and sedges, also common herbs such as Cranes' Bills (*Geranium*), Willow-herb (*Epilobium*), Docks (*Rumex*), Meadow-sweet, Dandelion, Stinging nettle and so on.

(4) Geophytes.   Truly underground buds on a bulb (Wild Hyacinth), corm (Crocus), or rootstock (Monkshood and Solomon's Seal).   They cannot occupy soil that is persistently frozen to a considerable depth in winter.

The sequence 1 to 4 shows progressive increase of a lack of tolerance of locally occurring changes in temperature and humidity of the free air, but the relation of geophytes to frozen soil shows that this is not quite the same as tolerance of changes of temperature *per se*.

Outside this sequence, marsh and water plants have the added protection of water, muddy or clear, shallow or fairly deep. Their buds may be on the floor of the pond or buried in the soft deposits of that floor.   The Arum Lily (*Calla*) withstands our winters if sunk in a pool, but not if planted in a garden.   Plants with buds in or under water are Hydrophytes, while Halophytes tolerate considerable amounts of salts in solution.

Plants with no resting buds may be considered apart from perennating ones which flower repeatedly.   They are called Therophytes and include annuals such as Chickweeds, Groundsels, Nasturtiums.   Biennials normally give a first season to germination and establishment and then in a second season derive part of their energy from stored food and flower and die.   In warm and arid climates plants like the agave may vegetate through several years, then set seed and usually die.   Some mountain plants have an analogous scheme, so a classification into annuals, biennials and perennials is subject to limitations of its value.

Raunkiaer's scheme was originally planned for temperate latitudes, and the percentage of species in each class is often called the local biological spectrum, though it does not always give a true idea of the local physiognomy of the vegetation, for it often happens that one species, such as *Pinus sylvestris*, is so dominant as to give the plant community its characteristic appearance. Another limitation of the percentage system is due to the fact that one locality may be far richer than another in the total number of its species. Another limitation of the scheme is illustrated by the fact that the phanerophytes of the coniferous forests of western North America reach as great a size as that of tall trees of the equatorial rain forest even though they are seasonally exposed to low temperatures ; they meet this difficulty by having their exposed buds protected by thickened scales, a coating of resin, hairs or some other device.

The Hemicryptophytes of deciduous woodlands in cool temperate latitudes often differ greatly from those of mountain pastures, and positions of buds are minor matters in many cases ; the buds may be specially protected in ways not considered in the definitions. Hemicryptophytes also may survive fairly rigorous conditions if the ground in winter be blanketed with snow or with slowly decaying forest-litter enclosing enough air to make it an effective non-conductor.

Though Chamaephytes are in general less protected from extreme seasonal atmospheric changes than are hemicryptophytes, yet the dividing line between the two groups is difficult to draw either morphologically or ecologically. Some chamaephytes develop mat-forms in Arctic or Alpine surroundings, with prostrate tangled shoots carrying leaves that allow only slow evaporation and also decay slowly. Both plant and litter hold snow and form a non-conducting layer which may protect the buds and so enable chamaephytes to form a relatively considerable proportion of the flora in rigorous environments. Hemicryptophytes, which thrive where temperature and moisture do not vary too greatly, also profit by schemes of bud-protection in soil-litter. Woody chamaephytes tend to be ousted by some of the other classes where conditions are reasonably favourable, but come to their own where drought or cold, especially if accompanied by high wind, is seasonally severe. They economize material as against the phanerophytes which would also suffer more from exposure to wind ; they also make their own shelter and thus have advantages as against the softer, less resistant herbs.

Needless to say, the dividing line between hemicryptophytes and chamaephytes is difficult to draw, while the limiting height of 10 inches for a chamaephyte as against a phanerophyte is somewhat artificial.

Fig. 10 shows graphically the spectra of two areas widely separated in latitude. Graph I is that of the cedar forest of Morocco, i.e. of a particular plant community, found in about

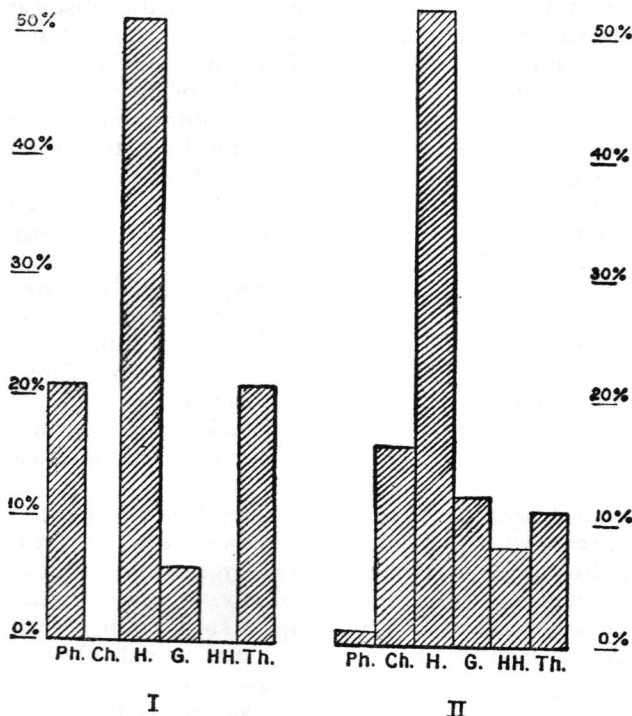

FIG. 10.—Biological Spectrum of (I) the Cedar Forest of Morocco compared with that of the whole of Iceland (II)

Ph., Phanerophytes; Ch., Chamaephytes; H., Hemicryptophytes; G., Geophytes; HH., Marsh and Water plants; Th., Therophytes

lat. 34° but where the Mediterranean climate is considerably modified by elevation (over 5,000 feet). Graph II shows the spectrum of the total flora of Iceland. The mean latitude is *c.* 65°, that is, marginal to the Arctic, but while on the one hand the highlands show practically Arctic conditions, on the other the position and the island form modify greatly the winter temperatures of the lowlands.

The first point to notice is that in both cases over 50 per cent of the species present are hemicryptophytes, which, for the reasons already given, tell us nothing of the climatic differences. In I phanerophytes form over 20 per cent of the total, in II but 1 per cent; it is thus clear that while the climate of the Moroccan Atlas is favourable to tree-growth, that of Iceland is unfavourable. In the Atlas annuals have the same percentage value as phanerophytes; the forest is of an open type with intervening glades, and during parts of the year the climate is suited to short-lived plants. Iceland has a much lower percentage of annuals. The only other class represented in the Moroccan forest is that of geophytes of which the percentage value is small, the mountain habitat with thin soils constantly exposed to erosion being unsuitable. The absence of chamaephytes appears to be due to two causes. The typical summer drought of Mediterranean areas does not occur at these elevations and this explains the absence of the woody forms. Grazing, whether by wild or domesticated animals, is intensive, and thus hemicryptophytes with their concealed buds have a better chance of survival than herbaceous chamaephytes with their exposed buds. This indeed is one of the factors which accounts for the wide prevalence of the members of the former class.

Iceland appears to have a much more varied spectrum, including marsh and water plants in its swampy lowlands and a quite considerable percentage of geophytes. The latter is a somewhat unexpected feature, but two facts have to be noted. Past and present glaciation means that the loose and light soils favoured are widespread. Further, while geophytes are normally infrequent in high latitudes because of the low winter temperatures and resultant soil freezing, Iceland, at least so far as the lower altitudes are concerned, shows distinct traces of 'oceanic' conditions. Thus over considerable areas the mean temperature of the coldest month is above or but little below freezing-point, and the winter temperatures everywhere are very notably higher than at corresponding heights in, e.g., southern Greenland. The moderate temperatures help also to account for the relatively high percentage of annuals, July temperatures both on the high grounds and the low being round about 50° F. Spitsbergen has a very much lower percentage of annuals (2 per cent). The special feature of the Icelandic spectrum, however, when compared with that of the Moroccan Atlas is the high percentage of chamaephytes.

Fig. 11 serves to indicate the effect of increasing altitude on the percentage distribution of the different classes in Iceland. Here the lowlands are excluded, Graph I showing the spectrum of the area lying roughly between 1,000 and 2,600 feet and Graph II that between 2,600 and 4,000 feet. The essential points about the contrast are that while the tolerant hemicryptophytes undergo little change with increased height, adapted chamaephytes increase enormously ; the two classes together account for over 90 per cent of the total at heights over 2,600 feet. Conditions at the upper levels are too severe for phanerophytes or marsh and water

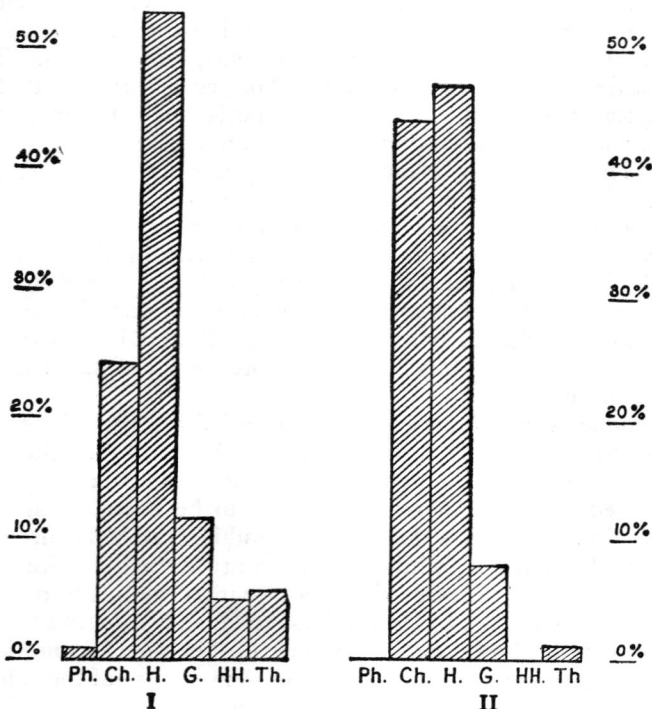

FIG. 11.—I. Spectrum of area between 1,000 and 2,600 feet in Iceland. II. Area between 2,600 and 4,000 feet

Ph., Phanerophytes ; Ch., Chamaephytes ; H., Hemicryptophytes ; G., Geophytes ; HH., Hydrophytes ; Th., Therophytes

plants, therophytes are keeping a place only with difficulty, while, presumably on account of the edaphic factor, the percentage reduction of geophytes is less marked. Again, a comparison between the spectrum of the whole flora as shown in Graph II with that of the area lying at moderate heights in Graph I, makes clear how strong is the influence of the ' oceanic ' climate of the lowlands, this being Scandinavian rather than truly Arctic or polar in type. True Arctic or polar features in the flora become accentuated only at the greater heights.

Where the polar climatic type is characteristic throughout, as in Spitsbergen and parts of Alaska, the chamaephyte percentage may run up to 60, most of the remainder being hemicryptophyte. On the other hand in the Sahara desert the percentage of annuals may be over 40, chamaephytes and dwarfed phanerophytes accounting for a large part of the remainder. Such examples illustrate the ways and the extent to which Raunkiaer's scheme enables us to interpret the local climate.

Raunkiaer's scheme is, of course, applicable to unstable as well as to climax communities. Indeed where the total flora of an area is taken, as distinct from that of a particular community within it, the resultant spectrum includes both. Thus in the spectrum of the whole of Iceland shown in Fig. 10, II, the percentages of marsh and water plants and of annuals are influenced by the presence in the island of many primary seres, or temporary plant communities representing successional phases of plant-occupation of a region. In consequence, the spectrum is not strictly comparable with that of the Moroccan cedar forest, in essence a climax community, whatever changes are brought about by man's activities, especially through his herds of grazing animals. A brief account of some primary seres may thus serve at the same time to supplement what has been said as to Raunkiaer's scheme.

In all successional seres, by definition, edaphic factors are changing while climatic ones have not had time to exert their full effect. There is usually a progressive change in the life-forms of the species present, the first colonists meeting with little or no competition but being at the same time fitted to exceptional and transient conditions. These first colonists modify and help to stabilize the physical habitat so that plants of other life-forms can enter. Thus the element of competition comes into play while at the same time climatic factors exert more and more influence till stability is attained. The point may be made clear by considering the simple case of the margin of a freshwater body where deposition is taking place.

Water and marsh plants will be the first to appear, and they obstruct movement of silt and so accelerate deposition, and help to raise the surface level. In time it is raised sufficiently to allow tolerant hemicryptophytes to come in, giving a more continuous cover of vegetation at least above the surface as distinct from the first very open community. So long as flooding occurs even occasionally, so that the water table remains high, organic remains decay slowly owing to insufficient aeration, and thus much raw humus is added which helps still further to raise the soil level. In time the area rises beyond the reach of floods and the water which then reaches it is due to rainfall, i.e. the local climate exerts its effect, while previously flooding or low water may have been due to the rainfall in perhaps distant hills. The local climate now begins to influence the soil, which acquires some at least of the features characteristic of the area generally. This means that the new surface can now be occupied by species much less tolerant of wet conditions than were the first colonists. In temperate climates like our own, where, as we have seen, hemicryptophytes are both abundant and diverse, this life-form will tend to predominate in the middle stages of the sequence ; but

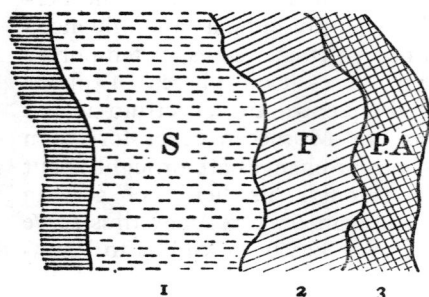

In 1, at the water edge, about 1 per cent of salt is present in the soil at a depth of 4 inches (10 cm.) and two species of Salicornia occur (S) ; in 2, only traces of salt are found at this depth, and sea-purslane or *Atriplex portulacoides* (P) appears ; in 3, salt is absent and sea-purslane occurs mixed with a species of Agropyrum (P.A.). Note that here there is no regular tidal flooding such as occurs on our shores, while summer precipitation is scanty; thus both soil moisture and soil salinity diminish as the water edge is left, and the zoning depends on the two factors. Salicornia requires soil moistened with saline water, and disappears as aridity increases and salt-content diminishes, Agropyrum is highly resistant to drought, and though salt-tolerant on occasion is not salt-demanding; Atriplex is intermediate in its requirements

FIG. 12.—Vegetation Belts on the margin of the Lagoon at Palavas, near Montpellier, Southern France
After Braun-Blanquet

the hemicryptophytes will drop down to their normal *c.* 50 per cent of the total as the conditions become stabilized and phanerophytes or chamaephytes (heath plants) come in, according to the local climate.

As a rule, successive seres become more and more complex. At first, indeed, as in the case of mangroves or of therophytes on a sandy beach, a single life-form may predominate, but the ultimate climax community is practically always composed of diverse elements.

The outstanding features of a few widely distributed types of primary seres may now be noted. Where a river enters the sea by a wide estuary, salt marshes tend to develop. Here we have both moving, silt-laden river water and salt ocean water influenced by tidal ebb and flow, the movements being markedly variable in force and amount. The tides, of course, show both diurnal fortnightly and monthly periodicity, while the mixture of fresh and salt water causes deposition of suspended material. Where the surface is subjected to rapid, alternating currents, fixed plants cannot establish themselves, and, apart from Zostera (p. 30), few plants other than Algae can tolerate constant or quasi-constant submergence in saline water. As deposition raises the surface above all but occasional tidal flooding, however, Salicornia or marsh samphire comes in as a pioneer. It belongs to the Goosefoot family (*Chenopodiaceae*) including a number of plants which occupy loose surfaces and are both resistant to drought and tolerant of saline soils. Thus they tend to occupy waste spaces, such as semi-deserts or areas cleared by natural causes or man's activities. Many Chenopods are halophytic succulents while others have a mealy appearance due to a coating of fine hairs. The genus *Salicornia* seems to be very variable, a common feature in the family, and the marsh samphires of Europe occur, in annual, biennial and perennial forms, as halophytic succulents.

The next stage is marked by the entrance of another marsh plant, the grass *Glyceria maritima*. This is a perennial with a creeping root-stock giving off fibrous roots and aerial shoots. By checking current action it facilitates deposition of silt. The annuals, like *Suaeda maritima* or sea blite, chamaephytes such as sea-purslane (*Atriplex* or *Obione portulacoides*) both Chenopods, with sea-thrift (*Armeria vulgaris*), another chamaephyte, as well as a variety of hemicryptophytes, arrive. Halophytic features conspicuous in the early colonists become less noticeable as the area is raised above tide water. *Festuca rubra*, a grass allied to sheep's fescue, helps to make the plant community a closed one, and thereafter grazing develops (saltings of English farmers and *prés salés* of French ones) and trampling and manuring by animals as well as diking and draining by man promote the establishment of an artificial grassland.

Sand beaches present rather different conditions. Wave and wind action tend to pile up sand above high-tide mark, where it is rarely submerged save during exceptionally high tides, especially when an onshore gale coincides with a high spring tide. Thus salting is due to spray rather than to flooding, the rooting medium is loose and liable to blowing ; but it is enriched by the decay of the flotsam and jetsam of the beach. Gales and therefore flooding are more frequent in winter than in summer, and thus all the conditions favour summer annuals, provided these are tolerant of a saline soil. Among such annuals are various Chenopods, e.g. species of *Atriplex* (orache) and saltwort (*Salsola kali*) also sea rocket (*Cakile maritima*), a Crucifer with fleshy leaves and stock-like flowers.   Sea sandwort (*Arenaria peploides*), a member of the Pink family, is on the other hand a hemicryptophyte with small thickened leaves.   It is more characteristic of shingle than of sand beaches, but since stones are not uncommonly mixed with sand, it may find the necessary stability on a sandy beach. The plants form an open community, very inconstant, for the annuals may occupy different sites from year to year as the beach deposits are continually shifting.

As against this constantly changing fringe of loose sand, just above average high-tide mark we may have deposits of rather more stable nature.   Here the chief colonist is sea couch grass (*Agropyrum junceum*).   In Raunkiaer's scheme it ranks as between a hemicryptophyte and a geophyte, for the much-branched creeping root-stocks can throw up shoots from the nodes even when they are deeply buried.   It is thus admirably adapted for colonizing loose deposit, and sea couch is tolerant of occasional but repeated submersion in salt water.   Because of its creeping rootstocks and upright shoots the plant checks sand-drift and thus forms miniature dunes, gradually raised above the level of even exceptional tides by the deposition of wind-blown sand.

Marram grass (*Ammophila arenaria*) grows more strongly. It has stout, stiff stems bearing smooth, inrolled leaves, and the whole plant is very resistant to drought.   It is intolerant of even occasional submergence, but once sand has been heaped up to a height sufficient to obviate the risk of this, it spreads quickly, helping to fix the dune and to limit ' blow-outs '.   Lyme grass (*Elymus arenarius*) has similar features.   These two and especially marram, are the great agents in fixing high dunes, and though occasionally and locally on our shores other species may be present, they are of minor importance in the early stages.

As the surface becomes stabilized, however, and added humus, partly from lichens and mosses, increases the water-holding power, other plants come in which must still be drought-resistant. They include grass of the dry pasture type, and such familiar plants as restharrow (*Ononis*), burnet rose, bedstraw, (*Galium*), milkwort (*Polygala*), ladies' fingers (*Lotus*), thyme, bracken and so on, of varied life-form.   The complete absence from this closed community of the scattered annuals of sand beaches is noteworthy, as is also the disappearance of marram save where the burrowing of rabbits leads to blow-outs, and the succession goes back to an earlier stage or ' retrogresses '.   The later stages are usually obscured by man's interference, but without this a stable community such as woodland or heath would no doubt develop according to the local climate.

The mangroves of sheltered bays and lagoons fed by torrential rivers rich in silt from summer rains within the tropics are a primary sere contrasting with those of temperate lands. Tidal ebb and flow, heavy deposition, warmth and torrential seasonal, often monsoon, rains all help to give the advantages to trees rather than to herbs, while the need for remarkable adaptations for root-breathing and other matters restricts the number of plant-genera involved. Rhizophora and Bruguiera are two of the chief genera

FIG. 13.—Stilt-roots of Mangrove (*Rhizophora conjugata*)

and belong to the order Rhizophoraceae, while Avicennia, the white mangrove, belongs to the Verbenaceae. These plants are best developed and richest in species in east Africa and south Asia with extensions to north Australia and the Pacific ; a few patches occur on the north-west coast of South America and on its continuation in central America. There are fewer species and less mangrove development on the shores of the Atlantic.

Very remarkable adaptations occur.

1. Typical mangroves of the genus Rhizophora develop inter-lacing stilt-roots. These ensure firm anchorage on the shifting surface, and as they develop successively higher and higher up the trunks minimize the danger of those first formed being stifled

in the evil-smelling mud as its level rises. Further, since the upper roots are exposed at least at low tide, oxygen can enter through their special pores or lenticels ; there is little oxygen in the mud owing to the rapid decomposition of organic matter.

2. Some mangroves have no stilt-roots but develop on their much-branched root system special breathing organs or pneumatophores, which project above the surface, bear complex lenticels and thus facilitate respiration (see Fig. 14).

3. In Rhizophora what is called vivipary occurs, that is, the seeds germinate while still attached to the parent, without the usual resting period, sending out a large primary root. The seedlings have a floating mechanism which allows them to be carried by the tide and thus ensures dispersal. If they drop direct to the mud they fall in such a position as to bury the root,

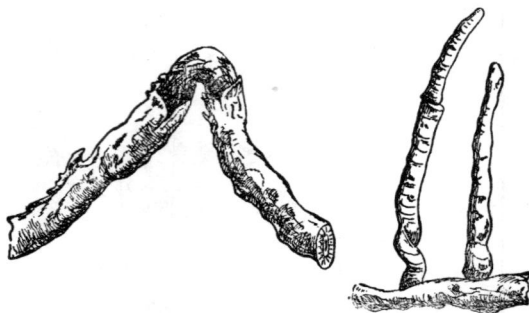

FIG. 14.—Roots of Mangrove (enlarged)
After Schimper

which grows with great rapidity and fixes the young plant. Germination would be difficult if the seeds escaped in the usual fashion owing to the low oxygen content of the mud.

4. Mangroves are drought-resistant, showing in their leathery, shining and thickened leaves features common in halophytes.

The stilt-roots, pneumatophores and viviparously produced seedlings result in exceedingly dense growth, which virtually prevents the entrance of other plants, and makes mangrove almost impenetrable by land animals or man. It has, however, a highly specialized marine fauna of its own, including the curious fish Periophthalmus, allied to the gobies, which, in this medium, neither land nor water, has acquired almost frog-like habits. Thus when the tide ebbs and the mud is exposed it ' hops ' about on the surface, using its strong pectoral fins and tail in the process. The eyes are near together at the top of the head, readily susceptible of motion, and can be protruded like those of a frog. By their aid Periophthalmus hunts the small crustaceans which leap over the mud in the same fashion as our sandhoppers and beach fleas. Amphibians, be it noted, are excluded here owing to their sensitiveness to salt, and there is no real resemblance between the fish and a frog.

A further point of interest in the mangroves is the presence of a large amount of tannin, forming the cutch of commerce. This seems to be a protection against the attacks of marine animals such

Fig. 15.—Mud-skipper (*Periophthalmus*)
After A. Günther

as the ship-worm (*Teredo*), a burrowing mollusc very destructive to wood.

Like the other successional seres described mangrove swamp forms but a narrow fringe on the seaward margin. Inland it gives place gradually to the forest characteristic of the local climate, whether equatorial, monsoonal or of scrub type. A curious fact is the presence of the same mangroves on both sides of the Atlantic. This is sometimes ascribed to their great power of dispersion by currents, though this is difficult to believe. Meantime we need note only that there are other if scanty indications of affinities between the plants of tropical West Africa and tropical America.

NOTE

The account of the spectrum of the Icelandic flora is based on *Studies on the Vegetation of Iceland*, by H. Mølholm Hansen, which forms Vol. III, Part I, of *The Botany of Iceland*, edited by L. K. Rosenvinge and Eug. Warming (Copenhagen, 1930). Though highly technical this contains much material of value to the plant geographer.

The value of Raunkiaer's scheme is best realized by actual handling of plants, in both the active and resting stages, so that a practical knowledge of gardening is important. Even the townsman can learn much by watching the sequence of events and the methods adopted in public parks and gardens. Thus a common sequence in flower beds is a spring geophytic community (bulbs) followed by a therophytic one (summer annuals); skill comes in with the intercalation of other life-forms to give variety, as when a semi-woody chamaephyte like the wallflower is introduced into a bulb bed, or the bulbs are interplanted with rosette or creeping hemicryptophytes like primulas, double daisies, violas or forget-me-nots.

For an elaboration of Raunkiaer's scheme see the translation of J. Braun-Blanquet's *Pflanzensoziologie*, edited by G. D. Fuller under the title of *Plant Sociology* (New York and London, 1932), a book which, though somewhat too technical for the ordinary geographical student, contains much valuable material and an admirable series of illustrations.

CHAPTER VII

FOREST COMMUNITIES

FACTORS CONTROLLING FOREST DISTRIBUTION

FORESTS in the strict sense are communities in which tall phanerophytes are individually so numerous that their crowns form a complete canopy shading the ground. Since the bulky tissues contain much fluid absorbed from the soil, while the buds are fully exposed to the local atmospheric conditions, it is clear that there must be a definite climatic control to their range. That they should occur where rainfall and temperatures are for a considerable part of the year favourable to vegetative activities is to be expected. But such a state of affairs prevails only over a limited part of the earth's surface, and the problem therefore is to find what minimum conditions must be satisfied before forest appears elsewhere in any of its varied types.

The limiting factors may be summarized as follows :—

1. Bearing in mind that bulky permanent tissues have to be built up, and that the shoots formed each season have to be ripened sufficiently to withstand the following unfavourable season, it is clear that there must be a long growing period. Apparently, herbaceous growth can often go on under conditions of temperature below the limit for woody growth ; for example, a mean July temperature of not less than 50° F. is needed for formation of dense stands of even the hardiest northern conifers. Low temperatures thus limit forest range both in high latitudes and at the greater altitudes.

2. The deeper layers of the soil must be permanently moist and the moisture present must be in a readily available form. The actual rainfall necessary to ensure adequate reserves of soil moisture varies greatly both with local temperatures as affecting evaporation and with tree type. Certain general points are, nevertheless, clear. Since trees are long-lived, the long-period fluctuations in the total fall must not be such as to lead to exhaustion of soil reserves ; regions of highly variable rainfall are therefore unsuitable. Demands on soil moisture are greatest

8

during the growing season ; therefore, other things being equal, areas of warm-season rainfall will be more favourable to forest than those with cold-season precipitation.   Since some moisture must be absorbed even during the ' dead ' season, a low total markedly seasonal in character inhibits forest development.

3. Where very low winter temperatures occur the air must be relatively calm.   Winds, especially dry winds, are indeed a notable limiting factor, particularly in high latitudes and at great elevations, where they tend to lead to a loss of moisture which cannot be made good by absorption from the chilled soil.

With these facts as basis it is easy to deduce the parts of the earth's surface which are likely to carry forest.   Beginning with the northern hemisphere and considering first the interior of the land-masses, we find that in the far north forests will be excluded by the shortness of the growing season and the low temperatures, so that here a fringe of cold desert or tundra appears.   As one goes south, the month of maximum rainfall in successive belts changes from August to July and July to June.   In the belt first reached coniferous forest is the result of conditions of slow evaporation.   In the next, forest may be predominantly deciduous or coniferous according to facts of soil or situation ; in the next again, with a lower rainfall and an increase in convectional storms in the warm summer, forest and grassland become interspersed. As these conditions become accentuated, the soil ceases to retain the necessary reserves of moisture, and grassland of the steppe type replaces forest.

Let us turn next to the conditions on east and west coast margins.   In both cases, if the continent concerned extends far enough to the north, tundra will tend to appear, though the more favourable temperature conditions on west coasts will limit its southern extension there as compared with eastern coasts.   On both also conditions favour forest development as the cold zone is left.   As we travel southwards, however, a striking difference becomes apparent and that for quite familiar reasons.   On west coasts in the cool temperate latitudes the onshore winds bring abundant rain, well distributed throughout the year but with a cool-season maximum.   Still farther south the total fall tends to diminish, absolutely or in relation to evaporation, without loss of the cool-season maximum, leading, apart from relief rains, to steadily increasing summer drought.   As this becomes marked, forest density diminishes, the trees thinning out till finally hot desert appears.   As rainfall once more increases south of the Tropic of Cancer, with a warm-season maximum, desert passes into savanna or bush savanna with forests along the watercourses, and the sequence—as is well illustrated in Africa—is completed by tropical or equatorial rain forest, the latter only when the total reaches or exceeds 80 inches and there is no definitely dry season.

East coasts with some exceptions get more summer rain and the winter maximum with summer drought does not occur. Asia shows at once great extension in latitude and monsoonal influences most fully developed, and here, save for man, forest extends in virtual continuity from the Arctic Circle to the Equator, conditions becoming increasingly favourable as we travel southwards.

Thus ignoring the effects of local topography and of the relations of land and water, we may get a broad view of forest distribution in the northern hemisphere. A great belt extends across the land-masses in the higher latitudes, including both coastal belts and continental interiors. In the interior of the continents, save where massive mountain ranges introduce modifications, the belt tends to fade out southwards into temperate grassland. On the western margin the forest belt shows a varying extension towards the interior but similarly fades out southwards into hot desert, and there is a definite gap before another forest type appears with increased rainfall, at first summer rain and later all-season. On eastern margins there is not this gap, and the tendency is for at least a fringe of forest to extend continuously—where the lands are continuous—and with increasing luxuriance to the Equator.

In the southern hemisphere forest distribution is similar in essentials with the notable difference due to the fact that the land-masses taper southwards and do not extend continuously into such high latitudes. Thus the great forest belt of the higher latitudes of the north is represented here only by a few scattered patches as in southern Chile, Tasmania and parts of New Zealand. Elsewhere conditions comparable to those found in the northern hemisphere tend to occur, modified by the size and shape of the lands and their relief. The wide continent of Australia, for example, shows with remarkable clearness the fact that, in the latitudes concerned, conditions are favourable to forest development on the eastern margin, where a continuous fringe is present, and unfavourable on the western where the forest is limited to the south-western area of winter rainfall.

THE MAIN FOREST TYPES AND THEIR RANGE

Range and Limits of Temperate Forests. Climate influences not only the distribution of forest but also that of forest type, and in noting the salient points here we may conveniently begin again with the northern hemisphere and a continental interior. European Russia in its western section (Fig. 16a) shows that the forest belt already defined falls into a northern coniferous belt and a more southerly tropophytic one.   But, as most text-books do not fail to indicate, the latter, as we travel farther into the interior, is, as it were, narrowed between the encroaching coniferous belt and the increasingly arid type of steppe till, in the vicinity of Kazan near the Volga bend, it is pinched out and disappears (Fig. 16b).   Comparable conditions occur, if not quite

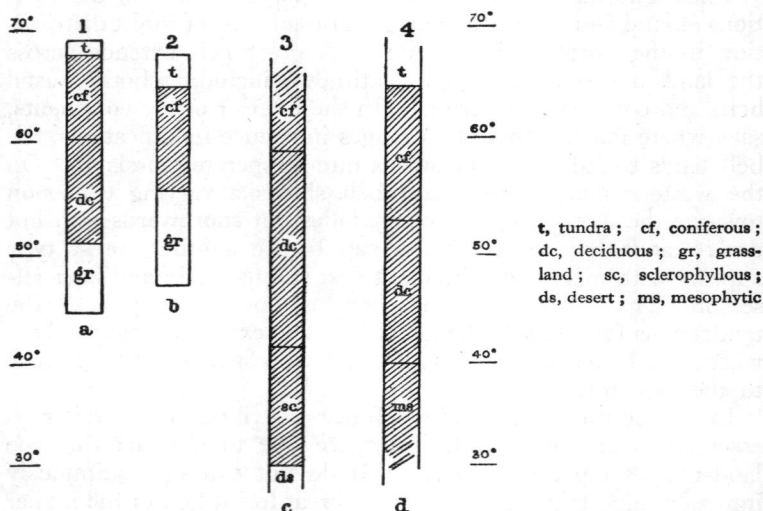

FIG. 16.—1. Russia from Murmansk coast to Gulf of Perekop.   2. Petchora River to mouth of the Ural River.   3. West Central Europe.   4. East coast of Asia

in so striking a fashion, in the interior of North America, while the mountainous character of inner Asia practically excludes a belt of tropophytic forest there.

Turning next to eastern and western margins we find that on the western border of the Eurasian land-mass (Fig. 16c) there is again a division between a northern coniferous belt and a more southerly summer-green one, the latter passing into the Mediterranean sclerophyllous type as summer drought becomes marked. In the absence of any continuous north-to-south mountain barrier both the first two extend well into the continental interior while the third has also a notable eastward extension owing to the presence of the Mediterranean Sea. Conditions differ on the west coast of North America, for here the tropophytic belt is not represented, a point to which we shall return in a moment, and the Cordilleran chain limits the spread of forest towards the interior.

On the eastern border of Asia (Fig. 16d) we find again a division into coniferous and tropophytic belts, and this occurs also in Atlantic North America. Southwards in both cases the latter gives place not to scrub forest but to what is called the mesophytic type. Here the component trees may be evergreen or deciduous, both conditions occurring in the very characteristic magnolia family. The trees differ from those of the sclerophyllous forest in not being drought-resistant, and from those of the tropophytic one in that they are not necessarily deciduous, so that the forest as a whole shows a less sharp contrast between summer and winter conditions, while their buds have less protection against winter cold. Both genera and species also tend to be numerous, so that the forest is highly varied in character and vegetation is luxuriant.

Thus in temperate and warm temperate latitudes four kinds of forest occur showing considerable differences in their component trees. The northern one has a great predominance of conifers, and under certain conditions gives place southwards to the tropophytic one, characterized by the presence of a comparatively small number of dicotyledonous genera represented by deciduous species ; with these, however, conifers may be mingled. East coastal areas under warm temperate conditions bear mesophytic forest, distinguished by its great wealth of dicotyledonous trees of varied type, with some monocotyledonous ones (palms), while conifers are again present. On west coasts the place of this type is taken by the scrubby, sclerophyllous forest, including mainly evergreen dicotyledonous trees, with a considerable admixture of conifers and again some palms. If it seems fairly clear that climatic influences control the range of the mesophytic and sclerophyllous types, the other two demand a little consideration.

The conifers of the northern forest are accompanied by a small number of species of dicotyledonous genera, such as birch, willow, poplar, alder, characterized by their small, somewhat stunted leaves. Like the conifers they are very resistant to low temperatures. Such trees make smaller demands on the soil than those like deciduous oaks, beech, ash, and so on which have more luxuriant summer foliage and more rapid metabolism. The conifers with their slower metabolism absorb fewer bases, including lime, require less water and lose less, and can thrive almost equally well where the soil is acid and heavily leached (podsolized), and where decomposition of its constituents is checked by moderate and markedly seasonal rainfall. The trophophytic trees are more sharply limited by climatic factors in their double effect on them and on the soil. They require, especially beech, abundant moisture in the growing season; they demand also that the chemical changes in the soil should be rapid so that the material derived from the shed leaves is promptly available, for the strain of producing within a brief period a whole new canopy of luxuriant foliage is great. Thus both temperature and rainfall conditions must be continuously favourable during a long season and the soil must be rich in bases, including lime. Then they can crowd out the conifers and their companions and form practically pure stands; any notable departure from the necessary norm enables the latter more tolerant forms to come in.

Note the result. In the first place, because of the generally rich soils over which they occur, man's influence has been continually exerted against the summer-green forest; vegetation maps are in consequence apt to be deceptive, for much of this trophophytic forest shown has long since ceased to exist. Again, any local change in climate due to relief or other physiographical factors, such as exposure, brings the conifers into what should be the broad-leaved zone. Any notable change in soil has the same effect. As already stated (p. 67), the parent material does seem to exert a marked effect in the case of the Brown Earths, the soils over which trophophytic forests are mainly found. Immaturity of soil also favours conifers and, if they succeed in colonizing such areas, their presence may delay the changes which would lead to the development of typical Brown Earths. Generally, then, even without man's influence the belt of trophophytic forest is more or less interrupted by conifers which may be locally abundant.

As we go into the interior of continents, forest ultimately gives place to steppe and trophophytic trees disappear before sclerophyllous ones because they are less resistant to drought. On eastern coasts the southern extension of the trophophytic forest is limited by the appearance of the richer and more diversified mesophytic forest, which may be said to begin in about 40° N. lat., roughly in the latitude of Peking in Asia and near New York in Atlantic North America. The presence of this type is associated with higher summer temperatures and abundant summer rainfall. In western Europe trophophytic forest occurs mainly between 40° and 55°–60° N. lat. with sclerophyllous trees, especially of the genus Pinus, to north and south because of slower metabolism and summer drought respectively, the species naturally differing in the two cases. Dicotyledonous trees are more abundant and varied on the eastern sides of land-masses and coniferous trees more important on the western sides, especially in North America. This difference complicates the comparison between western North America and western Europe.

The factors controlling the range of summer-green forest are thus complex. There is a climatic control ; for while winter temperatures are relatively unimportant there must be a long and fairly warm growing season, and total rainfall must be sufficient to keep the soil in a moist condition while a considerable part of it must fall during the warmer period. There is a soil control ; for this must be rich in bases and at best but mildly acid. There is a competition control ; for any disturbance of the necessary delicate adjustments will bring in the conifers. The actual composition of the flora is also important as is shown by the fact that conifers form nearly pure stands in parts of western North America where, judging from European conditions, we should expect to find typical trophophytic forest.

Distribution of Conifers. Let us note first the main points about the distribution of conifers in the northern hemisphere, for this throws light on the range of forest types. As already seen, in the more northerly latitudes the conifers, with their comparatively small number of dicotyledonous associates, reign virtually supreme. In dry continental interiors also they form the southern limit of forest. Broadly, then, we may say that few dicotyledonous trees can tolerate either cold climates or a combination of cold winters and low rainfall, conditions to which some conifers are perfectly suited. On the other hand, the conifers' power of competing with dicotyledonous trees on *lowlands* virtually ceases about 40° N. lat. This is roughly where, on western coasts, drought-resistant dicotyledonous trees come in and on eastern coasts those of mesophytic type. It is possibly the relatively warm and moist soil during the cool season which acts as a check to the conifers ; we find at least that where they are present in numbers on the lower grounds the soil is usually either sandy or derived from limestone rocks and in both cases does not hold water well.

Apart, however, from their appearance on the low grounds under special soil conditions, the physiological peculiarities which enable them to extend so far to the north permit them to thrive on uplands and mountains in the warmer belt. Thus both in eastern Asia and in western North America, both areas of high relief, they are present in great numbers in the lower latitudes, the genera being often peculiar to the area concerned and strikingly different from the more widely distributed ones found farther north. Thus Cryptomeria is peculiar to Japan, Sequoia to California, while the larch genus extends right across the northern hemisphere in the higher latitudes. Still farther south, within the tropical belt, the general limitation of conifers to mountains of considerable height becomes accentuated, so that there is, as it were, a gap before we find them again on lowlands in high southern latitudes. The forms present here differ notably from those of the northern hemisphere.

We may turn next to the influence of the floral elements present on the range of forest types. So long ago as 1884 the botanist Asa Gray drew up a list of tree species in Atlantic and Pacific North America as compared with those found in Japan and Manchuria to the east, and northern and central Europe on the western border of the Eurasian land-mass. His results are shown graphically in Fig. 17, and without laying any stress upon the actual figures we may use the graph to bring out some of the contrasts between eastern and western margins and between the two continental areas.

We see that the two eastern areas show an enormous wealth of dicotyledonous trees as compared with the two western. In part this is to be expected in view of the rainfall conditions ; it will be noted that Atlantic North America includes the zone of mesophytic forest, while part of the same zone in Asia is included in southern Japan. But the Ice Age appears also to have exerted some influence. In Asia especially the land-mass extends far to the south, and in neither area is there any notable or continuous transverse mountain barrier. It is believed that during the maximum glaciation the more delicate trees ' retreated ' southwards and re-advanced as conditions improved. The greater wealth of the Asiatic area in conifers is doubtless due to the fact that mountain refuges were available to the south from which a re-advance could be made.

The European area, on the other hand, is relatively poor in dicotyledonous trees and very poor in conifers. Prior to the Ice Age it had a much richer tree flora, and it seems clear that the combination of the transverse Alpine chains and the long Mediterranean Sea made a southern retreat impossible and led to large-scale extermination. The Balkan peninsula formed a sort of pocket within which certain of the Tertiary trees found a refuge, but not all of these have been able to re-colonize the ground lost.

Conditions are even more striking in Pacific North America. Here even the inclusion of the belt of sclerophyllous forest leaves the total number of dicotyledonous trees very low, and they are definitely surpassed by the conifers, which are much more

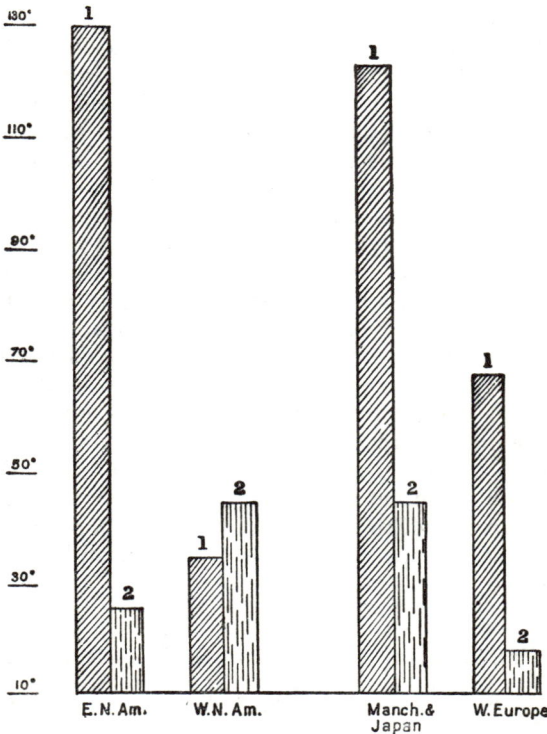

FIG. 17.—1. Dicotyledonous ; 2. Conifers
Eastern North America.   West North America.   Manchuria and Japan.   West Europe

numerously represented than in central and northern Europe. The extreme poverty of the dicotyledonous tree flora must be an effect of glaciation, and we have to note the presence of the longitudinal Cordilleran belt which must have offered a barrier to that re-colonization from the south-east which seems to have occurred in Europe.   The proximity of the mountain belt to the coast also, and the way in which it occurs in series of chains must have left little room for numbers of lowland trees to find a refuge to the south.   On the other hand, the complex topography and high relief doubtless enabled the conifers to survive glaciation in greater numbers.   The same factors, combined with the absence of competition from dicotyledonous trees, permit them to cover areas in, e.g., southern British Columbia and Washington which we should have expected to carry tropophytic forest.

To the subject of the Tertiary forest of the northern hemisphere we shall return later.   Meantime, it is worth note that where man has striven to enrich the scanty tree flora of northern and central Europe by planting exotics he has introduced both conifers and dicotyledons from eastern Asia, but from North America mainly dicotyledons from the east and mainly conifers (Douglas fir, Sitka spruce, Sequoia, &c.) from the west.   The Glacial Period, that is to say, impoverished Europe in both but especially in conifers, this effect reaching its maximum in Britain. It left Asia at least relatively rich in both and, while reducing the dicotyledons of North America enormously, especially in the higher latitudes, it left a number of economically useful conifers which are quite tolerant of European conditions.

This survey may serve to make clear the general nature of the factors influencing the range of types of forest in the northern hemisphere.   We need not pursue it into the southern one, for there the conditions are comparable so far as latitudes permit. It should however be emphasized that if ecologically the forest types are comparable yet the actual floral elements differ vastly. Not a few genera which formed part of the northern Tertiary forest and have disappeared completely there, still linger in the south.

CHARACTERISTICS OF THE MAJOR FOREST TYPES

1. *Equatorial Rain Forest.*   In looking in a little more detail at the chief forest types we may conveniently reverse the former order and consider first the tropical rain forest as representing the most luxuriant type of a woodland community.   It has three major characteristics : (*a*) the multiplicity of arboreal species present, for here we are far indeed from the condition present in temperate latitudes where one species, e.g. of pine or birch, may form an almost pure stand ; (*b*) the great development of stratification, several tiers of trees being present in addition to others formed by more lowly plants ; (*c*) the numbers and variety of climbers and epiphytes, the former including many woody types (lianes), the latter not only belonging to a great variety of systematic groups but showing (e.g. orchids) special

adaptations as contrasted with the ' accidental ' epiphytism of the lichens, mosses and occasional ferns of our woods.

The number of species of trees is, of course, responsible for the high percentage of phanerophytes (p. 113), and has also some relation to the number of tree tiers.   It is often said that under hot, wet conditions competition finds expression chiefly in the struggle towards the light.   In point of fact, however, the different strata have each their own species, and these, if they may be said to strive to reach their own level before attaining full development, make no attempt to pass beyond it, even if opportunity offers.   In other words, the arboreal species seem to fall into three or more groups, each possessing not only a particular height limit, but also a related degree of tolerance of the shading due to the canopy of the next tier above.   The species present in the topmost tier presumably demand, at least in the full-grown stage, complete exposure.   Thus the struggle towards the light mainly affects the sapling stages.   It may be added that some of the occasional herbaceous forms of the lowest tier have iridescent or violet leaves, apparently to help them to make the fullest use of the light rays which penetrate the forest gloom.   This again suggests that the members of the different tiers are not all striving to overtop their neighbours, but are definitely adapted to a particular stratum.

For root room, on the other hand, there does appear to be a struggle.   The rapid chemical decomposition and the intense leaching means that there is but a thin layer of vegetal mould within which all roots must occur.   Those of the trees are largely superficial, and there is probably not that kind of root statification known to occur in some temperate woodlands where the elements in the cover may have their roots or root-stocks at different soil levels.   Because of the limited and congested root-run the taller trees have not much holding power, a real danger since strong winds are not unknown, while the heavy foliage offers much resistance as compared with the yielding of some temperate trees, such as birches with their whip-like branches.   It is believed that the buttressed appearance of the lower part of the trunk in many of the taller trees of the hot rain forest is an adaptation to minimize wind-shaking and thus possible tearing of the roots.   The trees show wing-like outgrowths which may extend 10 to 25 feet up the trunk and give rise below to main roots standing above ground-level.   Other trees have what are variously called open buttresses or stilt-roots, that is, the wings are not continuous with the trunk but separated by a gap, giving a flying buttress effect.

Lianes also seem to be important in the upper part of the canopy, acting like stays. The point is interesting, because travellers tend to emphasize the strangling nature of the giant lianes, and to regard the size and number of these as another evidence of the struggle towards the light. Some lianes are indeed typical ' stranglers ', this being especially true of those belonging to the large genus Ficus, which includes the fig, the banyan and a large number of tropical lianes. Some of the last begin as humble epiphytes or modest creepers, but, owing to their power of throwing out both clasping roots and aerial roots which extend downwards to the ground and fix themselves there, can in time develop into independent trees which suppress completely the original supporting tree, the decaying tissues of which help to nourish the greedy supplanter. This is clearly an adaptation to get over the difficulty already noted which young specimens have in finding room in the crowded forest to grow up to the level for which they are best fitted. Many of the giant lianes, on the other hand, extend from tree to tree like great cables and must reduce the ' wind-shake ' which would otherwise be transmitted to the roots. In addition, the interlacing of the branches of the different trees offers some support against wind action.

The forest is often described as evergreen, which is true in the sense that leaves throughout are not simultaneously shed. They seem, however, as a rule, to be renewed annually, while the very resistant leaves of some temperate conifers may endure for five or even more years. In the rain forest individual trees devoid of leaves may be observed at any period, though a new crop soon develops. It would seem that those minor variations in rainfall intensity which occur even in the most truly equatorial climate exert an effect but that, owing to the multiplicity of species present and the varying adaptations shown by these, there is no uniformity of response. In consequence leaf-shedding, when the forest as a whole is considered, is a sporadic rather than a periodic phenomenon affecting all species at once. The leaves usually show adaptations to prevent water from lying on their surface ; they may be glossy so that water drains off, or else narrow to a long point (drip-tip) which carries it off.

Flowering, like leaf-shedding, occurs in quite sporadic fashion and not at any fixed season, an important point in connexion with animal life, for it means that fruits, including pulpy fruits, are available at all seasons. A common and peculiar feature also, the significance of which is not known, is the appearance of the flowers on the older stems or trunk (cauliflory) or occasionally even on roots instead of on terminal branches.

As a rule there is not a well-developed ground flora, presumably because of the diminished intensity of light. Grasses are infrequent as are also mosses. In temporary clearings, however, and also where periodical flooding checks the density of the tree stand, certain giant monocotyledonous herbs occur. Of much interest are those belonging to the order Scitamineae, including the four families of Musaceae (banana, plantain, &c.), Marantaceae (with several arrowroot-yielding plants), Cannaceae (note the bright-flowered cultivated Indian canna) and Zingiberaceae (with several economic plants, e.g. ginger, cardamom spice, East Indian arrowroot). Of these the banana family is almost confined to the Old World, the ginger family is chiefly represented in the Indo-Malay area, while the other two are mainly American. The distribution justifies us in saying that all the areas in which tropical rain forest occurs possess representatives of the Scitamineae, often peculiar to the area concerned.

The banana genus may serve to illustrate some of the special adaptations. It has a root-stock from which it throws up what looks like a giant stem bearing the flowers and fruit. But this stem is in reality formed only by the inrolled sheaths of the leaves which expand above into large oval blades. Because the plant is a monocotyledon the veins of the leaves are parallel and afford little support to so large a leaf. Under cultivation the leaves soon become ragged ; in the natural forest habitat they must receive much protection from wind and rain from the dense canopy above. The 'false stem' is clearly a device to ensure rapid aerial growth with the minimum of material, while the broad leaves are efficient starch-making organs. The fact that the root-stocks in some members of the order are used as a source of starch suggests that they are storing organs. Thus we arrive at the notion of these plants waiting, as it were, their chance underground, and then flinging up a great mass of leaves in order to make the fullest use of their opportunity when it comes. The illustration may serve to remind us that while many herbs in the equatorial forest must needs be epiphytes for there is little room for them on the ground, yet there are openings there for specialized forms. Further, as occurs if to a less marked extent in our woods, non-green parasites, independent of light, may appear on the tree roots, while saprophytes, or plants feeding on decaying organic matter, may also occur.

Generally, then, the tropical rain forest is characterized by its diversity, especially of dicotyledons, monocotyledons and ferns.

Conifers only come in with increased elevation, especially, for example, in East Africa where mountain cedar (an arboreal juniper) and the genus Podocarpus occur. Mosses and lichens are similarly crowded out at the lower levels, but come in as the forest thins with an increase in the height of the land. But the common idea that in this forest type species are ceaselessly struggling against each other for light and space must not be pushed to extremes ; it is a true community, the members of which show delicate adjustments both to each other and to the habitat conditions.

2. *Tropical Forests with a Seasonal Rhythm.* In its typical form the tropical rain forest has a limited range. An increase in elevation causes it to give place to mountain forest, some of the features of which we have already noted. Again, on the lower grounds as a definitely dry season appears with increasing distance from the equatorial rain belt it passes into a transitional type, characterized by a smaller number of species, diminished density and particularly by a more marked periodicity in leaf-shedding which alters completely the look of the forest. Apart from the true monsoonal areas of Asia and those, mainly coastal ones, elsewhere marked by a somewhat similar monsoonal indraught which increases total precipitation, this transitional forest type has an even more limited extension. As seasonal aridity becomes marked and total rainfall diminishes, true closed forest is replaced by parkland and bush savanna. Here the trees are more scattered save in favourable localities such as near watercourses, show increasing adaptations to enable them to resist drought, and are more and more mingled with tall grasses which may overtop the stunted trees during the wet season.

In the typical tropical monsoonal areas of Asia and the similar but more restricted areas elsewhere, conditions are different. Where the total rainfall is high the forest during the wet season at least may show a density and luxuriance analogous to that of the rain forest, though woody epiphytes tend to be fewer, lianes not being developed on the same scale, while the trees do not reach quite the same height. The theoretical distinction between this luxuriant monsoonal forest and true rain forest is that the former includes a considerable proportion of trees which shed their leaves during the dry season. Teak (*Tectona grandis*) may be taken as an example, and is a tree with a somewhat wide range in India and Burma. The actual appearance of the forests in any area depends on the competition between the hygrophytic species proper and those adapted to withstand seasonal drought. This appears to be only in part influenced by the prevailing moisture conditions, for man has undoubtedly exerted much influence. Note in the first place that while true rain forest has shown much resistance to human penetration, with the monsoonal areas in the wider sense we come to regions where cultivation, stock-rearing and effective forest exploitation become possible.

Presumably because of the small risk under natural conditions of fires caused by lightning, rain forest species show little fire-resistance. That is, if there is heavy preliminary clearing, and advantage can be taken of a brief dry period for firing, the trees are completely destroyed. It is, on the other hand, generally true that the species characteristic of areas with a well-marked dry season show notable fire-resistance, at least in the adult stages. This seems to be associated with the frequency of the risk under even natural conditions, for the intense insolation combined with the presence of much inflammable material in the form of the dead leaves and stems of the tall grasses ensures rapid fire spread from even a spark. In the more open tropical woods occasional fires are probably of some benefit to the dominant trees. They destroy the mat of dried ground vegetation and so facilitate the germination of the tree seeds, while the check to the growth of the grasses aids the seedlings to make a start. Where rainfall is heavier the character of the forest, i.e. the relative predominance of hygrophytic and deciduous species, seems to depend largely on the frequency or otherwise of forest fires. This has been noted especially in India, where the forests are carefully managed and the forester as a matter of routine endeavours to give as complete fire protection as possible. The result is not, how-ever, what might have been expected, for it is found that with complete fire protection rain forest species tend to creep in, including those herbaceous members of the Scitamineae already described.

In the forests of northern India (the Himalayan foothills and again across the Ganges) sal (*Shorea robusta*) is one of the valuable species. The tree has winged seeds, and the presence of heavy undergrowth prevents these reaching the surface, while the soil conditions which develop where this undergrowth is thick seem quite unsuitable to the growth of the seedlings. Thus, if complete fire protection is given sal may ultimately disappear, a forest of the hygrophytic type replacing it. Similar effects appear with teak forests, especially in the moister parts of their range, for teak is tolerant of a considerable range of moisture conditions.

To realize the true significance of this phenomenon we must go a little further back. It seems clear that if forests like those

in which sal or teak form a large element run back so readily to
a modified rain forest type when protected from fire, then they
are not strictly climax communities, but largely successional
series dependent on frequent firing.   Now, apart from burning
to extend cultivation, man at all stages of culture is always tending
to set fire to forest.   This may be accidental or done to assist
hunting or to encourage pasture grasses.   It is probable, therefore,
that we may generalize from the Indian observations and say
that the present range of that type of forest which is transitional
between the rain forest and the bush savanna type is rarely due
wholly to natural causes, but has been largely influenced by
human action.   This seems to be true especially of Africa,
where parkland, bush savanna and transitional types are widespread.

3. *Sclerophyllous Forests*.   In the Sclerophyllous or Mediterranean type of forest the plants present reflect the combination
of a hot dry season of varying length and a cooler, moist one,
the effects of these conditions being modified by edaphic and
physiographic factors.   All persistent forms, whether arboreal or
shrubby, must be able to resist periodic drought and yet, unlike
those of truly arid areas, adapted to utilize a fairly constant
rainfall, not necessarily small in total amount.   Herbaceous forms
requiring a considerable amount of moisture can, on the other
hand, thrive without difficulty, provided they do not demand high
temperatures and can limit their activities to the cooler, moister
periods.   Three main elements are therefore present : the tall
trees represented by a comparatively small number of species ;
a great abundance of shrubs, often highly drought-resistant and
frequently with brilliant flowers ; a variety of herbaceous plants
among which geophytes and annuals are well represented.
Epiphytes are rare, and when present are limited to mosses and
lichens.   Woody creepers are also infrequent and tend to be
slender as compared with the lianes of either the equatorial or
wet monsoonal forests ; herbaceous creepers, on the other hand,
may be abundant.   Succulents are not characteristic, and when
they occur seem to be immigrants from the bordering desert
which creep in especially where the soils are thin or sandy and
thus dry out readily.   That the climate under such conditions
does not forbid them is shown by the way in which exotic
succulents, such as Mesembryanthemum from the Cape and
cactuses from America, have spread round the shores of the
Mediterranean Sea.

As already seen, the trees include both conifers and angiosperms, the former especially in the northern hemisphere.   There

also evergreen oaks occur, but since the oak genus, apart from southern spreads both into Mexico and into the higher and damper parts of monsoonal Asia, is essentially north temperate, evergreen oaks are not found in the sclerophyllous forests of the southern hemisphere. There Chile has a fair number of arboreal species including in the peculiar genus Quillaja (rose family) forms with some superficial resemblance to evergreen oaks. In the Cape area, on the other hand, trees are few and belong mostly to the old-fashioned family of Proteaceae, the living members of which are almost confined to the southern hemisphere. Mediterranean Australia again shows dense stands of tall trees in a fashion hardly represented elsewhere save perhaps in the stands of tall conifers found on mountain slopes in California and less notably round the Mediterranean Sea. In Australia many of the trees belong to the genus Eucalyptus (myrtle family). This genus has now a very limited distribution (Fig. 18) and its members appear peculiarly adapted to semi-arid conditions. It is, however, a much-debated question how far the general poverty of arboreal species, and the thinness of the stands, in areas of Mediterranean climate is due to natural causes, including the influence of the Ice Age, and how far, especially in the northern hemisphere and in part in the Cape region, it is the result of man's influence exerted either directly by forest destruction or indirectly through stock-keeping. The fact that the aboriginal Australian is neither cultivator nor stock-keeper, and that the Australian area has not the same long history of European influence as the Cape one, may have influenced the density of the woods there. It may be added, however, that in afforesting areas of Mediterranean climate Australian trees, including members of the genus Eucalyptus, have been largely and successfully employed, so that, for example, parts of North Africa and of the Cape region are now almost as ' Australian ' in aspect as the continent itself. This certainly suggests that it has served as a centre for the evolution of trees particularly adapted to the Mediterranean type of climate.

As compared with the limited number of arboreal species shrubby plants are numerous and very diverse, both within the individual areas and when these are compared with one another. Where tall trees are few and scattered they form dense thickets (maquis, chaparral, &c.) often regarded as the characteristic vegetation type under Mediterranean climate. In Australia, owing to the light shade cast by the tall Eucalyptus, the shrubs constitute the rich undergrowth which helps to give the forest its luxuriant aspect.

9

Some interesting points arise in connexion with the multitude of families and genera represented. Many genera, such as Quercus in the northern areas, Quillaja in Chile and Eucalyptus in Australia, occur in both arboreal and shrubby species. There are also whole families in which trees are rare or even absent while drought-resistant shrubby forms well fitted to the Mediterranean climate occur. Various kinds of poppies in California, and such plants as rosemary in the Mediterranean area proper,

FIG. 18.—Distribution of Eucalyptus (Myrtle Family)

are interesting in this respect, for the poppy family and the Labiatae include mainly herbs. Even more striking are the conditions in the great Heath family (Ericaceae). The family as a whole is cosmopolitan save that its members avoid alike true deserts and hot wet areas, but are tolerant of seasonal drought, whether actual or physiological. It is natural, then, that its members should appear in areas of Mediterranean climate, where Arbutus is conspicuous as a tall shrub in the European area and a related genus (Arctostaphylos) in California. On the other hand, the true heaths (Erica and related genera) are virtually confined to Europe, its Mediterranean borderlands and Africa, particularly the Cape area. In the last the brightly coloured heaths are a very conspicuous feature and are mingled with many shrubby members of the Proteaceae, the type genus Protea including the South African sugar bushes. The Proteads occur again in great numbers in south-west Australia while a few genera only are found in Chile.

It is generally true that the shrubs characteristic of the different areas belong either to genera widely distributed in the continental area of which each forms a part, or to endemic genera nearly related to such widespread ones. Though this is to a considerable

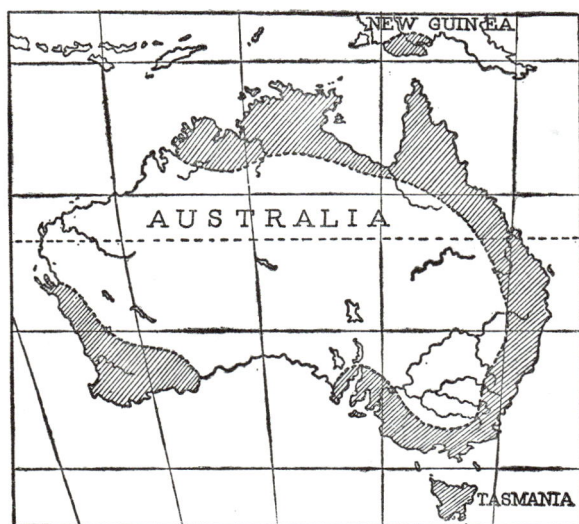

Banksia is a genus of mainly shrubby Australian Proteads whose distribution within the continent corresponds to that of woodland in the wider sense. The genus is best represented in S.W. Australia, where arboreal species form an important element in the sclerophyllous forest

FIG. 19.—Distribution of Banksia in forest area
After Engler and Drude

extent true of the trees also the greater number of shrubs suggests that adaptation to the specialized climate is more easily acquired by small than by tall woody plants. This is, of course, but another way of saying that the climatic conditions appear relatively unsuited to tall trees.

Little need be added to what has been already said in regard to the herbaceous elements. Bulbous monocotyledons are usually abundant and their adaptations are obvious ; annuals and hemicryptophytes also occur and, like the geophytes, tend to appear above the surface only during the moister periods, especially spring and autumn, when temperatures are favourable.

4. *Mesophytic Forests.* The mesophytic forest belts, that is, those occurring in warm temperate belts with plentiful summer rain, represent a great variety of types. It may be sufficient to note a few points in regard to the contrasted types found respectively in temperate and eastern Australia and south Japan, the latter showing much general resemblance to that of eastern North America. In extra-tropical Australia tall Eucalyptus, attaining heights of 300 to 400 feet, form the uppermost tier, though acacias and arboreal members of the Daisy family (Compositae) also occur. Tree-ferns, which reach a height of 30 to 40 feet, form a second tier, while ground ferns also occur in great quantity. The predominance of fern types is further emphasized by the fact that they include also creepers and epiphytes. In Japan the forests contain a much richer and more varied flora. Thus arboreal species are numerous and include evergreen oaks in great variety together with representatives of the laurel, magnolia and tea (e.g. Camellia) families. Stout, woody creepers are present, and the numerous epiphytes present include some orchids. A similar wealth of species, without so marked a tropical admixture, occurs in eastern North America where again the laurel and magnolia families are well represented. The presence of the Appalachian range, however, means that northern forms extend in a belt southwards along the higher ground, while the infertile sandy soils near the shore are responsible for a large development of coniferous trees there, forming the ' pine-barrens '. On the other hand, the fact that the mountain range has a limited southern extension and the way in which the interior lies open to the Gulf of Mexico, mean that the forest in its more luxuriant form extends well to the west of the Appalachians.

5. *Cool Temperate Forests and Heather Moors.* It seems needless to discuss further the features of the summer-green and coniferous woods, but there is one point which requires emphasis. In western and north-western Europe the latter give place over wide areas to the heather moors so characteristic of upland Britain and of parts of the north German plain. The dominant species is the social *Calluna vulgaris*, called heather in the north and ling elsewhere, mingled with species of Erica (bell heather) and with many berry-bearing members of the heath family (bilberry, cranberry, cowberry, bearberry and so on), as well as with the crowberry (Empetrum), which belongs to a

different family but has a striking resemblance to the berry-bearing heaths and grows under similar conditions.

Two important points have to be made clear in connexion with these dwarfed and sometimes trailing shrubs and the communities to which they give rise. The first is that the plants as a whole are common associates of the lighter coniferous woods, and especially of those in which birches occur in numbers. There the shrubs are quite comparable to those which form the undergrowth of the sclerophyllous woodlands, and indeed the same genera may occur (Erica occurs in the Mediterranean area of Europe, Arctostaphylos includes the circum-boreal bearberry and various Arbutus-like species in California). Second, as already noted, the true heaths in the limited sense are in the temperate latitudes of the northern hemisphere confined to Europe, with the single exception of *Calluna vulgaris* which stretches across Greenland to Newfoundland and then south to Massachusetts. This means that heather moors in our sense are virtually limited to north-western Europe, for the plant which gives them their characteristic physiognomy has but a limited extension elsewhere. In Europe the heather moors are intermingled with and pass into the wet moors with cotton-grass and Sphagnum moss, where the characters of the vegetation seem definitely controlled by the edaphic factor of the presence of thick deposits of peat (p. 68). The question at once arises— do the heather moors of Europe represent a true climax community or are they largely man-made and the result of forest destruction ? With this is bound up the economic problem of the possibility of afforestation. The subject is complex and cannot be discussed here, but it does seem important to emphasize the fact that the tailing out into heather moors of the thin and limited coniferous woods of upland Britain is not a general phenomenon when the northern hemisphere as a whole is considered. In North America and Asia the natural coniferous woods, mingled with birch and willow, and accompanied by their subsidiary shrubs, especially heath-like plants and crowberry, extend northwards till the tundra communities appear, whether these are of the Arctic heath type with greatly dwarfed or even miniature shrubby plants or consist chiefly of mosses and lichens.

NOTE

In addition to the books already mentioned, and especially Schimper's, the long series of monographs published under the title of *Die Vegetation der Erde* (Leipzig, 1896 onwards) and edited by A. Engler and O. Drude should be noted. Of the volumes Vol. XIII, *North America*, by John W. Harshberger (1911) and XIV, *New Zealand*, by L. Cockayne (1928) are in English, the others in German. See also *The Vegetation and Soils of Africa*, by H. L. Shantz and C. F. Marbut (American Geographical Society Research Series, No. 13, New York, 1923), and A. F. W. Schimper, *Pflanzengeographie auf physiologischer Grundlage*, 2nd Edition (F. C. von Faber), 1935.

CHAPTER VIII

GRASSLANDS AND DESERTS

GRASSLANDS AND THEIR DISTRIBUTION

THE previous discussion has attempted to clarify both the climatic conditions under which grasslands may be expected to occur and their essential features. We have seen that woodlands are highly complex communities including not only the tall phanerophytes which demand a long growing season and considerable supplies of moisture, but also a number of subsidiary forms, usually much less exacting both as to climate and soil. If then the sum-total of the conditions, climatic and edaphic, is such as to prohibit the presence of dense stands of trees, without preventing herbs or small shrubs forming a virtually complete cover, woodland gives place to what is called a grassland community. If the conditions are so unfavourable that the plants present are scattered, that is, no complete cover of vegetation is present, the resultant open communities are described as desert ones.

The removal of the trees of most woodlands would lead to rapid multiplication of the ground forms and thus to the formation of a new closed community in what had been previously the lowest tier of the forest. That is to say, while the presence of a natural grassland is proof that the conditions are at least relatively unsuited to arboreal species, the converse is not true. It is not either climatic or soil factors which prevent the appearance of grassland communities in the forest zone, but the competition of the trees. That competition finds expression in various ways. The cutting off of the light by the tree canopy may be less important than the greedy roots which take up both much water and large supplies of nutritive salts and may starve out the herbs. Tree branches are also arranged so as to allow rain water to drip to the ground within root range, and this concentrated drip, as all gardeners know, is fatal to many herbaceous plants. It is this element of competition between herbs and trees which has led to so much forest destruction. Many of the grasslands of the world are, in consequence, artificial, the result of the felling or burning especially of tropophytic and tropical forests, for these under natural conditions have glades and openings where the ground flora is particularly rich.   By extending such glades artificially man obtains at once room for those cultivated grasses which yield so large a part of his food and more ample pasturage for his flocks.

We may next note more precisely the climatic factors which prevent trees from forming dense stands, or even exclude them altogether, without at the same time causing desert communities to appear.   Broadly, it is a question of the length of the season favourable to vegetative activity.   In the more typical grassland communities, roots and root-stocks form a compact turf close to the surface.   This felted network checks the penetration of rain to the deeper layers of the soil, a factor which aids the grassland plants in their competition with trees in the transitional zone where total rainfall is barely sufficient for arboreal plants.   But that surface moisture is exposed to evaporation, and therefore frequent light showers during the growing season are important for the herbaceous forms.   A light winter snowfall, remaining till the spring rise of temperature and melting slowly while the deeper layers of the soil are still cold, also favours herbaceous as against arboreal species.   The essential point, however, is that the surface must be frequently moistened during the period, perhaps short, when temperatures are such as to permit active metabolism. Extreme winter cold is not an inhibiting factor provided a warm and sufficiently moist period follows.   Similarly, marked summer drought may not be prohibitive if it follows a period which has been both warm and moist.   Total rainfall matters little provided the amount and distribution are not such as to permit the growth of many competing trees, and that it is not so low and so irregular as to induce desert conditions.

Clearly, then, two major areas of climatically controlled grassland will tend to occur.   In temperate latitudes, as we have already seen, summer rainfall in the interior of continents tends to drop below the minimum total necessary to moisten the ground sufficiently for even the tolerant conifers, while the winters are often cold.   Here we find the great grasslands variously called steppes, prairies and pampas.   In such areas, intercalated between the winter cold and the late summer drought, there is a short growing season, of which many kinds of herbs can take advantage. Similarly, in tropical latitudes, as rainfall diminishes and becomes more definitely periodic in its fall, while temperatures in the lowlands remain persistently high, even the most drought-resistant trees cannot maintain themselves in close stands, and open woodland passes into savanna with usually a more notable admixture of woody species than in the temperate grasslands.

Of less wide distribution, though of much local economic importance, are those areas, technically grasslands, which border the cold deserts of the world.   Thus above the forest limit on mountains and on its borders in sub-Arctic and Arctic latitudes closed communities, mainly or exclusively herbaceous, often cover considerable tracts before conditions become so severe as to cause the plants present to be limited to specially favourable sites.   In such areas wind, as well as temperature conditions, exclude trees, so that the control seems to be climatic.   On the other hand the mountain pastures in particular are usually developed over areas where much rock waste has accumulated, especially as a result of ice action, so that edaphic factors play their part.

Smaller areas of grassland also occur where the edaphic factors are the predominating ones.   Some of these are successional seres (cf. the account of sand-dunes and salt marshes on p. 106 et. seq.).   Transported soils and subsoils of specially porous nature (e.g. loess and some glacial sands and gravels) and soils which have little water-holding power may give rise to grass-lands.   Edaphically controlled grasslands also tend to appear well within the woodland climatic zones where periodic flooding occurs.   Similarly, what are called grassland flushes, i.e. patches of typical grassland plants, are of common occurrence on heather moors where spring water of neutral or but slightly acid reaction comes out at the surface and permits various herbaceous forms to replace the acid-tolerant moor plants.   Generally grassland communities tend to appear wherever either temporary or per-manent freedom from the competition of woody plants is assured, unless conditions are such as to produce desert communities.

ELEMENTS OF GRASSLAND COMMUNITIES

The name given to the grassland communities naturally sug-gests that the grasses (natural order Gramineae) form their largest element.   This is not, however, necessarily the case, for cotton grass (sedge) moors and moss tundras are technically grasslands, while on many mountain pastures plants other than grasses may be very numerous.   Even if we take the economic view of the grasslands as the great pastures of the world, we find that a num-ber of grasses are inedible, while many other plants such as members of the Leguminosae (clover, &c.) may be more important than grasses as food for stock animals.   In other words, not all grasses are pasture grasses and some of the important food plants of pastures are not grasses.

Despite such facts, however, grasses do form the most conspicuous plants of grassland communities, and the reasons are worth a little consideration. It is not that there are more kinds of grasses than of other plants. Fig. 20 shows graphically the number of genera and species in the two largest orders of Dicotyledons and of Monocotyledons respectively. All the four orders

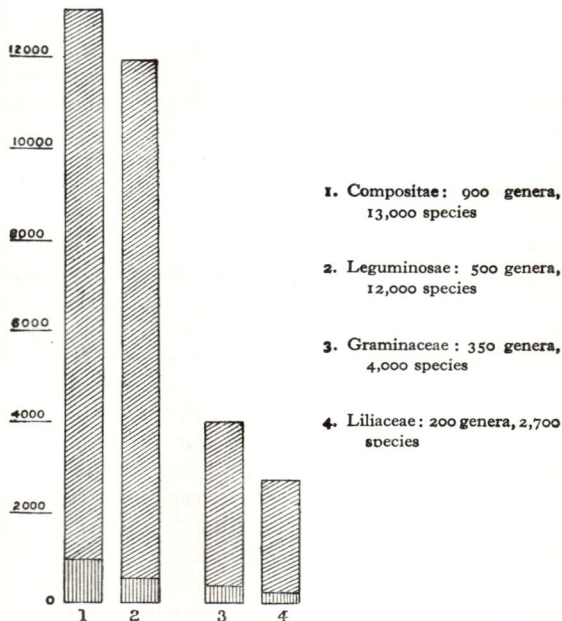

1. Compositae: 900 genera, 13,000 species

2. Leguminosae: 500 genera, 12,000 species

3. Graminaceae : 350 genera, 4,000 species

4. Liliaceae: 200 genera, 2,700 species

FIG. 20.—Genera and Species of herbaceous growing plants

are cosmopolitan and all contain a very large proportion of herbs. In the Compositae the number of trees and shrubs is relatively small. It is considerably greater in the Leguminosae, but there large genera, such as Acacia and Mimosa, include many drought-resistant trees and shrubs which form constituents of the tropical savannas, that is, of grassland communities, while herbaceous genera and species are extremely common in temperate grasslands. Bearing in mind the enormous number of species which both orders include and their world-wide range, we should expect, and indeed find, that both would be abundantly represented in grassland communities. In the ' semi-desert ' of the Great Basin of the western United States, for example, Compositae, especially wormwood or sage-brush (genus *Artemisia*) dominate over wide areas, and this is at least partially true of some steppes. Their importance in our urban areas is known to all.

What permits the grasses to predominate in most grassland communities is not the actual number of species but the social habit, the mode of growth and the wide range of adaptability. The first two points are correlated ; it is the mode of growth which enables the grasses to live in communities in which one species may predominate or many occur together without apparently competing with each other.   The adaptability again enables them to tolerate a wide range of climatic and edaphic conditions, and though in wet areas they tend to be replaced by the related sedges (Cyperaceae), many grasses are very tolerant of marked seasonal drought.

Grasses are herbs, the bamboos forming the great exception, for though these are only partially woody and possess giant root-stocks underground, they may reach heights of over 100 feet. Tropical bamboos grow in continually expanding clumps which may present the appearance of ' forests ', though in some cases the plants are short-lived, flowering at intervals of 10 to 15 years and then dying—a not uncommon feature in arborescent or shrubby Monocotyledons (cf. the agave).   Many at least of the bamboo brakes of monsoonal Asia may be regarded as the tropical equivalents of the successional grasses which appear on bare ground elsewhere ; they seem to be characteristic especially of burnt-over forest lands (cf. p. 127), for the root-stocks may escape the effect of fire.   The point is relevant here as emphasizing the fact that grasses in general are particularly well fitted to take advantage of the opportunity offered by the destruction or absence of other vegetation.

Other grasses may be either perennial or annual.   The perennial forms usually branch freely (' tiller ') at the lower nodes of the stems where these are in contact with the ground, and send up from these nodes tufts of narrow leaves which rarely show a distinction between stem and blade, while the leaf bases are sheathing.   Fertilization of the flower spikes included in these tufts is effected by wind, so that no energy is spent in producing brightly coloured and attractive flowers.   Except in the cultivated grasses the fruits are usually light enough to be wind-distributed without elaborate adaptations, though some have hooks or spiny bracts which cause them to cling to the coats of grazing animals. Not a few forms also, especially on mountains, can reproduce themselves viviparously if the weather is unfavourable to seed-setting ; that is, leafy shoots with adventitious roots replace the flowers and, dropping to the ground, fix themselves there.   This is not an uncommon feature in monocotyledons and a similar phenomenon occurs in some ferns.

The slender leaves with their sheathing bases are very resistant to wind and are not shed in the fashion common in dicotyledons by the growth of separating tissue.   Where cold or intense drought brings about seasonal death, they dry out from the tips downwards rather than rot.   This is, of course, economically important in that the grasses can be preserved as hay, while in, e.g., Alberta the chinook winds of autumn ' cure ' the leaves as they stand and so give rise to natural hay.   Generally, especially in the case of the more drought-resistant species of grasses, this drying of the leaves without separation from the stems is very important in helping to form the characteristic sod or turf, which is due both to the fibrous roots and root-stocks underground and to the mat of dead leaves above.   The whole sod is unfavourable to the germination of the seeds of other kinds of plants and helps the grasses to keep their hold.   Under natural conditions there is a check to sod formation owing to the grazing, manuring and treading of the large herbivores, but where these are destroyed and replaced by stock animals certain grasses may spread and form virtually monotypic communities.   Thus the so-called deterioration of many permanent (mainly upland) pastures in western Europe is associated with the spread of Moor Mat Grass (*Nardus stricta*).   This is tolerant of poor and acid soil, forms as its name indicates dense mats of dead leaves, and is avoided by sheep, often the only stock animals kept on such pastures.   Any other pasture plants originally present are nibbled down by the sheep, which are too light to tread down the mat grass as heavier animals like cattle do.   Thus other plants are increasingly crowded out and a mixed pasture is gradually replaced by an economically poor one formed mainly of mat grass.   The sod has to be torn open before any improvement can be effected in such pastures.

The illustration brings out one important point.   Grassland communities, whether under purely natural conditions—becoming increasingly rare—or under man's influence, are closely linked with the herbivorous mammals of which they form the natural home, and the relation between the grasses and the mammals is particularly close, apparently because the two have evolved simultaneously.   The grasses, more than most herbaceous plants, can afford to pay the toll demanded in pasture by the herbivores, for they gain something in return.   Once trees or shrubs or it may be tall and strong-growing herbaceous plants have got a start they can kill out even the hardiest grasses.   But both trees and shrubs must needs pass through a critical early stage.   During this stage the herbivores help the grasses both by nibbling the competing seedlings and by trampling down the young plants, the grasses showing much greater resistance to this treading effect which may even encourage their growth (cf. the rolling of lawns and of young cereal crops) because of the resultant tillering from the nodes of the crushed stems.   Almost everywhere, however, man has so upset the original balance that it is not easy to determine how far the appearance of the grasslands to-day is due to purely natural causes and how far to man's influence.   In particular the introduction of the sheep, originally a mountain animal with a limited range in the northern hemisphere, into many of the drier grasslands of other parts of the world has led to great changes.

But though it may be difficult to estimate the extent to which the existing grasslands of the world are true climax communities, the special adaptations shown by the grasses are at least clear. Much more than the conifers, they represent a systematic group which has become fitted for particular areas, in this case the drier continental plains.   As we have seen, even where the conifers occur in their purest stands, the fact that few shrubs and no herbs are included means that other kinds of plants can push their way in numbers into the communities of which they are the dominating elements.   But the grasses under certain conditions form communities in which other systematic groups are either absent or represented only by a comparatively small number of kinds and of individuals.

A word or two may be added in regard to the lily family which, as Fig. 20 shows, is also large, if not so large as the grass one. Though the majority are herbs, yet shrubs and trees also occur. They are mainly of xerophytic habit and confined to the warmer areas where aloes and others form a considerable element in the savanna flora.   The herbaceous Liliaceae are often numerously represented in temperate grasslands, but their mode of growth is as a rule very different from that of the grasses.   The aerial leaves which spring from the underground root-stock or bulb are often soft and decay readily, and most liliaceous plants appear above the surface for only a short period of the year.   Their adaptations, however, fit them as much to form elements in a woodland community as in a grassland one, and they cannot be said to be characteristic of the latter.   Their green leaves, sometimes bitter or poisonous, are of no importance as pasturage, but the stores of food in the underground bulbs make the latter important, especially to the steppe rodents.

Of the other orders and families represented in the grasslands we need only say that especially in the temperate zones a great number of familiar and widely spread families include herbs which can thrive within grassland communities and may be locally abundant. Among these are labiates, crucifers, the ranunculus, mallow and crane's-bill families, and so on. In such cases, however, the adaptations so far as the family as a whole is concerned are sporadic rather than general, and the presence or absence of such forms does not alter the main features of the community.

EXAMPLES OF GRASSLANDS

The Canadian Prairies. Without attempting to survey the grasslands of the world, we may illustrate by examples some of their outstanding features. The Canadian prairies may serve to indicate the main features of temperate grassland, and we can assume that the main points as to climate and surface features are already known to the geographical student. Broadly and with all the qualifications with which the concept of three prairie steps of increasing height and aridity as we pass westward must be taken, we may put the essentials as follows :

1. Over the first prairie step a considerable number of trees occur forming groves and miniature forests along the stream courses and on elevations, e.g. the Pembina scarp with the Riding and Duck mountains. The grasses are of the meadow type and the growing season is long enough for the prairie to show both a spring aspect and a summer one. During the former many small herbs, mostly with inconspicuous flowers, appear among the grasses. Later many composites, such as asters (Michaelmas daisies), goldenrod, sunflowers and so on, grow to considerable heights and flaunt their massed blooms.

2. Over the second prairie step trees restrict themselves to the hardier forms such as poplars along the streams. Stunted shrubs are the chief woody plants, and among these forms like buffalo berry (*Shepherdia*) and silverberry (*Elaeagnus*) are markedly drought-resistant. Both belong to a small family including shrubs characteristic of coasts and steppes in the north temperate region ; our native berry-bearing, silver-leaved sea-buckthorn is another example but it also lives on screes. Small cactuses which have come in from the south emphasize further the aridity

of the climate, while the tall herbs of the eastern ' weedy prairies ' are absent.

 3. Over the third step short (2 inches to 3 inches high) wiry and very drought-resistant grasses, tending to grow in bunches or clumps, are characteristic, especially buffalo grass (*Buchloe dactyloides*) and grama grass (*Bouteloua oligostachya*). Cactuses occur again, but these small, often creeping Canadian cactuses, half-hidden in the grass, should not be confused with the giant forms characteristic of, e.g., the deserts of Arizona. Among other plants present are small creeping vetches and other drought-resistant forms, while halophytic communities appear round the saline pools of the south. As the Rocky foothills are approached the plants become taller and more luxuriant.

Of special interest are the trees of the first prairie step, and bearing in mind that its western limit, the Pembina scarp, has a certain rough correspondence to the administrative boundary of Manitoba province, we may note a few outstanding points. In eastern Canada generally the distinction between coniferous and tropophytic forest is not sharp, the latter including as a rule a number of conifers though the species present differ from those of the coniferous forest proper. This mixed eastern forest comes to an end in the vicinity of Winnipeg where the prairie begins. That the hardier trees such as poplars, willows, birches with some conifers should creep into the prairie belt is to be expected, but three genera of hardwoods—maple (Acer), oak and elm (Ulmus)—are noteworthy as indicating the effects of the prairie climate on typical tropophytes.

Canada as a whole has nine species of maple, characteristic especially of the more luxuriant parts of the eastern forest. Of these two only occur in Manitoba. One is the mountain maple, a shrubby upland form extending from the east to find its western limit in Manitoba. The other, the ash-leaved maple (*A. negundo*), is in Canada confined to Manitoba but occurs on the other side of the international frontier. It has clearly come in from the south and is both drought-resistant and very frost-resistant ; the compound leaves have much reduced surfaces as compared with those of other maples. It will grow in eastern Canada without difficulty when planted, but the eastern maples are taller and finer trees. Again, Canada has twelve species of deciduous oaks, mainly characteristic of the richer eastern forest, and of these one only, *Quercus macrocarpa*, reaches Manitoba. It is significant that while in the south-east this is called the bur oak and has some economic value, in the north-west it gets the name of scrub oak and is often little more than a shrub. Of the three Canadian

elms only one, the American or white elm (*U. americana*), suc-
ceeds in entering the prairie belt and then in diminishing numbers
and size.   It may be added that just as the European beech has
a limited extension towards the continental interior, being absent
to the east of the Odessa–Königsberg line, so in Canada the
American beech extends westward only to the vicinity of Sault
Ste. Marie.   Facts of this kind make clear the meaning of what
we have called the tailing out of tropophytic hardwoods towards
continental interiors, and show how the reduction and final disappearance of the trees enable the grasses to form special communities.

The Sudanese Savanna.   As a contrast to the Canadian prairies
we may take the savanna or grass-woodland of Africa, the country
within which this type of community covers the widest area.   In
Africa the most northerly part of the savanna lands forms a wide
belt which abuts on the sea between the confines of Liberia and
Senegal, and stretches eastward through the Sudan till, as the
Abyssinian plateau is approached, a change occurs.   Northwards
this belt is separated from the desert proper by a zone of thorn
scrub, while southwards its boundary to the west and centre is
the tropical rain forest.   In the east it swings round the closed
forest to reach the west coast again in Angola.   In order to give
some precision to the description we shall limit it to the Sudanese
area, though the type is generally similar both north and south
of the Equator.

The first point to note is that throughout the open country to
which the name of Sudan is given the flora is generally similar and
is definitely African in type.   This is not wholly true of the
limited flora of the desert proper, for the latter is crossed by a
kind of floral divide, the plants to the north of this having Mediterranean affinities.   Traces of these are also visible in the mountain
forests and grasslands of Abyssinia.   Again, in marked contrast
with the conditions which we noted in Canada, changes in the
savanna communities tend to occur in the south–north and not
the east–west direction.   That this must be so is clear when we
recall the fact that total rainfall diminishes from south to north
while at the same time the length of the dry season increases
without notable changes in the temperatures.   Nowhere within
the savanna belt, however, do the climatic conditions exclude
trees, and the contrast between the more southerly and the
more northerly sections expresses itself chiefly in the greater
height of the grasses in the former and the increased number
and diversity of the trees, the species not being identical
throughout.

For the savanna belt as a whole the name of grass-woodland has been suggested in order to emphasize the presence throughout of trees, whether in clumps or scattered specimens (parkland effect). The trees do not reach the stature common in closed forests, and are characteristically deciduous, with light foliage not throwing heavy shade. Further, the way in which the tall grasses interpenetrate at least their lower branches is evidence enough that under the prevailing climatic conditions the competitive power of the grasses is great. Stimulated by the high temperatures and the seasonal rainfall they grow with a rapidity which the trees cannot emulate, the latter remaining in a state of permanent check. It is this inability of even full-grown trees to dominate the grasses which leads the ecologist to regard the communities as essentially grassland ones even though trees may be locally numerous. In books of travel some types of savanna are often described as ' forests ', and they may resemble forests in that travel through their dense vegetation is difficult, whereas we tend to think of grasslands as areas easily traversed. But however dense the plant cover may be during the wet season, there is no closed tree canopy as in the true forests and it is the grasses, i.e. herbs branching at ground-level, which are mainly responsible for the dense cover.

The grasses vary in height according to the rainfall, from 3–5 feet to 5–12 feet (contrast the Canadian prairie grasses, p. 143), and those of the millet type (Pennisetum or spiked millet, Andropogon, related to the cultivated Guinea corn, and so on) predominate ; elephant grass, which reaches a height of 12 feet, is a species of Pennisetum. They are mainly bunch grasses more or less distinct from each other at the base, that is, not forming a dense interlacing turf. For the reasons already given conifers are not present among the trees, but Monocotyledons are represented by some palms, especially doum palm (*Hyphaena*). Among the dicotyledonous trees those belonging to the Leguminosae are common. Acacia is perhaps the most characteristic genus in the Sudan, but a number of other less familiar leguminous genera are also represented. Of other trees most belong to tropical families not represented farther north. Mention may be made of the economically important shea tree (*Butyrospermum*) from whose oily seeds an edible fat (shea butter) is obtained, and of the baobab with its swollen, water-storing stem, a tree widely spread in the drier parts of Africa.

The vegetation undergoes modification in the swampy areas such as the sudd swamps of the Nile and the region round Lake Chad. Here sedges, such as papyrus, are mingled with reed-

10

like grasses and bulrushes, such forms in response to the more abundant water supply attaining heights of even 20 feet. Here again, however, we have illustrated the tendency for trees to appear without being able to dominate the grass-like forms. The chief tree of the swamps is ambatch (*Herminiera*), a leguminous form which reaches about 20 feet but is extremely light for its bulk. The lightness is due to the great development of intracellular air-spaces, a not uncommon feature in marsh-plants (cf. the spongy pith of our own rushes), and believed to be a means whereby oxygen can be carried to submerged parts. It has economic importance in ambatch, for the tree is used extensively to make raft-like canoes and floats for timber.

DESERT AREAS

If it is true that the word forest is used loosely in common speech this is much more true of desert, for reasons which are clear enough. Any area devoid of surface water becomes for the traveller a desert, since its absence will bring in its train a deficiency or absence of wood for fuel, of fodder for transport animals and a probable lack of wild animals or berry-bearing plants to serve as food. If the experiences of an unfortunate journey through such an arid area can be crystallized in a telling phrase, its desert character is apt to be regarded as established.

It is interesting in this connexion to note the wide currency of the statement that most of the interior of Australia is a waste of ' spinifex and sand '. Here the alliteration counts for much, while the use of the scientific name of a spiny, drought-resistant grass seems as it were to settle the matter. It is all the more curious, therefore, to find that the name is inaccurately used. Spinifex is a genus of grasses of the millet group, the members of which are characteristic especially of coastal sand-dunes and are distributed from Australia through Ceylon to Japan. The ' spinifex ' of the arid interior areas of Australia on the other hand, more accurately called porcupine grass, consists chiefly of a couple of species of the genus Triodia which is represented in Britain by a heath grass. If we discard the ' spinifex ', the interior of Australia takes on at once a less arid look ; true deserts there have indeed not nearly so wide a distribution as is commonly believed.

There is another point of some importance. The subdivisions of the grass family are based fundamentally on minor features of the flower spikes, and these are rarely associated with those modifications of the leaves, such as the thickening of the epidermis, inrolling, tendency to become hairy or prickly and so forth, which enable particular grasses to resist highly arid conditions. This means in its turn that only rarely does the systematic position of a grass afford us much hint as to its ecological characters. Triodia, for example, belongs to the group which includes some of our common meadow grasses, such as Poa, Festuca (fescue) and so on. It is one of the great difficulties in dealing with the more arid parts of the world that their grasses have rarely precise common names, while the Latin genera to which they are referred

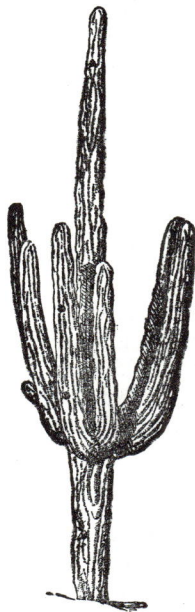

FIG. 21.—Giant cactus (*Cereus giganteus*). Arizona. Grows about 40 feet high. Birds nest in cavity of trunk

often tell us little of their distribution, for many genera are widely distributed (cf. Triodia), or of the appearance of the various species included. Thus our British species of Triodia has the specific name of *decumbens*, indicating merely that the plant spreads along the ground and then sends up erect tufts—in other words, to the untrained eye it looks much like any other grass. That the Australian desert species look very different is suggested by their specific names of *horrida* and *pungens*, but none the less they belong to a genus which includes much more commonplace forms and to a subdivision most of whose members are widely distributed meadow types.

The point of this digression is to make clear first that, from the ecological standpoint, a desert requires rather careful definition ; and second, that at least so far as the grasses are concerned, we cannot say that certain genera or sub-groups are definitely characteristic. This latter statement can also be made, if not quite to so marked an extent, of most other groups and sub-groups. It is true that in the Americas the cactuses form an important element in the flora of most deserts, but even they extend beyond the limit of true deserts (cf. p. 143). Generally, indeed, we can hardly say that deserts have a characteristic flora of their own ; rather is it true that the plants which occur represent stunted remnants of the vegetation of bordering areas, and may or may not display special adaptations.

We may note some points about such bordering areas. We have already seen that the Sudanese savanna is separated from the Sahara desert by a belt of thorn scrub. This is not an uncommon feature and scrub, running into a variety of special types, is particularly well represented in Australia. Some types are characterized by the prevalence of thorny, highly drought-resistant acacias. Thus the Brigalow scrub, found especially in the more arid parts of the tropical north and north-east, consists of a species of acacia which forms dense thickets with a limited development of grasses. In the extra-tropical south and south-west, Brigalow scrub seems to give place to mulga scrub where a different acacia predominates and more grass is present. Still more tolerant of very arid conditions is the mallee scrub which covers large areas of what are sometimes called deserts. Here the dominant species are not acacias but several kinds of dwarfed eucalyptus mingled with other stunted forms including species of Casuarina (see Fig. 22, p. 149), a genus which, like eucalyptus, is represented in Australia by both forest trees and shrubs.

Such transitional communities, combined with our previous studies of types of grassland, help us to reach the ecologist's conception of the world deserts. A markedly seasonal distribution of rainfall is increasingly unfavourable to tall phanerophytes and prevents these forming closed communities, except where running water keeps the soil in a moist condition. Where temperatures are also seasonally low, the formation of woody tissue appears to be difficult and the necessary exposure of the buds on even dwarf phanerophytes checks the development of these. Under such conditions, therefore, the temperate grasslands appear, characterized by the great predominance of herbs. Where there is no

definite cold season dwarf phanerophytes and woody chamaephytes can thrive even though the rainfall is both definitely
seasonal and not more than moderate in total. Then the balance
seems to swing between stunted shrubs of highly drought-
resistant and often thorny type and herbaceous plants including
grasses of various kinds, the former appearing the more resistant
to great aridity when this is combined with high temperatures.
In all cases, however, the vegetation cover is at least quasi-
complete, at any rate during the moist period.

Where rainfall is at once very low and irregular in its incidence,
one of the limiting factors of plant life drops to or below the
necessary minimum ; where even a short continuously warm
period ceases to be present, the same thing happens with the
second major limiting factor. At the same time, in either case,

Fig. 22.—1. Equisetum arvense. 2. Casuarina stricta. 3. Enlargement of
Casuarina

that complex of organic and inorganic conditions which leads to
the formation of vegetal mould ceases to act in normal fashion.
The result is that no continuous vegetation cover can develop ;
higher plants if they appear at all occur in sporadic fashion and
not in interlocking communities. The struggle for existence
expresses itself mainly as an individual effort to carry on metabolism under more or less constantly unfavourable conditions,
rather than as an adjustment between competing organisms. In
other words, deserts appear.

The characteristically scattered plants again fall into two main
groups so far as their relation to moisture is concerned. One
set, exemplified by the annuals and in part by the bulbous forms,
may be thought of as taking advantage of the fact that desert
rainfall is variable. The annuals in particular play as it were the

waiting part, the seeds remaining inert it may be for years and then, if exceptional rain comes, running through their life-history very rapidly. Such facts as the long-period changes in the nature and intensity of the Peruvian current, and their effects on rainfall in the normally arid parts of western South America, suggest that variations of this kind may be great enough to account for the presence of a number of such types in areas with a rainfall which on the average is very low. Plants of this kind need not show very special adaptations to desert conditions, for by hypothesis they are active only when the desert ceases temporarily to show the characteristic features.

The second group includes the plants tolerant of the full rigour of the local conditions and therefore necessarily showing more obvious adaptations. Here, however, the time factor comes into play. It is easy to see that if a particular area becomes progressively more and more arid, there will tend to be during the process great elimination of plants, the moisture-demanding forms disappearing first. If the process of desiccation is not continuous but oscillating, the survivors will tend to be those tolerant of long-continued drought without necessarily being able to reduce their water requirements to an absolute minimum. Before specially adapted plants can evolve, arid conditions must persist over a very long period. There is much evidence that in geologically recent times the Sahara was much moister than it is at present, and this is true also of the semi-deserts of the western United States. In both cases, and especially in the latter, many of the plants present belong to widely spread genera characteristic especially of waste spaces, the species in some cases differing comparatively little from those found elsewhere.

Note in this connexion that the western prairies of Canada contain a number of plants of ' desert ' type, as witness the few cactuses, various annuals, which remain as ungerminated seeds in dry years, as well as many halophytes. Thus the elements of an unspecialized desert flora are already present in rudiment ; and, if the climate changed in the direction of increased dryness, the killing out of the water-demanding forms would leave the bare spaces characteristic of deserts, while the drought-resistant forms, though able to maintain themselves, could not extend their territory. Thus without any notable evolutionary changes a desert flora would develop. Only if desiccation went on slowly and continuously over a very long period of time should we expect new specially adapted forms to arise. In point of fact there are comparatively few of such perfectly adapted kinds of plants, which suggests that many existing deserts are of relatively recent origin.

In sum then, from the ecologist's standpoint, deserts are areas in which the sum-total of the physical habitat factors is so unfavourable that a complete cover of vegetation cannot develop. Locally, higher plants may be entirely absent ; when present, they are separated from each other by unoccupied tracts.

FEATURES OF DESERT PLANTS

In noting some of the features of desert plants we may begin with what is perhaps the most remarkable of all such plants. This is Welwitschia (Tumboa), a gymnosperm with an extremely limited distribution in the coastal desert of south-west Africa, especially in the vicinity of Walvis Bay. This desert, it will be remembered, shows extreme aridity combined with high temperatures and has several very peculiar plants. Welwitschia (Fig. 23) stands out not only on account of its special adaptive

FIG. 23.—Welwitschia mirabilis
After Kerner and Oliver

features but because of its isolated systematic position. It belongs to the Gnetales (p. 35), but while the two other genera, Ephedra (Fig. 22) and Gnetum both include a number of species and have a fairly wide distribution, the one in warm temperate and the other in tropical latitudes, there is but one species of Welwitschia and this is confined to a comparatively small area.

The plant consists of a short but thick woody stem not rising many inches above the rocky ground on which it grows, and narrowed below into a stout tap-root. It lives for a century or more, but though the stem grows thicker it never elongates. The top is bi-lobed and hollowed in the centre, while from its edges spring two gigantic leaves which are never shed. They develop after the cotyledons and continue to grow throughout life at their bases while the tips wither and decay. Thus the plant is ' evergreen ' in a more literal sense than any other known form, for the leaves of conifers have but a limited duration in relation to the life of the individual tree. The sprawling, ribbon-like or starfish appearance of the leaves, well shown in the drawing, is due to the fact that though originally simple they become torn and split down to the base as the years pass by.   The flowers appear in groves on the top of the stem, the pollen-bearing on one plant and the ovule-bearing on another.   Pollination is by insects, a very remarkable feature in a gymnosperm and believed to be a special adaptation.   Insects in this arid area only make their appearance in ' wet ' years, and it is only in such years that the seeds of Welwitschia would have a chance to germinate.   But flowers are produced annually—on the off-chance as it were—and it is an advantage that seed should be set only in the years when it could germinate.   The fertilized seeds are winged and thus can be carried by wind.   Seed is said to be produced on occasion in large quantities, but yet the plants are scattered and not abundant within the area occupied and are apparently unable to extend their range.   It would appear that the plant has originated within the area within which it is found and that the physical conditions there must have been constant during a long period of time.

In the same desert occurs another peculiar plant, the naras or desert melon (*Acanthosicyos horrida*).   The genus again includes but a single species not known outside the region, but from the systematic standpoint the plant has not the isolated place of Welwitschia, for related genera are widespread in tropical latitudes.   Remembering what has been already said as to the part played in taxonomy by the reproductive organs, the meaning of this statement is not difficult to grasp.   It signifies in brief that the flowers and fruit are broadly similar to those found generally in the Cucumber family to which the plant belongs, while the vegetative organs have become modified to fit it for life in a sandy desert.

It is indeed essentially a dune plant, growing on sand-hills, while Welwitschia clings to the rocky hollows between these. Most of its allies, variously called gourds, melons, cucumbers and so on, are water-spending and water-demanding plants of very rapid growth and lush foliage, climbing or scrambling by means of tendrils, and often annuals.   At first sight, then, one would not expect that adaptation to desert life on the part of such plants would be easy.   But even in desert areas underground water may be present, however dry the surface may appear. Looking at the plant purely as a piece of mechanism, we may say that a double problem has to be faced—the limited supplies of underground water must be tapped over a wide area, and surface loss must be minimized.   We find that the root system attains an enormous length—a common feature in perennial desert plants of this type.   It has been traced for 40 feet, which at once shows that deserts are not quite so scantily peopled as one is apt to suppose.   The dryness of the air and surface means that that growth in size occurs underground rather than above so that when we look at the plants as a whole they are not so stunted as they seem.   In this particular case what appears at the surface is a woody shrub not more than 4 to 5 feet high, with green, well-protected branches, rudimentary leaves and strong thorns.   The resistant stems are very apt to be buried in the shifting sand but readily grow up through it and as they branch tend to fix it. From grazing animals they are protected by their bitter taste.

In appearance then Acanthosicyos is a typical desert plant as far removed as may be from the familiar melon or gourd.   As if to show, however, that the adaptations are but ' skin-deep ' it develops rounded, grape fruit-like, ' melons ', juicy and bland, relished greatly by the natives, the rare travellers and by the jackals, all of whom regard them as a gift of providence in a thirsty land.   The plants indeed represent natural pumps bringing to the surface and storing in their miniature reservoirs lost water. Their squandering in the fruits of the precious fluid so jealously guarded in the stems is justified because it ensures the spread of the seeds, jackals being stated to be the main agent under purely natural conditions.   In a region so naturally repellent, also, some attraction must be provided to draw visitors from afar.

As already stated, Acanthosicyos has a very limited distribution which, together with that of some other highly peculiar plants, underlines the aridity of Damaraland.   Another gourd, however, much less specialized and more widely spread, shows that under certain conditions adaptations to desert life may be readily acquired.   This is the bitter or colocynth gourd (*Citrullus colocynthis*) widely spread in the dry belt which extends from North Africa to India and common on sandhills in the Egyptian and Nubian deserts.   It belongs to the same genus as the cultivated water-melon, and has rounded orange-like fruits with a thin rind and a bitter pulp from which the purgative drug colocynth is obtained, an early article of trade in Europe.

At first sight the plant seems to disprove what has been already said as to the characters of desert plants, for its shoots are plump and juicy and bear large soft leaves.   Neither shoots nor leaves have any special protection against drought, for they flag quickly if separated from the parent.   Here the explanation is found in the great length of the roots and the fact (cf. p. 152) that owing to its limited lifting power sand, however dry it appears on the surface, may have considerable reserves of water below.   Presumably the hillocks on which the colocynth gourd occurs must have exceptional supplies of water below, readily tapped by its great root system.

In a desert environment some generalized forms maintain themselves, especially since competitors are few, if they show some adaptation to aridity. The colocynth gourd profits by easy root penetration, also in sandy deserts ground-water protected from evaporation by the loose surface cover may be present locally even though rain falls but rarely. In consequence most families which include a large proportion of tolerant ' weeds ' are well represented in deserts, though their members are apt to be ignored because they are unattractive and seem to offer little of interest. Among such families may be noted the widespread composites, the chenopods (goose-foot and spinach types) and the crucifers. A dull greyish-green colour, due to the clouding of the chlorophyll by a surface covering of fine hairs, wax or resin ; leaves reduced in size or absent ; low stature with the frequent occurrence of mat and cushion forms ; a tendency to develop either succulence or thorns : all these are common features and their presence helps to give deserts their dreary look.

One other point requires emphasis. Just because deserts by definition cannot carry a continuous plant cover, the problem of seed spread offers special difficulties. Suitable sites for new plants are those where underground water is present within reach of long roots and is not being already tapped by existing plants, or, for the short-lived forms, those particularly exposed to the occasional rains and yet not in such a position that rain water runs off speedily without moistening the soil. However unspecial-ized desert rain plants may appear in other respects, their seeds must show a very special sensitiveness to moisture, and some means of ensuring transport to the widely scattered suitable sites is a great advantage.

Two plants, to both of which the name of Rose of Jericho is sometimes applied, and both occurring in the arid and semi-arid lands round the eastern Mediterranean, have always aroused interest because they seem to be steppe plants which, by virtue of a special adaptation, have been able to extend their range into the desert proper. One (*Anastatica hierochuntica*) is a crucifer, the other (*Odontospermum pygmaeum*) a composite. The former, which belongs to a genus with but a single species, is the more specialized of the two. Fig. 24 shows its main features. As the fruits mature with the onset of the dry season the leaves drop off and the dry branches roll inwards forming a ball of wickerwork protecting the pods. In Palestine, where the plant is common near Jericho, the normal sequence appears to be that the ball remains in position during the dry season and when the rains come again uncurls, allowing the seeds to escape and be washed away by runnels. But the plant has little hold on the soil and high winds may detach it in the balled-up form when it rolls easily over the dry surface. If it reaches a moistened spot the branches uncurl and the liberated seeds may germinate. Thus an adaptation adjusted primarily to a climate where the rainfall, if small, is regular permits the plant to spread into true desert.

The other Rose of Jericho shows a development of a kind of adaptation not uncommon among composites. Its massed florets are enclosed in stiff bracts, and after seed-setting these bracts close over the numerous small fruits, forming tight knobs from which these cannot escape. Normally, it would seem, these knobs open when the rains come and the seeds have a chance of

FIG. 24.—Rose of Jericho (*Anastatica Hierochuntica*)
I. Dry. II. Wet
After Kerner and Oliver

germinating. Again, however, it seems that either the whole plant or the separate heads may be torn off and swept away, remaining inert till access of moisture causes them to open and shed the bottled-up fruits.

Both plants emphasize once again the way in which plants from bordering areas may creep into the desert proper. The deserts indeed show but an accentuation of the climatic type which prevails in those bordering regions. It is probable that a complete analysis of a desert flora would show that its ' rain plants ' are either the little-modified descendants of an earlier flora or recent immigrants, while some at least of the forms showing intense adaptations, like Welwitschia and Acanthosicyos, are the much-modified descendants of forms which occupied the area before it possessed the same degree of aridity as at present.

We have said nothing of the true cold deserts, that is of the areas bordering Arctic and mountain snows and ice. The problem here is simpler, for such deserts are in contact with but one vegetation belt, not encircled as other deserts may be. It is generally true that the scattered plants of high mountains and Arctic regions are the more resistant of those which occur in the adjacent grassland or tundra belt. Some points in regard to those occurring in the northern hemisphere will be discussed later when we come to consider the effects of the Ice Age, and one aspect has already been dealt with in Chapter V.

NOTE

The literature on the American prairies and on North American vegetation generally is extensive. An interesting article by F. E. Lloyd will be found in the *Handbook of Canada*, published for the Toronto Meeting of the British Association for the Advancement of Science (Toronto, 1924). For the savannas of northern Africa see T. F. Chipp, ' The Vegetation of Northern Tropical Africa ', *Scott. Geog. Magazine*, XLVII (1931), p. 193. Further details as to both grasslands and deserts will be found in the general works already mentioned.

CHAPTER IX

LAND ANIMALS AND PLANT COMMUNITIES

ANIMAL HABITATS

WE have seen that plants tend to form communities which are a direct response to factors of habitat, especially climatic ones. That response again is expressed in the nature and relative numbers of the life-forms in different communities, in the lateral spacing of the plants and in the extent to which they are arranged in tiers. The survey has made clear how diverse the resultant communities are. Even defining forest as a closed canopy of tall phanerophytes, we find that forests not only vary greatly in their composition, in the density of the tree stands, in the degree to which tier formation occurs, but can exist also under a wide range of climate, with a corresponding diversity in character and appearance. Similarly, while it is convenient for some purposes to regard as grasslands communities in which the closing of the canopy is due to herbaceous plants, yet grasslands differ greatly among themselves and again occur in a variety of habitats.

For land animals the word habitat takes on a very different aspect. Most terrestrial animals can tolerate a wide range of variation in the purely physical factors ; neither climate nor relief is as a rule in itself of outstanding importance, while, save with burrowing animals, soil exerts little influence. It is indeed in the general case to the characteristic plant cover and not to details of climate or relief or soil features that land animals must be adjusted in structure, function and habits. In other words, habitat for them is defined not by the physical factors themselves but by their expression in the plant communities present. A particular amount or distribution of rainfall may matter little in itself ; it matters enormously in so far as it is reflected in a type of plant community to which the animals present must be adapted.

Diversity of plant communities involves diversity of terrestrial habitats for animals and a wide range of animal adaptation. The ocean shows a much greater degree of uniformity, and the con-

trast has two consequences. In the first place we find that the
lands, despite their much smaller area, despite also the presence
of purely negative tracts such as those drowned beneath land ice
or a permanent snow cover, have a far greater number of kinds
of animals than the seas. Again, marine animals show little
analogy to that wide range of adaptive adjustment to habitat
which is so marked in the case of land forms. These adaptations
occur especially in connexion with the kind of food habitually
taken and with the usual mode of movement, for, in contrast
with marine animals, many of which are either sedentary or float
in the water, almost all land animals have well-developed locomotor organs definitely related to the plant cover—the South
American sloth hanging back downwards from branches in the
tropical forests and literally unable to put foot to ground, our
squirrel almost equally at home in the trees and on the ground,
wild horses galloping over the plains, the snake gliding through
the grass, and so on. In the ocean, on the other hand, plants
rarely occur in such size and numbers as to exert any special
influence, and the animals capable of free movement for the
most part either swim in the water or crawl over the sea floor
unhindered by the small number of bulky plants present. The
two major oceanic habitats are thus that in which the animals
are dependent on the solid substratum and that formed by the
open water. On the lands, on the other hand, habitat is determined mainly not by the nature of the substratum but by the
plant communities which it bears. Upon those communities
depends largely the extent to which free movement is possible
and the kind of movement which is easiest.

These plant communities, again, vary enormously in the
amount and nature of the basal food supply which they furnish,
in the extent to which this shows seasonal variation and in the
degree of its accessibility to plant-feeding animals. It is true
that both in the ocean and on the lands the end of the food-
chain, and that however numerous the intervening links, is the
living, chlorophyll-containing plant cell. But in the ocean the
most numerous and most widely distributed plants are single-
celled, floating algae drifting with the surface currents, while the
remainder consist chiefly of the larger fixed algae which are
structurally hardly more complex. The predominating land
plants, on the other hand, are complex fixed forms varying greatly
in the nature of the plant body, in the details of structure and in
the extent to which they are built up of tissue elements at once
rich in food and capable of being assimilated. The woody and
corky tissues which enter so largely into the make-up of many

land plants not only are poor in essential food elements but will not yield to the digestive fluids of most animals. Some insects among terrestrial animals, some crustaceans and molluscs among marine ones, seem able to digest wood, but otherwise, like cork, it is practically valueless in this connexion. Further, even the softer parts of land plants differ notably both in their food value and in their availability. In consequence, most vegetable feeders among land animals show a delicate adjustment to a particular kind of food, some insects, for example, limiting themselves strictly to the leaves of a single species of plant. Generally, it may be said that associated with the great range of variation of land plants we find that vegetarian terrestrial animals tend to be adapted to a particular type of diet and thus constrained to frequent the plant communities which yield the food they require.

In sum, then, the kinds of places in which land animals live—that is, their habitats—are determined mainly by the nature of the plant cover, and to that plant cover they are adapted just as the plant communities are adapted to the prevailing physical factors. But while the plants are fixed, the animals are capable of free movement within the limits set by the nature of their locomotor organs and their demand for suitable food—that is, by their specific adaptations. Two interesting topics thus present themselves for discussion. In the first place we have to inquire how far it is true that the various kinds of plant communities we have described have each their characteristic fauna, the range of whose members is limited by that of the community. Secondly, there is the more detailed problem of the actual structural adaptations which fit particular animals for the various types of country as defined by their plant cover. The latter problem we shall consider in another chapter, taking the more general question here.

One point, however, may be emphasized. In dealing with plant communities we noticed that, while homologous communities occur under similar climatic conditions in the different continental areas, the actual species present may differ widely. Thus sclerophyllous forest occurs under ' Mediterranean ' conditions of climate in various parts of the world, but the actual species present differ enormously, e.g. as between California or Chile and the Cape area. The same sort of thing happens with animals, e.g. while the tropical forests of both Africa and South America contain many monkeys, yet the monkeys present in the two areas differ greatly. Both, however, show adaptations to life in a particular kind of plant community, which is the point with which we are concerned here.

THE EQUATORIAL FOREST AS AN ANIMAL HABITAT

In considering the question of how far it is true that particular plant communities serve as habitats for animals too specialized to extend beyond them, it is convenient to begin with the equatorial rain forest. It is not only well defined, but seems to be uniquely favourable so far as the basal food supply is concerned. It is indeed the only kind of community in which fruit-eating animals can find their chosen food throughout the year, the only one where continuously renewed green leaves are available. But the climate which makes this possible means that tall phanerophytes predominate over all other life-forms, and this in its turn implies that vegetal food is mainly present in the upper tiers and can be reached only by animals able to fly or climb. At ground-level, movement for bulky animals is difficult because of the close spacing of the trees with their massive, buttressed trunks and spreading surface roots, while at the same time the general scarcity of ground plants means that pasturage in the ordinary sense may be non-existent. Further, since social species of plants do not occur, individual trees with specially succulent fruits or some other attractive quality are found only as isolated specimens and have to be sought. Again, though the trees are constantly shedding their leaves and putting forth new ones, this also is a sporadic phenomenon ; thus animals which require fresh herbage may similarly have to make considerable journeys in search of it.

There is also, though at first sight it may seem absurd, a water problem. The leaves of the trees, as we have seen, are adapted to allow rain water to flow off them, a film of surface water being a hindrance to the starch-making process. It is probably true that animals which feed mainly on leaves and succulent fruits obtain from them sufficient fluid and do not need to drink, but others must make a long and difficult journey to the ground, food and water being widely separated. Total conditions are thus not quite so favourable as they seem at first sight.

Consider also the two main modes of movement. Some power of flight is clearly useful, but in itself is insufficient and is often combined with climbing power (modifications of the beak and toes in birds, &c.). Indeed, the density of the forest prohibits swift and soaring flight and the power to climb up trees and along branches is more important. Even the birds, therefore, tend to have limited powers of flight compared with those occurring in other types of habitat.

Climbing in the literal sense is best achieved by grasping limbs, sometimes associated with a prehensile tail (New World monkeys), while the difficulty of the jump from one tier to another or from one tree to another may be got over by great agility and the power to use the lianes as ropes (Old World monkeys), or by the presence of a parachute (flying squirrels, the flying lemur, flying phalangers, and many others). But the conversion of the vertebrate limbs, whether both pairs or mainly the forelimbs, into grasping organs involves structural changes which make swift quadrupedal movement on the ground difficult. The presence of a parachute as distinct from true wings (birds, fruit bats) has the great advantage in a vertebrate that it leaves the fore-limbs free to act as grasping organs ; but the parachute even when folded is a hindrance to movement on level surfaces and at the same time far less efficient as an organ of flight than a true wing. Generally, that is to say, the adaptations necessary to make life in dense forest possible tend to limit animals possessing them to forested areas ; but—and this is the point—not necessarily to the equatorial forest in the strict sense. Any forest, provided it can be reached, and provided it contains suitable food, will be equally suitable.

The true equatorial forests of the globe are so widely separated in space that movement from one of the areas to another is rarely possible. The gorilla and the chimpanzee are confined to the hot wet forests of Africa and are absent from those of South America and of Asia, the latter of which has the gibbon and orang-utang peculiar to itself. It is possible enough that either of the two groups of the great apes would suit either of the other regions just as well as the one it inhabits, but means of transport are lacking. On the other hand, in all the areas concerned, as we have seen, the equatorial forest passes into transitional types, differing in steadily increasing degree as rainfall becomes more markedly seasonal, and present also locally even within the equatorial belt where elevation or flooding or other causes bring about a change in the habitat factors. These transitional types differ especially in their increased periodicity in plant growth and reproduction, and in the reduction in the number of species represented. From the point of view of the vegetal-feeding animals, the food supply is both less varied and less continuously present. But what it lacks in these respects it makes up for in that at certain times and in certain places it may be abundant and more readily accessible ; abundant because, e.g., leaf renewal or fruiting is concentrated in time and place instead of scattered ; more accessible because the forest is less dense as well as because species of trees producing valuable food may be present in proportionately larger numbers. That food is not in reality so easily got within the equatorial forest as it seems is shown by the

II

way in which many of its denizens raid the limited patches of cultivated land within it. A garden or plantation acts as a centre of attraction just because edible substances are concentrated there. Compared with the equatorial forest it represents the setting out of a solid meal as against a sparse spread of hors d'oeuvres.

Note the consequences. There are certain animals, including, however, a comparatively small number of mammals (the sloths among Edentates, many Primates, some Marsupials), which do appear to be limited to forests of the equatorial type and scarcely extend beyond them. A larger number have a wider range, extending into tropical forests generally. Such animals move in a leisurely and irregular fashion towards the areas where food is most abundant, their movements being determined by the local response of the plants to the whole complex of the physical habitat factors. For many of them, however, the presence of a closed forest canopy is essential, so that they avoid the more open parklands and savannas. In other words, the more definitely they are adapted to forest life, the less able are they to extend beyond the forest limit. At the same time, while it is not difficult to make general statements about the animals characteristic of inter-tropical as compared with temperate forests, it is not easy in either case to draw up lists of animals rigidly confined to one particular forest type.

TEMPERATE GRASSLANDS

As a further illustration we may take the temperate grasslands, which offer the completest contrast possible with the equatorial rain forest. Here tall phanerophytes may be locally absent and the herbaceous kinds of life-forms are endlessly repeated. When represented by the social grasses, these afford seasonally an enormous supply of green leaves at ground-level. But the absence of phanerophytes implies that the climatic factors limit plant activity sharply to a relatively short period of the year. As the lush green of their leaves fades, the herbs prepare for regeneration and for the unfavourable season by laying up reserves in seeds and in underground stems and roots. From the point of view of herbivorous animals, then, we have a great abundance of herbage in early summer ; a prolongation of food supplies into autumn in a somewhat different form ; and, finally, a winter at least intermittently so severe that few animals can tolerate its rigours in the open, accompanied by sufficient frost and snow to render the underground parts of plants inaccessible.

How far is it possible for such communities to form permanent animal habitats ?

Examination of their faunas shows that the animals present fall roughly into three groups. Some, especially many of the insects and the land molluscs, show almost as direct a response to the varying conditions as do the plants. Thus the herbivorous land snails feed greedily when lush herbage is available, storing up reserves within their bodies. Either extreme summer drought or winter cold causes them to pass into a state of suspended animation (aestivation or hibernation) in some sheltered spot where they seem able to wait almost indefinitely till warmth or moisture brings fresh food and awakens them to activity. The insects here as elsewhere have a more complicated and varied life-history. Some feed only in the larval stage and when full-fed surround themselves with a protective coat from which, after what may be a prolonged resting stage, the perfect insects emerge to reproduce and die. In essence, however, the adaptations are similar in kind. Food is taken when available in excess of the immediate needs and stored internally, and the insects, whether as passive pupae or as over-wintering eggs, bide their time till plenty comes again.

A second group includes those mainly social forms which seem to show an intelligent prevision of events and make a combined effort to provide against both winter severity and winter scarcity. Thus among the mammals the rodents, many of which are characteristically steppe-animals, while again feeding greedily when food is plentiful and so becoming fat, and often spending much of the winter in sleep, display a more complicated response than snail or caterpillar. This is seen both in their habit of laying up winter provisions and in excavating burrows in which they can pass the winter in relative comfort. In consequence, neither their period of activity nor their food supply is so rigidly determined by weather conditions as those of the members of the first group or of the plants. They show, at least in germ, something of that power of freeing themselves from ' geographic control ' which is so characteristic of man himself. At the same time, the fact that their bodily structure makes it possible to construct only one kind of shelter—the burrow—limits them to areas where the soil is loose, well drained and easily excavated, that is, of the grassland type.

Examples are the oddly named prairie dog of the North American steppes, the bobac marmot of the Eurasian steppes, and the Alpine marmot of Europe. Such forms tend to take a variety of vegetable food, not being limited to fresh green leaves, and this means that for them the season of plenty is prolonged as compared with animals of more restricted diet. Seeds, bulbs, roots, &c., are eagerly taken and stored for winter use. Further, it seems a common feature in grasslands that the sudden onset of desiccating winds in autumn leads to the leaves of grasses being ' cured on the stalk ' as natural hay before the plant has time to withdraw their valuable contents to the underground storing organs. Such natural hay, therefore, retains food value and is collected by the rodents both as bedding and as a reserve. Crowded together in their hay-lined burrows the animals can resist both low winter temperatures and the occasional storms so characteristic of steppes, while mild intervals can be taken advantage of, for the length of the winter sleep seems to vary with the local conditions.

There is still, however, a third group, including those forms which can evade winter scarcity by their own movements—that is, are to a greater or less extent migratory.   Birds and the larger mammals are the most important of these, and because of their mobility they can respond easily to the pull towards the grasslands in summer which results from the superabundance of food then. The reasons for that summer abundance may be briefly noted.

Beginning with the land plants we find that, so long as the sun shines and occasional showers fall, these can readily make good the losses due to grazing or other forms of attack.   Thus the rodents as well as the plant-eating invertebrates multiply rapidly both because food is easily got and also as an adaptive response to the risks of the coming time of famine.   The breeding power of some of the steppe rodents is indeed phenomenal, several or even many litters being produced in the course of a single season. The same sort of thing occurs among the insects ; there may be several summer broods, while in some cases, as with various kinds of plant-lice, the generations succeed each other without pause and without the intervention of a sexual process, this taking place only with the onset of autumn and leading to the production of resistant, over-wintering eggs.

The bodies of fresh water also add their quota of food substances. As the micro-organisms of the soil become active and break down humus, producing nitrates in the process, some of the nutritive salts are washed out by rain and reach the ponds and lakes. The presence of the salts permits the fresh water algae to divide and multiply, and they in their turn serve as the basal food supply for a multitude of aquatic forms, such as minute Protozoa, ' worms ' of many kinds, molluscs and so forth, as well as for larvae of terrestrial forms of insects and amphibians.

Such larvae are particularly important because they mean that the ponds and streams not only furnish food to water-feeding animals, e.g. such birds as ducks and geese, but also replenish the food supply of land forms. Thus among insects, gnats and mosquitoes spend their early life in the teeming water and emerge as winged adults in countless swarms. That is, the salts washed out of the soil by rain are, as it were, returned to the lands in the living tissues of insects which have fed in their early stages on minute water organisms themselves nourished by those salts. In so far as the adult insects are eaten by larger land animals, e.g. birds, the droppings of these again enrich the soil and promote bacterial activity there—and so the unending cycle goes on.

The winter freezing of lakes and rivers, while on the one hand it checks organic growth and multiplication within them, on the other checks the loss of salts from the lands to the sea in drainage water ; and such loss is again reduced by the diminished run-off during the late summer drought. Generally, that is to say, the sum-total of the climatic conditions leads to enormous summer abundance associated with checks so sharp, so effective as regards every element in the food-chain from its base in quiescent soil micro-organisms and quiescent diatoms upwards, as to ensure a conservation of those mineral salts which will permit life to flower anew when sunshine and moisture come again. As the grasslands awaken, then, hosts of migrants, especially birds and mammals, are drawn towards them to take advantage of the brief season of plenty.

As the tide of life ebbs over the grasslands, the birds, which usually have great powers of flight, depart to seek food and shelter elsewhere. Many birds, it will be remembered, cross the Equator in their seasonal migrations and can thus find in another hemisphere conditions comparable to those that have prevailed in the lands they leave. Clearly, however, the larger mammals, unable to burrow, demanding large quantities of food and often very particular as to the kind of food they will take, present a very special problem. The problem is accentuated by the limited extension of the temperate grasslands in latitude as compared, e.g., with the African savannas. Those savannas carry an enormous number both of individuals and of species of herbivorous mammals, and it is interesting to recall (see p. 144) the fact that in East Africa they are continuous across the Equator, so that the herbivores can literally follow the sun with its accompanying rain mantle in its back-and-forward swing, and so find food throughout the year in what is essentially the same kind of plant community. Obviously the herbivores of the North American and Asiatic steppes cannot follow the sun in the same fashion ; they have to meet the problem of winter scarcity in a different way.

We may take the bison (' buffalo ') of North America as an illustration of what happens. It is commonly regarded as a typical denizen of the plains and was indeed formerly the basis

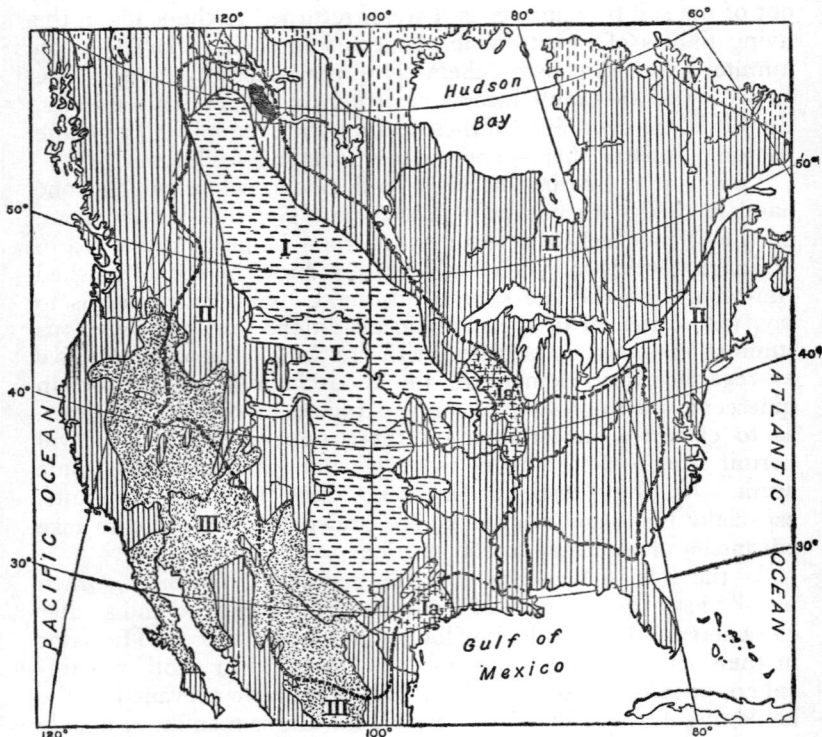

FIG. 25.—Former (broken line) and present (solid black) range of the Bison in North America in relation to main types of plant communities
I, grasslands ; Ia, mixed grasslands and woods ; II, various types of forest ; III, deserts and semi-deserts ; IV, tundra ; V, area with Bison
(Plant regions generalized from Harshberger, range of bison after Kitto)

of the social economy of some groups of plain-dwelling Indians. Now all but extinct as a wild animal, it was formerly very abundant and it has been found possible to trace the limits of its earlier range. In Fig. 25 this has been plotted on a map showing the major vegetation belts of the continent, and the map shows that the bison was not limited to grassland areas. It extended indeed, especially at certain times, into a variety of forest belts, avoiding the tropical forests of Mexico, the semi-tropical ones of Florida, the Pine Barrens of the south-eastern States and having a limited spread into the semi-arid and arid areas west of the Rocky Mountains. The small group of truly wild survivors is confined to an area in Canada within the northern forest belt but including wide pasturages.

In trying to explain this range we have to bear in mind the fact that the animal is purely grass-eating, requiring large supplies of pasture grasses at all seasons. Because the grasses on which it feeds are of the drier type, it needs much water, without which the digestive process cannot go on. Like most herbivores it needs salt, and in areas remote from the sea frequents, at least at times, those dry regions where saline deposits occur. Its mobility is great, and, though it is best fitted for open areas, forest is not an obstacle provided it be not too dense. Under-growth must, however, be overcome by brute force rather than by agility, and in the old days the animals followed regular tracks on their migrations. These tracks were kept open by the passage of the herds, for the animals are social, as the grasses on which they feed are social.

But the mere physical possibility of penetrating forested areas would be of little importance were it not that these yield food and shelter at a time when parts of the grasslands are devoid of both. Here, then, we have to recall what has been already said about the inter-relation of trees and grasses. The climates which favour forests do not exclude herbaceous plants ; indeed, many herbs are adapted to live in association with trees of the tropophytic type. Locally also edaphic and physiographic factors favour the grasses as against the trees, so that open glades occur. That is, within temperate forests there is a considerable amount of pasture without that sharp alternation of seasonal abundance and scarcity characteristic of the steppes. Further, the presence whether of forest in the strict sense or of scattered trees or groves proves that effective rainfall and rainfall distribution are alike more favourable to plant life than in the grasslands proper. Thus the growing season for the grasses will be longer and the period of complete barrenness shorter. Such wooded areas thus yield food resources which help to tide over the period of scarcity.

In summer, then, in the olden days bison occurred in enormous numbers in the open plains. There they bred, the lush grass ensuring not only that the adults could withstand the strain of reproduction but that the cows could produce milk to feed the young. The absence of shelter against attacks of carnivores, especially on the young, was compensated by the size of the herds and the strength and powerful horns especially of the males. As the grass withered, the herds tended to break up, their members scattering in search of food and shelter from storms either in ravines and valleys within the grasslands or in the marginal plant communities, the migrations being often of great extent, and to areas of less extreme cold. Their limit was set in part by the need for grass, whether in the growing state in the areas of less extreme climate or as natural hay elsewhere. But we have to remember also that being large, markedly social and purely grass-eating animals, the continuity of the species depended upon the utilization of the spring flush of grass on the plains; only there was sufficient bulk of food available in the breeding season. The distance over which the animals could travel in the off-season was thus limited by the need for a return in time to take full advantage of the first flush of growth. Though they were not rigidly limited throughout the year to grasslands in the strict sense, it was yet those grasslands which made the continued existence of the great herds possible.

As a further illustration of the fact that the larger herbivores are not rigidly limited in their range by the distribution of any particular plant community, we may consider three other North American Ungulates. The three selected are the moose or North American elk ; the wapiti, often called in error the American elk, though it is in reality more nearly allied to the red deer of Europe ; the prongbuck, the nearest American approach to an antelope, though its horns differ notably from those of the true antelopes. They form an interesting series so far as food is concerned, each being adapted in the main to a particular kind of habitat, though, as Fig. 26 shows, their ranges, in the days of their glory, showed a certain overlap, and all occurred at times within the grasslands.

The moose is definitely a northern form. Like the wapiti it belongs to the deer family, most of which prefer forested country, for the nature of their teeth prevents them feeding exclusively on the drier grasses as the hollow-horned ruminants do. The moose occupied originally the belt of forest, of very varying type and density, which stretches obliquely from the Maritime Provinces of Canada to the interior of Alaska (Fig. 26). It avoids equally the Barren Grounds or tundra, frequented by caribou and musk ox, and also that drier tract which extends from the state of Washington into the interior of British Columbia. It occurs, however, in the woodlands on the slopes of the Rocky Mountains in Idaho and Utah. A short-necked animal, unable

Typically the moose is a denizen of the northern forest belt (cf. Fig. 25), the presence of the Rocky Mountains permitting it to extend southward in the west; the wapiti occurs in the more varied and luxuriant southern forest, while the prongbuck frequents the drier plains. The ranges of the three, however, overlap in the northern grasslands and parklands

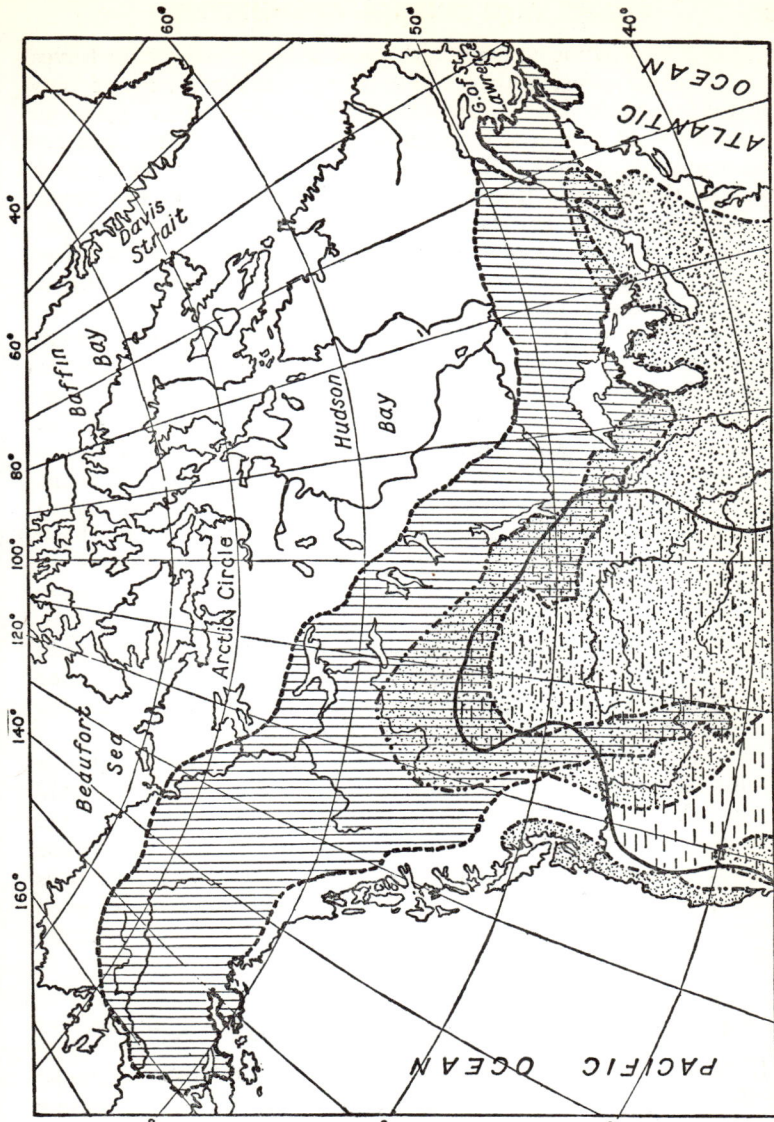

FIG. 26.—The Former Ranges of (I) Moose, (II) Prongbuck and (III) Wapiti in North America

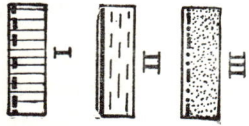

to crop low-growing grasses with ease, it feeds largely on leaves and shoots of trees, both coniferous and deciduous, and avoids the drier prairie lands.   But the tall grasses which grow in summer round swamps, rivers and lakes, draw it into what are technically grasslands.   The wapiti, on the other hand, is a more southern form, frequenting especially forests of the mixed or deciduous type, and taking a great variety of food.   It eats the leaves and shoots of deciduous trees but almost no kind of ground herbage comes amiss, and in earlier days large numbers occurred at times in the open prairies.

In contrast to both, the prongbuck is essentially a plains animal, avoiding heavily timbered country and feeding by preference only on dry grasses and ground plants.   It was never present in the eastern forested area of the United States.   By far the swiftest of the North American Ungulates, it is a poor jumper.   This excludes it from mountainous areas and rough ground, while its dependence on speed as a means of escape from attack makes it unwilling to become entangled in dense forest.   Its northward extension is more limited than that of the other two, but, on the other hand, it extends into south-western semi-arid areas from which they are excluded.   If not in appearance yet in the capacity to digest dry herbage and in some details of structure it shows an approach to those hollow-horned ruminants, such as bison and antelope, which seem so perfectly fitted for life in the natural pasture lands of the world.

Examples could be multiplied almost indefinitely.   Those given may serve to show that, while, as a rule, animals are adapted to their habitats as determined mainly by the plant cover, yet they are not necessarily confined throughout the year to a single habitat.   So far as the mammals at least are concerned, it is rarely possible to draw up a list of species characteristic of even those generalized types of plant communities we have described and of these alone.

LAND MAMMALS AND PLANT COMMUNITIES

If on one side this is due to the mobility of most mammals, on the other it drives home the point already hinted at that our analysis of the plant cover has been a very summary one.   For the geographer the essential is to prove that the distribution of the major plant groupings corresponds broadly to that of the climatic zones.   But no sooner does the ecologist get down to actual field survey than he finds himself compelled to abandon the pioneer plan of splashing bands of colour on a map to represent what used to be called plant formations. No grassland or forest community when examined in detail is a true unit ; a multiplicity of names and symbols may be required to express the facts brought out by a survey of quite a small area within either. This is because minor differences in structure or topography by their influence on shelter or exposure, amount and reaction of ground-water, soil characters and so on are reflected by the plants in a fashion which may mask locally the influence of the climatic factors.

Thus, while it is true to say that habitat for a land animal is mainly defined in terms of the plant community characteristic of the area occupied, we have yet to bear in mind that even within a single climatic zone a number of minor communities may be present. A steppe is an area where the climatic factors are unfavourable to trees and favourable to grasses. But locally trees or bushes may be abundant, or grasses may give place to halophytes in the saline tracts, or the drier types of grasses to tall marsh ones, and so on. Thus even in steppe areas forest-haunting animals can co-exist with those adapted to life in open country, those tolerant of dry conditions with those demanding much moisture.

There is even more than this, for the ecologists find that in many cases observation during a single season gives an incomplete picture of a community ; for a number of forms may then be invisible at the surface and exist only as seeds or underground parts. In addition to recognizing a multitude of minor groupings therefore, they lay emphasis also on what they call the seasonal aspects. The changes from season to season may be such as to alter entirely the appearance of a community considered as an animal habitat. A woodland of the sclerophyllous type is a forest in the sense that the characteristic plant response is the sparsely leaved evergreen tree or shrub. In the cooler, damper season, however, its essential feature is the abundance of ground herbs which are fodder for herbivores. Semi-deserts, again, have often two sharply contrasted aspects, one in which the plant cover is nearly complete and one in which it is very open ; as animal habitats they differ notably in the two periods.

Thus we see that our general distinction between forests, grasslands and deserts fails to take account of all the facts. No forest, no grassland, no desert is completely uniform in space or in time ; each includes a number of minor habitats.

So far as the animals are concerned, again, just because uniformity is so rare, so limited in the lands as compared with the oceans, it is a disadvantage rather than an advantage in the struggle for existence for terrestrial animals to show too rigid a structural adaptation to a particular habitat. The great ocean plains seem to be uniform over vast areas—pressure, temperature, salinity, oxygen content, possible sources of food varying very little. No land area shows anything like a comparable uniformity. Further, the terrestrial animals as compared with those of the ocean deeps have greater powers of movement and, especially the higher forms, well-developed sense organs and the ability to profit by their resultant awareness of their surroundings. The most successful groups, then, are those which are not so strictly adjusted to one kind of habitat as to be forced to remain permanently within it.

Attempts have been made to apply to the study of the distribution of land animals those ecological methods which have proved so fruitful in the case of plants ; but rarely with much success. There is, for example, some evidence that in the equatorial rain forest each tier of the canopy has its own invertebrate fauna, insects and their allies especially being apparently localized in a fairly definite fashion. But that is not the case to the same extent with the vertebrates. Uniform habitats are so small in relation to the locomotor powers of most of the larger animals, and absolute uniformity throughout the year so rare, that their range is usually considerable and may transgress the limits of more than one major type of plant community. Land animals, especially vertebrates, are not earth-bound in the sense that land plants must be.

At the same time, in all the continents a certain zoning of animal life is always observable ; nowhere is there a complete jumble of forms. This is well illustrated by the examples we have already given in the case of the North American Ungulates. The ranges of bison, prongbuck, wapiti and moose may show a certain overlap, but nevertheless each animal is adapted to a particular type of habitat and these adaptations set a limit to their possible movements. Some detail as to such adaptations and their effects must be given. We shall limit ourselves here to the mammals and attempt to consider the major kinds of adaptations present in the different orders. This method has the advantage of preparing the way for our later study of the faunas of the continental areas, and seems more suitable for a necessarily brief survey than trying to note the features of the animals most characteristic of the different plant communities already described. It necessitates, however, a brief survey of the chief kinds of living mammals, a subject to which the remainder of this chapter must be devoted.

GENERAL SURVEY OF TERRESTRIAL MAMMALS

While all mammals are warm-blooded vertebrates characterized by the presence of hair and the fact that the young are nourished after birth by the mother's milk, the range of variation among them is great. It is indeed sufficient to make it necessary to divide living forms into three sub-classes, the Monotremes, the Marsupials and the Placentals. Of the Monotremes we need say little. There are but three living kinds, all confined to the Australian area, all with certain reptilian features of which the most noteworthy is the fact that they lay eggs in place of giving birth to living young like other mammals. The three are the aquatic Ornithorhynchus, or duck-billed platypus, found in the rivers of Australia and Tasmania, and two kinds of burrowing spiny anteaters, Echidna in Australia, Tasmania and New Guinea, and Proechidna in New Guinea. They appear to be the persistent but specialized remnants of a very primitive stock which formerly had a much wider distribution.

Apart from details which we may neglect there are two major differences between Marsupials and Placentals. In the former the young are born after a very short period of gestation as very imperfectly developed embryos, incapable of even the simple muscular movements involved in sucking the mother's milk, which has to be forced into them. After birth they are placed by the mother in the pouch or marsupium within which the later stages of development occur. In Placentals, on the other hand, the young are born as miniature adults and during the long period of gestation are nourished through a complex organ called the placenta by which they are attached within the mother's womb. There is a sense, indeed, in which we may say that during the developmental stages the young of Marsupials are ' external parasites ', while those of Placentals are ' internal parasites '. Vestiges of the placenta occur in certain Marsupials. In the Placentals birth is a catastrophic process involving serious risks to the mother, both because of the size of the young and because of the rupturing of blood-vessels by which it is accompanied. The increased chance of survival of the offspring has, however, more than justified the maternal sacrifice, and the Placentals have gained ground at the expense of the more primitive Marsupials.

The second major difference between the two is that the brain of the Placentals is much more complex, and with this is associated a power of profiting by experience which culminates in the intelligence of man, and in extreme acuteness of certain senses, notably in some of the Ungulates and Carnivores. The two features are correlated, for without their intelligence, acute senses and social or family instincts the dangers of the Placentals' method of reproduction would be too great for survival.

Though there is abundant fossil evidence that in the recent geological past Marsupials were widely distributed, they seem unable to withstand the competition of the more highly evolved Placentals. Only in the Australian area, where they are free from this competition, have they been able to multiply and become differentiated along many lines. At the present time, outside of Australia, Tasmania, New Guinea and some of the islands of the East Indian archipelago, living Marsupials occur only in the Americas. Further, of the comparatively few kinds found in South America only one, the Virginian opossum, has been able to maintain its hold in North America. Within their own isolated area, on the other hand, and especially within the continent of Australia, living Marsupials are not only numerous and diverse but have evolved in directions which show a curious parallelism to those followed by the Placentals in other parts of the world. Australia is indeed the Marsupial Continent, and, just as it shows all the major types of plant communities represented elsewhere, though these are composed largely of peculiar species or genera, often of primitive type, so also each of these communities contains mammals showing structural adaptations analogous to those characteristic of forest, grassland, mountain and desert forms elsewhere. With insignificant exceptions, however, these mammals are Marsupials and not Placentals. The giant kangaroo of the Australian plains shows certain analogies to the Placental herbivores of the similar plains elsewhere ; the Tasmanian wolf recalls the Placental wolves which prey on those herbivores ; the forests include squirrel-like and bear-like animals and so on. It seems as if the physical conditions of climate and relief tend everywhere to produce a similar type of organic response both in plant and animal ; only the level at which that response takes place differs. The plants and animals of Australia are ' primitive ' as compared with those which occur elsewhere ; their fossil allies lost their hold in the northern hemisphere as more specialized types developed there ; but saved by isolation within this southern continent, the Marsupials have been able not only to persist but to evolve along many lines. Many of the forms present seem to have originated within the continent, and never to have existed outside of it.

In classifying both Marsupials and Placentals much stress is laid upon the nature of the teeth. Living Monotremes are either devoid of teeth (Echidna and Proechidna) or those present are lost at an early stage (Ornithorhynchus) ; but with rare exceptions other mammals have highly specialized dentitions and these have a twofold interest. In the first place they give a key to the diet and so to the habits. Again, mammalian teeth are readily preserved as fossils and it is largely from such fossil teeth that the evolutionary history of living mammals has been worked out.

As compared with those of reptiles, mammalian teeth are limited both in total number and in the extent to which they can be replaced. Different functions are performed by different groups of teeth which are variously developed in various cases, while some groups may be altogether absent. Those in the front of the jaws are the incisor or cutting teeth ; behind them stand the stabbing or canine teeth, never more than one at each side of each jaw ; farther back stand the cheek teeth, used in mastication and varying greatly in nature and complexity according to the nature of the diet—that is, the use to which they are put. Mammals which feed exclusively on the flesh of other animals tend to have numerous, small and simple incisor teeth, powerful canines, and cheek teeth of which some at least show cutting edges (cusps). Those feeding exclusively on vegetal food have usually fewer but larger incisors, the upper often meeting the lower with a scissor-blade action ; the canines may be absent ; the cheek teeth tend to have broad grinding surfaces, often with an alternation of ridges and hollows. Where the food is mixed, which often means that insects, &c., are mingled with the softer kinds of vegetal food, this definite specialization is absent, and the cheek teeth instead of being complexly ridged have blunt tubercles with hollows between. Man, like his allies the apes and monkeys, has a generalized dentition of this type. It may be added that while Placentals have two sets of teeth, the adult dentition replacing the ' milk ' teeth of the young, this succession does not occur in the same fashion in the Marsupials, though a few show vestiges of it.

Chief Kinds of Marsupials. These fall into two sets according as the food is mainly animal or mainly vegetal, called respectively Polyprotodonts and Diprotodonts. In the former the incisor teeth are numerous, small and similar in both jaws ; in the latter there are only two incisors in the lower jaw and the centre ones in the upper jaw are larger than the side ones. Each division includes four families.

Polyprotodonts include (1) the Opossums, limited to the Americas, mainly arboreal and feeding largely on insects ; (2) the Dasyures, a large family, whose members vary greatly in appearance : some are rat-like creatures feeding on insects, but the true Dasyures are cat-like, while the

Tasmanian wolf is the largest of the Polyprotodonts and the Tasmanian ' devil ' reaches the size of a badger and is extremely ferocious ; (3) a special family has been erected to include the Marsupial mole of central Australia which in habits and appearance recalls some of the Placental moles of other parts of the world ; (4) the Bandicoots are rat-like or rabbit-like and take a variety of food, including insects and earthworms.

Diprotodonts include (1) two species of Selvas (Coenolestes) small, rare, mouse-like creatures confined to South America and forming the only family apart from the opossums still living outside the Australian region ; (2) the Wombats, a small family of bear-like creatures, feeding only on vegetal matter and confined to Australia and Tasmania ; (3) the Phalangers, some of which are called opossums by the Australians, a much larger family of mainly arboreal animals with a wider distribution, for they extend into New Guinea and some of the islands immediately to the west (Timor, &c.) : some have a parachute and show a curious resemblance to the Placental Flying Squirrels ; the diet is varied, insects being often taken ; (4) the Kangaroos and Wallabies are the most specialized of living Marsupials and purely vegetarian in diet : while the typical forms inhabit open plains there are some arboreal forms and these extend into New Guinea.

Orders of Terrestrial Placentals. Living Placentals may be grouped in nine orders ; but of these, two, the Sirenia or sea-cows and the Cetaceans (whales, dolphins, porpoises), are aquatic. Of the remaining seven orders Ungulates and Rodents are both vegetarian ; the Carnivores are predaceous ; Insectivores are all small forms preying mainly on invertebrates ; they lead up to the highly specialized bats or Chiroptera ; the Primates include lemurs, monkeys, apes and man, and, while showing, at least in the lower forms, certain affinities with the Insectivores, have a more mixed diet and attain a much larger size. All these are modern types while the remaining order, that of the ' Edentates ', is from the systematic standpoint quite unsatisfactory. It includes a small number of old-fashioned mammals, probably not nearly related, and with as the only common feature the fact that teeth when present differ from those of other living mammals.

The Edentates fall into three very different sets. In South America occur the vegetarian and arboreal sloths, the hairy, insect-eating ant-eaters, and the burrowing, omnivorous armadillos, the last remarkable among mammals in having a bony covering to protect the body. Africa contains two species of aard-vark (Orycteropus), curious burrowing pig-like animals feeding on white ants (termites). In both Africa and the Indian region are found the pangolins, which also feed on termites but have the body covered with overlapping horny scales.

Ungulates are mainly large mammals, often social, and very diverse, relatively primitive groups like pigs and tapirs co-existing with very specialized types like oxen and horses. The claws or nails of other mammals are replaced by hoofs and the cheek teeth are large and complex in structure. A notable feature is the tendency to the loss of some of the five digits typically present in land vertebrates, this being correlated with increased speed over firm ground. The elephants, however, retain the full number of digits on both feet and are aberrant Ungulates. The latter statement is also true of the small rock conies (Hyrax) of Africa and Syria which seem to be intermediate between Rodents and Ungulates proper and lack true hoofs. In the remaining Ungulates the weight of the body is borne mainly or wholly on either the middle (third) digit or on the third and fourth together, giving rise to a distinction between the odd-toed and even-toed forms. Living odd-toed Ungulates are few in number, including only the tapirs, the rhinoceroses and the horses, the last with but one functional toe on each foot. Even-toed forms are more numerous and include the pig group (hippopotamus, the true pigs of the Old World, and the American peccaries); the camels and humpless llamas of South America; the chevrotains, somewhat deer-like animals including the smallest of living Ungulates, and the ruminants. The last comprise deer of many kinds, the giraffe, the prongbuck (p. 170) and the hollow-horned ruminants (antelopes, goats, sheep and the various kinds of oxen).

Rodents form by far the largest order of mammals but are mostly small inconspicuous animals easily recognized by their chisel-edged

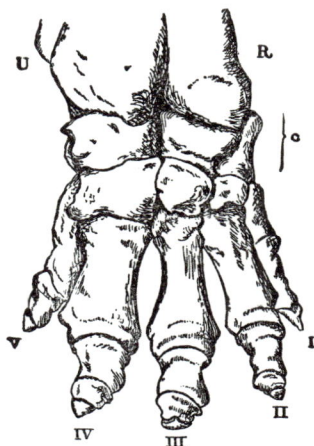

FIG. 27.—Right fore-foot of Indian Elephant (*Elephas indicus*)
R, Radius; U, Ulna; c, Carpus; I–V, Digits
After Flower and Lydekker

incisor teeth used in gnawing. Apart from the ubiquitous rats and mice, they include rabbits, hares, squirrels, porcupines, beavers and many others.

Carnivores are divided into the terrestrial forms and the aquatic seals and walrus. The former fall into three groups, the cat-like forms, of which the true cats (lion, tiger, leopard, puma, &c.) are the most specialized; the dog-like forms (wolf, fox, jackal, &c.); the bear-like group which is heterogeneous, for in addition to the true bears, which are at least partially vegetarian, we have such blood-thirsty forms as stoat, weasel, polecat &c., preying largely on Rodents, as well as otters, skunk, badger and raccoons.

Insectivores (hedgehogs, moles, shrews, &c.) include also as a very aberrant form the flying lemur (Galeopithecus) which has a parachute by which it can take flying leaps from tree to tree. This however differs notably from the true wings of the bats, which are very perfect organs of flight supported by the four elongated digits of the fore-limb, the first digit or thumb being short and clawed. Chiroptera are divided into two groups, the small, insect-eating forms being widely distributed while the larger fruit-eating bats or flying foxes are limited to the warmer parts of the eastern hemisphere.

In the Primates the lemurs are somewhat like monkeys in appearance but have foxy faces and simpler brains. The remainder fall into five families, the small marmosets of South America, the American monkeys, the Old World monkeys, the anthropoid apes and man himself.

CHAPTER X

ADAPTIVE MODIFICATIONS IN TERRESTRIAL MAMMALS

THE FOOD OF MAMMALS

WE can hint at only a few major adaptations here and there among the nearly 3,000 species of living mammals. Because mammals are active, highly organized animals, two problems of feeding present themselves. There is, first, the obtaining of the crude material in sufficient amounts and, second, the details of the mechanism by which this is made to yield the substances essential for growth and reproduction as well as to make up for the waste due to the vital processes.

As regards the second point, we must note the essential differences between plant and animal tissues. Living plant cells, and this whether the plants are aquatic or terrestrial, simple or complex, have a coating of the carbohydrate cellulose round the proteid contents. Animal tissues are made up of naked cells and thus bulk for bulk are richer in nitrogenous organic matter and more easily attacked by digestive fluids. Further, apart from the cellulose coat of individual little-modified cells, such as those which form a large part of green leaves, land plants contain much protective, supporting and vascular tissue which is in the main both indigestible and virtually devoid of proteid. In the higher land plants also this non-nutritious matter interpenetrates the plant body in a fashion to which land animals offer little analogy. Even a soft green leaf contains strands of tissue with thickened and modified cell-walls at once difficult to digest and of little nutritive value. The indigestible parts of animals are mainly external (hard coats of insects, shells of molluscs, scales of reptiles, hairs, feathers, &c.) and, though in vertebrates the bones and tendons may be unavailable, the muscles are both rich in proteid and easily digested, and this is also true of blood. On the other hand, of course, we have the fact that muscles are contractile, that is, possess the power of movement. Thus if one animal is to feed on the muscles and blood of another it must be able to capture and kill that other whether by strength or by guile. The inferiority of plant tissues as a source of proteid is as it were compensated by the fact that they are more easily obtained—land plants cannot run away from a hungry foe.

If then we divide mammals into those feeding respectively on animal and on vegetal matter we find that the latter require a proportionately greater bulk of food, for much of the material ingested may pass through their bodies little altered. Again, herbivorous forms must have means whereby the parts of plants taken are finely ground, thoroughly mixed with the digestive fluids to render their rather scanty nutritive elements soluble, while the absorbing surface of the alimentary tract must be extensive. Generally, indeed, vegetarian mammals must either make a very careful selection of the parts of plants consumed so as to include a high proportion of nutritive matter in relation to that which is useless ; or, if they are more indiscriminate feeders, they must have elaborate masticatory and digestive organs to deal with rough material. Such organs take up space and mean that the body must be bulky. To see that this must be so, one has only to think of the elaborate care with which the squirrel removes every vestige of the outer protective coats of a nut before beginning to chew the kernel, and compare the confidence both in its grinding teeth and in its digestive organs displayed by the elephant. If again we compare either squirrel or elephant with the domestic cat and note what acute senses, agility, intelligence and powerful weapons in the shape of teeth and claws are needed before even such relatively feeble animals as small birds and Rodents can be caught, it becomes clear that the carnivorous habit demands very special adaptations. Once such animals capture their prey, however, the flesh can be ‘ bolted ’ without elaborate chewing, for digestion is easy.

Given then the fact that mammals require considerable quantities of proteid, they are faced with the difficulty that for the smaller, less differentiated types, it is difficult to make plants yield a sufficiency of this, while, on the other hand, high as is the food value of the flesh and blood of other mammals and birds, these are not easy to capture. The result is that many small mammals are what is called omnivorous, and the meaning of the term requires a little elaboration.

If we begin with the vegetal element of the food of such mammals we find that green leaves, especially during the period when starch-making is active, contain a relatively large amount of carbohydrates but only a moderate amount of proteid. There seems in consequence to be a limit of size below which exclusive dependence on herbage is impossible ; it seems, indeed, to be physically and physiologically impossible for small mammals either to swallow enough leaves to supply their needs or to digest these completely. Seeds, on the other hand, are usually rich both in carbohydrates and proteids but are often small and enclosed in indigestible husks. Succulent fruits are usually rich in sugar and some accessory food substances such as useful salts, but, apart from the included seeds, are poor in proteids. The storing organs of plants, especially buds, young shoots, bulbs and other underground stems as well as some roots, contain in proportion to their bulk and to the indigestible residue larger amounts of both carbohydrates and proteids than the other vegetative parts of plants. All such food supplies, however, require to be sought and collected and in most climatic belts are not all present simultaneously.

Most of the small mammals which take storage organs of plants greedily when they can be got, require supplementary sources especially of proteid. Of these supplementary sources, that furnished by the class of insects is the most important. There is almost no organic substance, living or dead, whether of plant or animal origin, which does not enter into the diet of some kind of insect, and as a result the insects are the great intermediaries in the food-chains of terrestrial animals. They take up material which is absolutely useless to most other animals and convert it into their own living substance, which is then available. Further, the facts that the life-history of most insects includes a metamorphosis and that the larvae have as a rule limited powers of locomotion and softer coats than the adults and are almost always voracious feeders, mean that they are easy to catch and digest and are particularly rich in food substances. Great numbers of mammals, therefore, both Marsupials and Placentals, even when nominally vegetarian take in addition insects, especially insect larvae. Where the larvae are themselves vegetarian the body as consumed by the mammal includes both animal tissues in the strict sense and much semi-digested vegetal food already made partially available. The plump caterpillar has chosen, masticated and swallowed parts of green leaves, and the bird or mammal which swallows it has had part of what would otherwise have been its work done for it and is also getting a mixture of animal and vegetal food. Earthworms, another potential food supply, suffer on the other hand from the disadvantage of containing a large amount of quite useless earth. Generally it is safe to postulate of an omnivorous mammal that insects will enter into its diet as well as other terrestrial arthropods (millipedes, spiders, &c.).

The smaller weakly armed mammals can also get animal food from the eggs and nestlings of birds, carrion, the remnants of the kill of larger animals and so on.   It will be noted, however, that in the general case the omnivorous habit is most easily acquired by mammals which are either arboreal or burrowing, for the resultant modifications of the fore-limbs and body are an important factor.   The sensitive finger-like digits of many kinds of arboreal mammals, the sensitive pointed snouts of such burrowers as shrews and other Insectivores are obviously great assets in picking up miscellaneous food substances.

The term insectivorous, it may be noted, whether as applied to the Placental order of Insectivores or to other kinds of animals is somewhat deceptive.   Many kinds of mammals eat insects when obtainable, but an exclusive dependence on winged adults, such as occurs in some birds, almost always implies the power of flight.   In this sense the chief true insect-eaters are certain of the bats (p. 178), for mammals live too fast for it to be possible for non-volant forms to depend on the slow method of stalking adult insects practised by so many lizards among the cold-blooded reptiles.   Here however we have to recall the fact that certain insects, particularly the true ants and the not-nearly-related white ants or termites, show an extraordinary development of the social instinct.   Some kinds of both ants and termites construct ant-hills of a size which in relation to that of the individual builders is enormous.   These ant-hills are nurseries as well as dwellings, and many of the adults are wingless, wings being present often only during the short pairing phase when the nuptial flights occur. Ant-hills thus contain an enormous potential food supply, available provided (1) the protective covering of the ' house ' can be torn down and (2) there is some means of collecting both the helpless young and the wingless adults as they scatter.   In consequence, at various levels in the mammalian sequence, we find forms which are not omnivorous, not insectivorous in the general sense but specifically ant-eaters or termite-eaters.   The adaptations present are mainly those which facilitate the two processes already mentioned ; teeth are sometimes present and sometimes absent without apparently making much difference, and no special modifications of the alimentary tract seem essential.   What is essential is that powerful claws should be present on the fore-limbs, while as a rule the tongue is much elongated, as is the head in which it is lodged, and sticky with a glutinous saliva so that it forms a collecting organ.   Such ant-eating mammals occur among Monotremes (Echidna and Proechidna), among Marsupials as in the Dasyure family (banded ant-eater), among

Edentates (hairy ant-eaters, pangolins, aard-vark). Even such highly differentiated mammals as some of the bear group, as for example the sloth-bear of India, seem to depend largely on ants and termites, though the sloth-bear also attacks the nests of the social bees both for the grubs and for the stored honey, and takes also fruits, flowers and other kinds of insects.

Apart from aquatic fish-eating forms the remaining terrestrial mammals, including the larger quadrupeds, are either herbivores, depending on various kinds of fresh herbage, or carnivores, feeding on the flesh and blood of warm-blooded vertebrates, especially members of the Ungulate and Rodent orders. In both cases the structural adaptations are numerous and varied and something must be said of these.

ADAPTATIONS IN HERBIVORES

Among mammals the higher Ungulates show the most perfect adaptations to a diet consisting wholly of herbage. Certain of

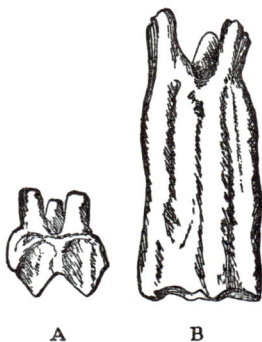

A   B

FIG. 28.—A. Last upper molar of pig (brachydont form), left side. B. Left upper molar of Nilghai or Indian antelope to show hypsodont type

the Diprotodont Marsupials are, however, little inferior in this respect and some of the larger Rodents are at least mainly dependent on such food and correspondingly specialized.

The major features of the dentition have been already outlined (p. 175), but there are a number of peculiar adaptations in the different groups. Thus the higher even-toed Ungulates are remarkable in having no incisor teeth in the upper jaw, the large lower incisors working against a hardened pad in the upper jaw. Upper canine teeth are also absent while the lower canines resemble the incisors and lie close beside them. That these are adaptive features is shown by the fact that the true pigs, the simplest of the even-toed series, retain the full complement of upper incisors, and have upper canines as well as lower ones, the latter not being incisor-like.   As we ascend the scale this condition gives place progressively to that found in antelopes and oxen.   Since the pigs take a variety of food it is tempting to regard the loss of the upper incisors as in some way making grazing easier.   But this cannot be the case, for the horses, the highest of the odd-toed series, have at once the full number of upper incisors and are as definitely grass-eating as the higher even-toed forms.   Here, however, another point is worth noting. In the even-toed series the higher as compared with the lower forms possess bony head appendages (antlers, horns) either in

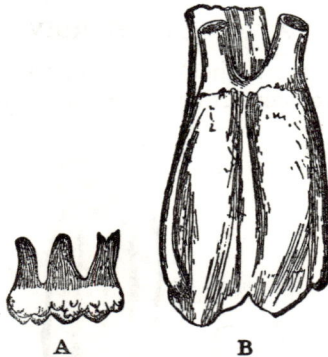

Fig. 29.—A. Outer view of second molar tooth of Anchitherium (brachydont form).   B. Upper second molar tooth of horse (hypsodont form)

both sexes or in the males only.   Apparently it is difficult to obtain from a diet of herbage sufficient lime salts to permit of the calcification of the massive cheek teeth, the head appendages and the bulky skeleton, so that the loss of the upper front teeth may represent a necessary economy of lime.

A tendency to lose either the upper canines or both upper and lower ones is at once more general among herbivorous mammals and more easily explained.   In mammals generally these teeth tend to be weapons, and this tendency reaches its maximum in the Carnivores where they are long, strong and sharp.   Herbivorous mammals cannot hope to compete with them in this respect and, save in the case of some of the less specialized Ungulates such as the pigs, either depend on flight for escape or have weapons of another type.   Further, it is an advantage for a herbivore to have a notable gap between front and cheek teeth, for these have different though equally important functions, and there must be no jarring of the front teeth while the cheek set are engaged in laborious mastication of dry food.   The suppression of the canines, especially of the upper ones, is a means of attaining this end.   In other words, in herbivores generally canines are ineffective as weapons, and inconvenient for animals which do much chewing, and they tend to disappear.

Note some examples.   In the Rodents there are no canines in either jaw and a hairy pad divides the mouth cavity into an anterior gnawing chamber and a posterior masticatory one.   The incisors are large but few, and if cornered the animals can use them to give an ugly bite.   The higher even-toed Ungulates cannot give an effective bite, but the antlers or horns combined with the powerful head muscles are used to try to prevent the Carnivores from making an approach near enough to use their teeth and claws.   The horses, which at least in the males retain the upper canines, use their powerful incisors rather than these in the vicious bite, but their main weapon lies in the powerful hind-limbs armed with the heavy hoofs.

It is however in the characters of the all-important cheek teeth that the herbivorous mammals show the most obvious adaptations.   Where the drier grasses are taken these must be thoroughly chewed, and the problem of maintaining, throughout a life which may be long, efficient, self-setting millstones is one which has been solved in several different ways.   The problem is complicated by the fact that one feature of mammals, the limited degree to which the teeth can be replaced, had apparently been fixed before the modern herbivorous forms appeared.   Placentals have two successive sets and two only, Marsupials one complete set only.   In the Placentals an obvious adaptation is to retain the milk set as long as possible so as to diminish the strain on the adult or second set.   This occurs among the Ungulates as a general feature but, rather oddly, not in the same way among the Rodents.   There, within the limits of a single family, some forms shed their milk teeth early and others retain them for a considerable period.   The living elephants, which have peculiarly massive and complex teeth and are very long-lived, make their cheek teeth last longer by the device of using only one or parts of two at each side of each jaw at any one time.   As the functional tooth is worn down it is shed and the next one grows forward to take its place. This is a development of the condition seen in man where the last cheek tooth (wisdom tooth) at each side of both upper and lower jaws normally develops later than the other members of the adult set. The wisdom teeth in civilized men not infrequently fail to develop fully, but where the food is of a coarse nature, involving heavy wear, it is an advantage to have new unworn teeth coming into position late.

Generally, however, specialization in herbivorous mammals shows itself mainly in the size and complex structure of the cheek teeth.   While the details are beyond our scope we may note the distinction between the long-crowned teeth of the hollow-horned ruminants and the short-crowned ones of, e.g., the deer (cf. p. 185).   In the former only a small part of the crown is exposed and as this is worn down the lower part is pushed up so that the teeth are adapted to withstand prolonged wear.   In the deer the crown is short, the whole depth being exposed from the first and this passing direct into the roots ; such teeth wear down readily and make it impossible for the deer to masticate the wiry grasses favoured by the hollow-horned ruminants.   It is notable that Africa, south of Mauretania, with its enormous tracts of savanna carrying coarse grasses, has no deer but countless herds of antelopes ; deer tend to frequent areas where the softer kinds of grasses occur or where other kinds of herbage are available.

In the Ungulates, however, the teeth are usually rooted, that is to say, once formed they cannot grow larger, for the pulp cavity is narrowed below and permits only sufficient blood to enter to maintain the tooth alive.   In some Rodents (e.g. beaver), on the other hand, the pulp cavity of the cheek teeth remains unconstricted, that is, there is no distinction between root and crown, and the teeth continue to grow throughout life, being renewed below as they are worn down above.   This may seem a more effective method, but Rodent teeth never attain, even relatively to the size of the animals, either the massiveness or the complexity of those of the higher Ungulates.

It is the size of their cheek teeth which tends to give herbivorous mammals their long heads as compared with the multitude of short-jawed, plump-cheeked Carnivores.   Further, the lower jaw can be freely rotated, an essential for prolonged mastication.   It will be noted that man, like his structural allies the monkeys, has some power of rotating the lower jaw.

As compared with the thin-flanked Carnivores, herbivorous mammals tend to have bulky bodies owing to the length and complexity of the alimentary canal.   Here two main types of adaptation occur.   A complex blind outgrowth, often long and wide, called the caecum, placed at the junction of the small and large intestine, increases the absorptive surface but, though generally present in mammals, it reaches great development only in certain herbivorous forms, and tends to be small in those which take a mixed or animal diet. In man, for example, the caecum is rudimentary and has associated with it that too familiar organ the appendix. The other type of adaptation is an enlarged and complex stomach. This condition reaches its maximum in the higher even-toed Ungulates where the organ is divided into four compartments with arrangements to ensure that only finely shredded material is exposed to the gastric juice. Such ruminating Ungulates feed in the open and swallow their food after only perfunctory mastication. They then retire to some sheltered spot where this material, now somewhat softened, is returned to the mouth cavity and re-ground till it is fine enough to pass through a filtering chamber to the true digestive stomach. While extremely efficient this method has the disadvantage that a period of passivity is required after feeding—hence the metaphorical use of the term ' ruminating '. Ruminants by choice therefore frequent country where areas rich in grasses alternate with those offering shelter from weather and insect pests as well as some protection from Carnivores ; most of them perform regular diurnal migrations in addition to those determined by seasonal variation in the food supply.

Of the numerous modifications of the skeleton we can say but little. In the higher true Ungulates, odd-toed and even-toed alike, both pairs of limbs are adapted for swift terrestrial progression over firm ground. This involves an elongation of the bones to give length of stride and a union of bones normally separate to diminish the risk of fracture. Of the tendency to lose the lateral digits we have already spoken ; it should be noted also that the limbs can move only in the back and forward direction and this means that the range of movement of the fore-limbs is very limited as compared with that in most mammals and notably in arboreal forms. It is necessary only to recall the varied uses to which the typical fore-limb with its separable and flexible digits can be put to perceive that the Ungulate speed has been attained at great cost. The elephants, so different in many ways from the true Ungulates, possess what may almost be described as a fifth limb in the long and flexible trunk ending in one (Indian elephant) or two (African elephant) finger-like processes and the presence of this organ brings in its train many contrasts in habit and function. Because it can be used like a hand to carry food to the mouth cropping incisors are unnecessary. There are no lower incisors at all and the upper ones are converted into tusks. These serve both as weapons and, particularly in the African elephant, as the equivalents of the digging sticks of primitive folk.

As compared with the specialized Ungulates the elephants are indeed eclectic feeders, being able to obtain food at ground-level, below ground by ploughing up roots and bulbs, and from trees. In the last case they are not even limited to herbage within reach of the trunk, for they can overturn small trees and so obtain the fresh leaves of the crown. Again, since the trunk is used in drinking, the long limbs do not necessitate a corresponding elongation of the neck. Note by way of contrast the giraffe, which feeds mainly on the leaves of small trees. Despite the very long neck, the length of the fore-limbs forbids the animal

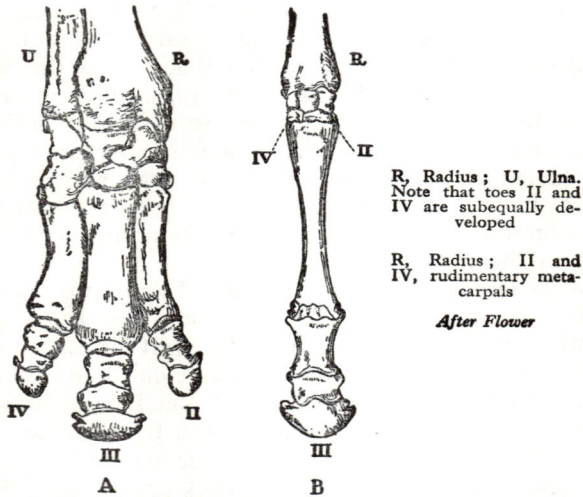

R, Radius ; U, Ulna. Note that toes II and IV are subequally developed

R, Radius ; II and IV, rudimentary metacarpals

After Flower

FIG. 30.—A. Right fore-foot of Rhinoceros (*Rhinoceros Sumatrensis*) B. Right fore-foot of Horse (*Equus caballus*)

grazing, and only by straddling the fore-limbs widely can it drink.

There is still another point about the trunk of the elephant. The long legs and neck of many of the higher Ungulates bring the head with its delicate sense organs well above the level of the ground vegetation so that the animals are warned from afar of the approach of enemies. The short-necked elephants would be at a disadvantage were it not that the nostrils lie at the end of the mobile trunk which can be raised high above the body, extended laterally or dropped to the ground. Though neither sight nor hearing appears to be acute the animals have a sense of smell of a delicacy beyond our conception, and by the free movements of the trunk obtain warnings of danger without the need of turning the head or the bulky body. But compared with the higher Ungulates the elephants are of course slow and clumsy animals, unable to jump or to maintain their maximum speed of some fifteen miles an hour for more than a short time. They are adapted to a type of country different from that frequented by the higher Ungulates.

Apart from those specialized Ungulates, the other herbivorous mammals which haunt open areas display as it were a compromise between the different needs outlined. The fore-limbs in particular tend to be less specialized and to retain a greater freedom of movement at the joints. Consider for example the giant kangaroo of the open savanna lands of Australia. The fore-limbs are short and retain the typical five-clawed digits. Though capable of supporting the weight of the body they are not adapted for rapid movement. On the other hand the hind-limbs are long and powerful and have one well-developed clawed toe, another of about half this size and two rudiments. In feeding the animal goes down on all-fours. On an alarm it rises on the hind-limbs, the large tail serving as an additional support. In this position the large eyes and mobile ears come into play and if the alarm proves justified the animal seeks to escape by the magnificent bounds for which the hind-limbs are so well fitted. If cornered it can use the fore-limbs in a throttling hug or, supporting itself by the tail and one hind-limb, can use the other with its powerful claw to give a rapier-like thrust. The two small toes, while useless so far as support is concerned, can be used in combing the fur, a very important function inasmuch as herbivorous mammals are much exposed when feeding to the attacks of parasitic insects some of which lay their eggs on hair or skin. Curiously enough, somewhat analogous modifications occur among the Rodents, where the jerboas of steppes and deserts have short fore-limbs and long hind ones used in leaping. They are however small burrowing animals. As a general rule indeed, and except in South America where Ungulates are few, grass-eating Rodents are unable to compete in the grasslands proper with the more specialized Ungulates and tend to be pushed to the more barren and inhospitable tracts.

As has been already suggested, the evolution of the more specialized herbivores has taken place side by side with that of the modern types of plants, particularly the grasses among Monocotyledons and the more numerous Dicotyledonous orders including a number of herbs (Leguminosae, Compositae, &c.). Because of the growth habit of such plants, food, during the favourable season at least, is superabundant and makes possible a development among the animals of a social instinct of quite special type. Then at least there is no direct competition for food—there is enough for all. Among Carnivores the dog types are more or less social, but they combine only for the specific purpose of bringing down prey, and once this is achieved each member of the pack fights for his share. Many of the monkeys also live in bands, but competition among the members is none the less fierce ; tasty morsels form the prize of the strongest, and the constant scuffling offers a marked contrast to the peaceful grazing of Ungulate herds. While therefore the latter often break up into smaller parties during the unfavourable season, a communal mode of life is practised so long as food is plentiful. With this are associated many modifications of habit and function. The young at birth are characteristically long-legged and the period of complete helplessness may be very short ; for the mothers dare not lose touch with the herd. This is especially true of the smaller forms where individuals have little chance against the attacks of predatory foes, bird or mammal. It leads to some curiously persistent instincts. Note for example that even the domesticated lowland sheep, well fed, carefully enclosed, will not permit her lambs to satisfy their hunger, moving on in an apparently heartless fashion as they strive to reach her udder. Under natural conditions both she and they must always be able to fly before their enemies, and to permit the young at any given moment to be full-fed is to run too grave a risk. This contrasts notably with the facts about the helpless young of the Carnivores, born within some kind of den, necessarily visited by the mother at infrequent intervals only, and then allowed to absorb milk enough to ensure that a long period of quiescence follows.

Nominally the Ungulate herds are ' led ' by the ruling male. In point of fact, however, the actual leader on the march seems usually to be a mature or even aged female, who takes this position by right of her specially acute senses, the ruler of the flock acting as rearguard to defend the retreat. It is clear that the females are especially exposed to danger both during the actual process of birth and when hampered by the young at heel. Thus the fact that a particular female has survived several successive breeding seasons is in itself evidence that she possesses much intelligence and it is on this that the safety of the herd depends.

Awareness to danger on the part of the leader would however be of little value unless her premonitions were instantly communicated to the rest, and here again there are a number of interesting adaptations. Among Ungulates visual signals seem to be usual, and the tail is sometimes a signalling organ, a change in its position indicating the beginning of a stampede. Among the antelopes it is frequent to find conspicuous markings at the end of the body; thus flashes of white indicate that the advance guard has taken the alarm and there is an instantaneous response on the part of the remainder—death being often the penalty of delay. The Ungulates strive to weary their foes by speed while most Rodents dash for their burrows or other shelter. The latter sometimes depend on aural signals, as witness the whistling of the Alpine marmot. The white scut of the rabbit, however, is a

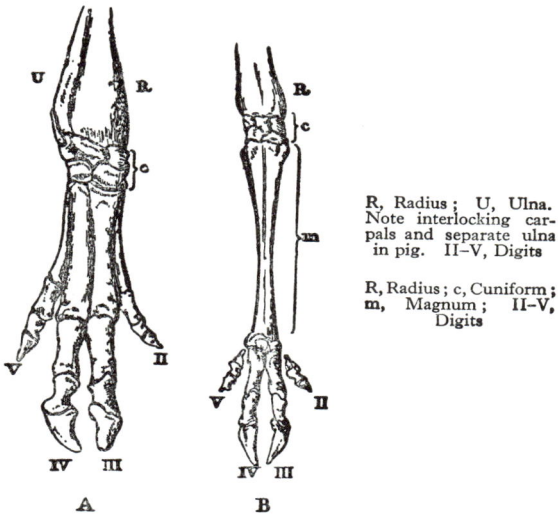

R, Radius; U, Ulna. Note interlocking carpals and separate ulna in pig. II–V, Digits

R, Radius; c, Cuniform; m, Magnum; II–V, Digits

FIG. 31.—A. Fore-foot of Pig (*Sus scrofa*). B. Fore-foot of Red Deer (*Cervus elaphus*)

visual signal comparable to the antelope markings, for it is obvious only when the animals are in rapid movement. A small point of some interest in this case is the presence of a special nerve in the neck—a nerve woefully familiar to many generations of biological students, for the making of a neat dissection in the examination hall requires some skill. Its function is to slow down a heart accelerated by rapid movement. Practically this means that the rabbit does not suffer as man does—or may do—from a choking feeling after sudden exertion. The illustration may serve to suggest what a number of minor adaptations must be present before the herbivore's power of putting on a sudden spurt is possible.

ADAPTATIONS IN CARNIVORES

For our purpose the carnivorous mammals are less important than the herbivorous ones. They need not show such a direct relation to the plant cover ; so long as suitable prey is present indeed almost any climatic zone, any type of relief, may serve. In consequence the range of genera and species tends to be wide. Most of the genera of Ungulates are limited to particular parts of the world land-masses and within these the species tend to be limited to particular types of country. Among the Carnivores the true cats of the genus Felis are all but cosmopolitan, being absent only from the Australian region and the large island of Madagascar so far as the larger land areas are concerned. Even species such as the lion in the Old World and the puma in the New, range widely, the latter with an extension from British Columbia to Patagonia, showing an astonishing indifference to variations both in climate and topography. Like the grasses and the composites among plants the higher Carnivores seem to have conquered the world and to be able to adapt themselves to almost every kind of physical condition. Civilized man's adaptability is, however, even greater, and since he took certain of the Herbivores under his protection he has proved the great enemy of the Carnivores.

Of the three groups included in the terrestrial Carnivores the cat-like forms are the most specialized, this reaching its maximum in the true cats of the genus Felis. These, so far as bodily structure is concerned, may be regarded as the highest of the mammals. Apart from his brain and his sensitive fingers man himself seems anatomically a poor thing beside them, showing little of that perfect adaptation of means to end so obvious in every detail of the feline body. That end, however, is the destruction of other warm-blooded vertebrates.

Among the adaptations shown by the cats we may note the shortening of the lower jaw to give increased leverage and its limited range of movement at the finely moulded articulation to ensure a firm grip on the prey. In the short jaws there is no room for massive grinding teeth, but these are not required. The hindermost cheek teeth are suppressed, the anterior ones have cutting edges to separate flesh from bones, a process assisted by the rasping tongue. The separated shreds of flesh are swallowed with but little chewing and are rapidly and readily digested. The fore-limbs possess five clawed digits and the claws when not in use are drawn back into hoods so that their sharp points are not worn down during walking (contrast the blunt, non-retractile claws of dogs). Since the armed fore-limbs combined with the stabbing canines form the attacking weapons, the range of movement of the former both at shoulder and wrist is great. The constituent bones of the fore-arm also do not show that tendency to fusion which occurs among the Ungulates. A striking feature is the enlarged middle ear which is provided with what seems to be a resonating chamber, giving great acuteness of hearing. The animals' own movements are characteristically silent.

Cats are not social, and though the mother shows great devotion to the young during their period of helplessness and much apparent altruism in bringing them food, later she soon turns against them, for no one locality can support many predatory forms of this type. The play of the young, so obvious in the domesticated cat and directly stimulated by the mother, is of course a training for adult life. There is a very critical period when the mother's guidance is withdrawn and the young have to apply these lessons for themselves, and this before they have come to their full strength. It is at this stage that the struggle for existence occurs in its most acute form and ensures the survival of the fittest stocks.

The dog-like forms lack the sabre-edged claws of the cats and the fore-limbs have a more limited range of movement ; but the animals have more power of sustaining speed than the cats. Cheek-teeth are more numerous and less specialized for a flesh diet. In the typical forms (wolves, hunting dogs) prey is brought down by a combined attack assisted by speed and cunning. Hearing is scarcely less acute than in the cats, there being again an enlarged middle ear though its structure is not identical in the two cases.

In the bear group the range of variation is so great that many systematists regard the group as artificial. Thus while the true bears and the members of the weasel family possess in common certain anatomical features whose significance is not clear, they differ very widely in habits and mode of life. The bears are thought to have had a common origin with the dogs, the two having evolved in different directions. Bears are large, slow-moving, clumsy animals, dull of hearing and, as their cheek teeth show, not fitted for a purely flesh diet. The fore-limbs are powerful and armed with five strong non-retractile claws. Several species do on occasion attack large Ungulates, but most take a considerable amount of vegetable food. Apart from the polar bear, they frequent wooded and hilly country and are good climbers ; bears are not social. Being thus without the very specialized weapons of the cats and the speed and power of combination of the dogs, the land bears have followed a line of their own and utilize the varied food resources of the woodlands. Several hibernate after growing fat on the autumn harvest of the woods, the tendency being more marked in the females, who carry their unborn young throughout the winter season. The habit of hibernation is remarkable considering the size of the body.

If the bears follow as it were the middle way between the evolutionary paths which lead on the one hand to complete dependence on flesh and on the other to the risks and limitations associated with a diet of herbage, their seeming allies the weasels have taken another course. It is possible that their line of descent could be traced back to some ancestor common to them and the civets. The civets are small cat-like Carnivores with longer bodies, shorter legs and less specialized teeth and claws than the cats proper. All are confined to the Old World and mainly to the lower latitudes there. Their small size and relative weakness mean that they must prey chiefly on small mammals, birds or even (in the case of the mongoose) reptiles. Now vast numbers of birds migrate to high northern latitudes to nest and rear their young, while the cosmopolitan Rodents are abundant in high latitudes generally. Thus a large potential food supply for carnivorous mammals is present, provided these can either climb trees or pursue the Rodents into their burrows and along their runs among herbage. The weasel group, though it includes such relatively large forms as the badger and such specialized ones as the aquatic, fish-eating otter, consists typically of small, slender-bodied, very blood-thirsty mammals whose ferocity and agility is the counterpart of the Rodents' fecundity. These weasel-like forms are widely distributed but reach their maximum development in the northern hemisphere and in its temperate regions.

Thus the range of habit among the Carnivores is wide and transcends the anatomical details on which their classification is based. While the evolution of herbivorous mammals has been mainly determined by that of the plant communities to which they are so closely linked, that of the Placental Carnivores has been influenced rather by the differentiation of their herbivorous prey. The curious side-track followed by the bears suggests that the Ungulates are not so helpless against attack as one might suppose.

PART III

TAXONOMIC DISTRIBUTION OF PLANTS AND ANIMALS

CHAPTER XI

THE MAJOR FAUNAL AND FLORAL AREAS
AND THEIR SIGNIFICANCE

SUMMARY though our survey of living plants and animals has been, it has at least made clear that it is impossible to discuss the present range even of the chief groups. It is estimated—to take but two familiar classes—that there are nearly 10,000 living species of birds and nearly 3,000 of mammals, the vast majority of the latter falling into the Rodent order. Even the specialist might well quail at the thought of discussing the distribution of all the living Rodents, much more that of the mammals as a whole. Clearly then our study of taxonomic distribution must have well-defined limits, set by a definite aim.

That aim is clear. For the student of geography it is of much interest that the different parts of the earth's surface are characterized by different assemblages of plants and animals and that, within limits, it is possible to give a reasoned explanation of that fact. Our study of systematic distribution then must be such that on the one hand the essential contrasts between the different areas are brought out, and on the other are explained. The material selected can only be representative, and because of their geologically late origin and their relative familiarity the mammals among the land animals form the most important group.

ZOOGEOGRAPHICAL REALMS AND THEIR FAUNAS

Looking at the land-masses as a whole we can make a first division which not only transcends in part the traditional limits of the continents but shows a large measure of independence of the climatic belts. Thus the island continent of Australia, with the adjacent islands of New Guinea and Tasmania, has a fauna and flora showing unique features. Here and here alone do those strange egg-laying mammals, the Monotremes, exist. Here also and here alone do we find a multitude of kinds of Marsupials, mostly quite unknown elsewhere. Not less remarkable is the fact that, apart from a few cases where human influence cannot be excluded, such as a wild pig in New Guinea, the dingo or native dog of Australia, and some rats and mice, terrestrial Placental mammals were entirely absent at the time of European discovery.   Other features are the presence of peculiar running birds, the emus and cassowaries, and of the Dipnoan fish Ceratodus in certain of the rivers of Queensland.   The plants are no less remarkable.   Though the myrtle family is wide-spread over the globe, the outstanding genus Eucalyptus is virtually confined to Australia and its satellite islands.   The great Protead family is definitely limited to the southern hemisphere, but includes a number of genera such as Grevillea and Banksia, which are restricted to the Australian area.

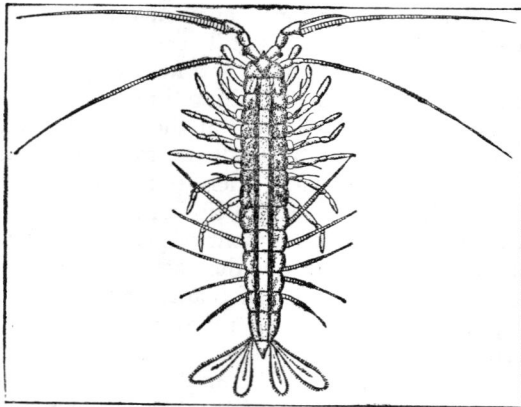

FIG. 32.—Tasmanian Mountain Shrimp (*Anaspides tasmaniae*)
After Geoffrey Smith

This series of peculiarities, combined with the fact that Australia is the only southern continent which at the present time has no direct connexion with the northern hemisphere by land, has led to its being given the name of *notogaea* or *notogaeic realm*— the southern land.   Even at this stage we may note two other points of interest.   There is clear evidence, as shown for example by the range as fossils of Ceratodus and Eucalyptus, that the present isolation of Australia, though it is geologically very old, did not always prevail.   Further, in the absence of Placentals no less than in a number of other features, Notogaea shows certain resemblances to the northern lands at an earlier geological epoch.

Hardly less remarkable are the flora and fauna of South and

Central America. Neither plants nor animals, it is true, show the distinctiveness, the completely ' old-fashioned ' air, which characterizes the assemblage in Notogaea. But then we have to remember that there is a definite if relatively narrow land-link between North and South America. What is here the striking feature is that despite this link, despite also the fact that some animals range throughout both North and South America, South America has many peculiar forms. The first seamen who have left records of their observations recognized clearly enough that many of the plants and animals of north-eastern North America were either identical with or closely similar to those of Europe. It took longer to realize how completely strange to Old World experience were most of those of South America. This was partly because so much of South America is inter-tropical. It was scarcely to be expected that familiar forms would be found in the great Amazonian forest or in the less dense tropical forests elsewhere. But even when we try to discount the effect of differences in climate, the contrast between the two continents is vast.

South America has no Monotremes, but it is the only part of the world outside the Australian area which has a number of Marsupials. The number of species is much smaller than in Notogaea, only two families being represented as against six in Notogaea, while all the South American forms are completely different from those of Australia. Of the South American forms only one, the common opossum, extends into North America, and no other great land-mass contains living Marsupials, though a few occur in some of the eastern islands of the Malay archipelago. Among the other striking peculiarities of South and Central America we may note its Edentates—the sloth, hairy anteaters and armadillos—these three forms not being known elsewhere save that an armadillo reaches Texas. There are virtually no Insectivores, abundant in North America ; the Ungulates show many peculiarities, both positive and negative, and while the forests contain no Old World monkeys nor apes, they have peculiar New World monkeys and marmosets of their own. Leaving further detail for the moment, we may note simply that the essential features are a certain primitiveness, recalling with a difference that so marked in Australia and speaking to isolation, combined with clear evidence of a late and partial intermingling with forms derived from North America. An obvious explanation is that the present connexion with North America is not, geologically speaking, very ancient.

Huxley, on the basis not of total fauna but of the distribution of a particular group of birds, first suggested that the resemblances between Australia and South America were so notable that the two might be grouped together. But since Australia--at least till the time of European settlement—was free from that northern invasion which has so changed the aspect of the South American fauna in a geologically late period, this grouping is undesirable. The term *neogaea* (' new land ') or *neogaeic realm* has therefore been applied to the South American area. Its significance should be clear to the geographical student. We still speak of the two Americas as the New World despite the fact that the northern continent at least has been largely ' made over ' by immigrant Europeans, modified by their new environment. There is more than a hint of an analogy with the native flora and fauna of Notogaea. We have every reason to believe that for at least the greater part of the Tertiary era South America had no link with the north and that then the plants and animals were almost as peculiar, as old-fashioned, as those of Australia. Then after the formation of the isthmian link, and especially after the onset of the Glacial Period in North America had rendered much of that continent unsuited to its earlier fauna, came the great immigration. The existing fauna of Neogaea, so peculiar, so different from that of other parts of the world, consists of a combination of the modified descendants of its original animals and of those of its late-Tertiary and Pleistocene immigrants. It thus exhibits a special combination of old-fashioned indigenous with newly immigrated forms.

As contrasted with these two southern areas, the remaining land-masses of the globe show a considerable measure of unity as regards their floras and faunas. This is true despite the great contrasts in climate between temperate Eurasia and North America on the one hand and equatorial Africa and sub-equatorial south-eastern Asia on the other ; despite also the notable contrasts in build and relief between the different parts and the double ocean gap between Eurasia and North America. Why this should be so, why it is that areas apparently so completely different as North America, Europe, tropical and temperate Asia and the African continent should be included in the single Zoogeographical Realm of *arctogaea*, or ' northern ' land, as contrasted with the much smaller areas of Neogaea and Notogaea demands some consideration. This is all the more true because the faunal features common to the whole Realm seem far less impressive than those differences between the parts which are a matter of common knowledge. Further, if the appropriateness of the name Notogaea seems clear enough in view of the isolation of

Australia from the northern land-masses ; if as we have seen we are justified in regarding South America as zoologically a ' new ' land because since late-Tertiary times an original fauna has been intermingled with an immigrant one : yet it is far from obvious why we should give the name of ' northern ' to a Realm which in Africa not only extends far south of the Equator but actually reaches southern sub-tropical latitudes at least comparable to those attained by Australia. The Cape of Good Hope area all but reaches 35° S. lat. which is that of the south-western corner of Western Australia.

Note first what general statements we can make about the fauna of Arctogaea as contrasted with the two other Realms. The list of species absent from the two other regions is not imposing. The rivers and lakes contain Ganoid fish which are absent from Notogaea and Neogaea. Except in Africa there are on the other hand no Dipnoan fish ; the African Protopterus seems, however, to be related to the Lepidosiren of South America. Except for the African ostrich (Struthio) there are no living Running Birds, but the African ostrich seems to be related to the Rhea of South America. Except for the common opossum in North America the mainland of Arctogaea contains no living marsupials. Two important positive features are that, as contrasted with Neogaea (and necessarily with Notogaea), Arctogaea is characterized by a wealth of Ungulates and by Insectivores. Insectivores, as already stated, are virtually absent from Neogaea, completely so if we exclude the West Indian Islands from that Realm. This is not true of Ungulates, but Neogaea has comparatively few kinds and in particular the Hollow-horned Ruminants (sheep, goats, cattle, antelopes) are unrepresented there, while they occur throughout Arctogaea. As against this scanty list of resemblances we have notable differences between the parts of Arctogaea. Meantime we need take but two examples.

S.E. Arctogaea is characterized by the presence of two living elephants, the African and Indian. Both have a limited distribution, but it is a sufficiently familiar fact that, so far as Eurasia is concerned, the reduction of elephants to a single species confined to a small area in the south-east is geologically a very recent event. Among the minor resources of Siberia is included so-called ' fossil ' ivory, derived from mammoths so recently extinct that frozen fragments of the hairy skin remain. The mammoth was widely spread in Eurasia in Glacial times, having been common in the British Isles, especially England. A tusk found in a peat bog in the Forth valley in Scotland proved to be so well preserved that there was competition between the museum authorities who wanted the specimen and a billiard-ball maker who appreciated the commercial possibilities of the ivory ; which again suggests how recently, from the geologist's standpoint, the animal disappeared from temperate Eurasia.   The long east-west belt of mountains in Eurasia, heavily glaciated during various episodes of the Pleistocene, hindered the southward retreat of many forms of life, including mammals, pushed out by the growth of the northern ice sheets, and this led to reduction of numbers while the later spread of forests pressed out some of the types more suited to open country.   Neither North nor South America contains elephants or elephant allies, though as we shall see later this was not always the case ; even the mammoth at one time lived on the coast of Alaska, as is shown by the finds of bones.

The second example relates to the deer.   The true deer with their nobly branched antlers belong to the genus Cervus and occur throughout Eurasia, tropical and temperate, extend into the more northerly part of North America, but are entirely absent from Africa south of the Sahara desert—a remarkable fact.   Further, in the more southern latitudes of North America there live deer with antlers of a different type belonging to the genus Cariacus and it is these which extend into Neogaea where the members of the genus Cervus are absent.

The bearing of these facts is complex.   We may note first that the extinct mammoth is so closely allied to the living Indian elephant that some authorities consider that it was only a variety, the hairy coat being an adaptation to a colder climate than that in which the Indian elephant lives.   Therefore we may conclude that the Indian area has served as a refuge in which a northern form has been able to maintain itself, with minor modifications, when it lost ground elsewhere.   A multitude of other examples, some of which must be considered later, permits us to put this point in a more generalized form and say that India south of the Himalayas as well as Africa south of the desert have received at least the majority of the animals now living within them from a northern source.   Arctogaeic then as applied to these parts of the Realm has no reference to latitude but to the fact that their living mammals can in the main be traced back to near ancestors which lived to the north of the Tropic of Cancer.   Africa, both because of the recently intensified desert barrier and because of the wide-stretching Mediterranean Sea to the north, and also because of its size and great length, is to a much greater extent than India and Farther India an appendage rather than an integral part of the Old World land-mass.   It shows, as we have suggested in speaking of its ostrich and Dipnoan fish, at least hints of an ancient analogy with South America. Even its mammals show traces, more marked than in the case of India, of that feature which we have emphasized in the case of South America. That is, there are suggestions, unfortunately only confirmed to a slight degree by fossil evidence, that there was here an earlier fauna largely exterminated or modified by northern immigrants. But for the most part that fauna, if it ever existed, has disappeared so completely that we cannot say as with South America that there is a definite inter-mingling of an earlier and a later element. In the main the living fauna of Africa south of the desert section shows close resemblances to that of India, with certain differences, while at the same time there is sufficient fossil evidence, especially in southern Europe and its margins, to show that the animals now characteristic of these areas formerly lived much farther north than at present.

Again, the example of the deer in North America is but one of a number which show that the fauna of that continent is not a unit. This fact is the more remarkable in that the great physiographical features of the continent tend to run in a north-to-south direction. There is no transverse mountain barrier such as that which separates India from temperate Asia ; there is no continuous east-to-west arid belt such as that which now cuts off the greater part of Africa from the north. So far as the Interior Plains of North America are concerned, there is no barrier, apart from that due to progressive climatic change, in all the length of the continent from the Mackenzie delta to the Gulf of Mexico. That climate itself need not be a bar to the range of mammals is shown by the puma, which spreads throughout the whole Cordilleran belt of the two Americas from British Columbia to Patagonia, crossing both tropics in its extension. It is then very striking that we have quite a definite contrast between the mammals of the northern and southern halves of North America, the one with species of Cervus in reindeer, elk and wapiti, the other with Cariacus deer, peccary and opossum, all shared with South America. Is it only climate that produces the contrast ? The American zoologists have devoted much toil to the task of proving that the range of the different kinds of mammals within the continent can be related to particular climatic elements and that the animals generally fall into groups according to the temperatures that they require. But it is difficult to see why, if deer of the genus Cervus can live in India and sub-equatorial Ceylon, temperature alone can prevent members of this genus from extending far south in the United States. To put the matter in a different way, we find that in Eurasia members of the genus Cervus are able to live in almost any type of climate, under any latitude, but in North America those present are species adapted only to the plant formations characteristic of the higher latitudes.   Here is a problem which has to be faced.

Meantime we may sum up the conclusions already arrived at. On the basis mainly, though not wholly, of their mammals we can divide the continental areas of the globe into three Realms. Of these Notogaea has such a unique fauna as to allow us to say that its present isolation has endured throughout a very long period of geological time ; the existing fauna has followed its own lines of development scarcely influenced by external impacts. Neogaea shows as it were the next stage.   Now connected with the north through Central America but yet isolated in the sense that North America itself is separated by a double water-belt from the lands of the Old World, it has a peculiarly complex fauna.   In part that fauna seems to have originated *in situ*, but the llamas, related to the camels of the Old World, the tapirs, belonging to the same genus as the tapir of south-eastern Asia, with other elements, suggest both that the present connexion with North America has been in existence for a considerable period and that North America itself must at one time have had a land connexion (or connexions) with the Old World which has now ceased to exist.

Finally, the remaining land-masses are included in Arctogaea. Here the distinguishing feature of the fauna, superimposed upon all the existing differences between the parts, is that at least the majority of the mammals present can be shown to be the more or less modified descendants of forms which originated and underwent progressive evolution in latitudes to the north of the Tropic of Cancer.   To a considerable extent the evolutionary process followed independent lines in North America and Eurasia.   Both areas, however, show certain common characters.   Thus fossil evidence proves that in each there was continuous evolution among a number of different stocks, followed by a tendency, accentuated as the Glacial Period approached, for waves of migration to spread outwards from the centres of evolution.   To such migratory movements Africa south of the desert and India with Farther India owe at least the greater part of their present fauna, while the ' modern ' element in the fauna of Neogaea has a similar origin.   Finally, as the brief note on the former distribution of the mammoth shows, the temperate lands of Arctogaea, eastern and western, have lost many mammals which they formerly possessed. Some of these, like the sabre-toothed tiger, the woolly rhinoceros, the cave bear and others, have completely disappeared from the face of the earth ; others like the lemurs which formerly lived in Europe have left modified descendants in the more remote parts of tropical Africa and tropical south-eastern Asia.

Put in the most generalized form we may say that the result of our preliminary survey has been to suggest that the living representatives of the more specialized orders of terrestrial Placental mammals have originated well within the northern hemisphere. Like all living things they have tended to spread outwards from the area of origin in waves, and the degree to which they have penetrated the southern continents has clearly been determined by the ease of access to these. From that standpoint Australia, South America and Africa south of the desert form a series, and Africa is included in Arctogaea just because the possibility of access has been greatest in its case. This statement in its turn permits us to say that mammalian distribution suggests that there is some deep-seated difference, veiled by the present distribution of land and water, between the northern and southern landmasses, and that the former have apparently tended, throughout later geological time, to show a measure of continuity across the lines of longitude wholly absent in the latter.

FLORAL REGIONS AND ZOOGEOGRAPHICAL REALMS

Before elaborating these contrasts between the northern and southern land-masses we must pause to inquire how far plant distribution corresponds to that of mammals, that is to what extent we can correlate Floral Regions with the three great Zoogeographical Realms already defined. There is a measure of correspondence ; but botanists have not reached the unanimity as regards even major divisions which is so marked with the zoologists, while different schemes vary notably in regard to the number and status of the subdivisions.

It is not difficult to understand why this should be so. In the first place, the fossil record is very imperfect in the case of plants. We have little direct knowledge either of the main centres of evolution or of the stages by which differentiation occurred in the higher forms. Mammals present a great contrast. As we have seen, the teeth, which are readily fossilized, give clues to the diet and habits, while the markings on the bones which show where the muscles were attached make it possible for the anatomist to make some reconstruction of form and function. Thus mammals are not only well represented as fossils in some Tertiary beds, but the material is such as to make it possible both to draw valid conclusions as to the areas in which the distinctively modern types arose and to follow, more or less precisely, the tracks by which migration took place.

So far as non-volant terrestrial mammals are concerned also we can recognize quite definite barriers to migratory movements. Though a number of the land mammals are good swimmers and take voluntarily to the water, yet there is little reason to believe that even these are likely to cross belts of water exceeding some twenty miles in width. Floating ice or raft-like masses of vegetation may be responsible for some passive transport, and it is possible that the mammoth crossed from Asia to Alaska either over a frozen surface or on broken masses of ice. In the general case, however, we can be reasonably sure that when several identical or nearly allied species of mammal occur on either side of a wide belt of water, then there must have been in the not very distant past some kind of land link. It is very different with plants. The fruits and seeds of some kinds are definitely adapted to water transport so that it is water and not land that functions as the track of migration. The coconut palm is the outstanding example, for it is distributed throughout the warm zone and is one of the few genera of palms with such a range, for it is true generally that the parts of that zone have endemic, that is peculiar, palm genera. Thus the doum palms (Hyphaene) are limited to Africa and the wax-palms (Copernicia) to tropical America. We cannot lay any particular stress, however, upon the wide range of the coconut, for the trees tend to occupy coastal sites and the fruit is capable of floating long distances uninjured and will then germinate if cast up on a beach. The members of the screw-pine family or Pandanaceae (not to be confused with the coniferous pine) also have fruits adapted for sea transport and are widely distributed in the inter-tropical belt of the Old World. Thus the members of the genus Freycinetia extend from Ceylon to New Zealand and the Polynesian Islands; but we cannot regard this as a proof of affinity between the flora of Ceylon and that of New Zealand.

There are other possible ways in which plants may be transmitted across belts of water or even over those deserts and transverse mountain chains which seem to block the movements of most mammals. Fruit-eating bats or birds on migration may have within their bodies seeds which when finally voided are still capable of germination. Thus the Bermuda Islands contain an endemic 'cedar', really a species of juniper whose nearest ally is found in Cuba, nine hundred miles distant. But we need not here assume a former land connexion, for birds eat juniper 'berries' freely and the Bermudas are visited by a number of migrant forms. Seeds and fruits may also cling to the bodies of flying animals and be thus transported, or, when small or furnished with a parachute, may be carried great distances by air currents. Man also is a potent if often unwitting agent of dissemination and it is much less easy than with animals to trace the effects of his influence. If again we recall the fact that the single large and cosmopolitan order of the Composites among the Dicotyledons contains more species than the two classes of birds and mammals put together, it is not difficult to realize that to make a satisfactory subdivision of the globe into floral regions based even on the Angiosperms alone, is a problem of great complexity.

It is partly because of the multitude of kinds of plants that most schemes of floral regions lay so much emphasis on climate. Not only has climate far more direct and obvious effects on plant life than on animals, but even to those with a limited knowledge of systematic botany it is clear that there are certain broad distinctions between, for example, the plants of the inter-tropical belts and those of temperate climates. We have already seen that conifers tend to accumulate towards the poles, largely avoiding inter-tropical areas. As positive features of the latter we have the tendency for arborescent forms of Monocotyledons to occur, as exemplified by palms, bamboos, screw-pines and many others, while in the higher latitudes even monocotyledonous shrubs are rare. Again, if the names of most of the tropical dicotyledonous orders are unfamiliar the fact that they sound strange to ears well accustomed to hear of the Ranunculus groups, the poppies, the saxifrages, the crucifers and so on, but serves to emphasize the greatness of the contrast between tropical and temperate plants. Among the numerous families which are mainly or wholly tropical we may note the Sterculiaceae, which include the South American cacao tree, the Anonaceae, including the custard apples, the Piperaceae or peppers widely spread in tropical latitudes, the Sapotaceae also with a wide range within the tropics, and with an economically very important species in the African tree from the fruit of which shea butter is made.

But if tropical America, much of tropical Africa and at least the eastern section of tropical Asia fall in this way into a wide pan-tropic belt, with a number of common features so far as orders are concerned, tropical Australia, as indeed one would expect, stands markedly aloof. Not only has the continent in the main a flora of its own, very different from that of the other land-masses, but there is not that contrast between tropical and extra-tropical families and genera which is so marked in South America and Africa.

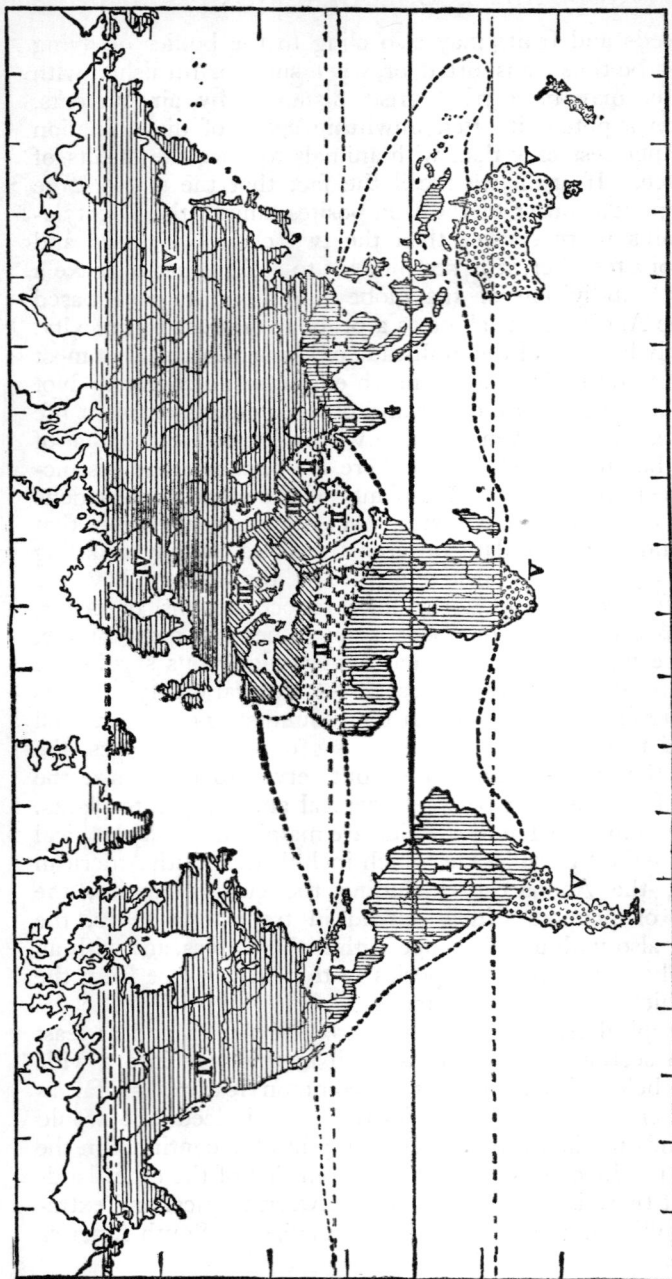

FIG. 33.—Major Plant Regions

Region I. Inter-tropical. Note that limit cuts off extreme south of peninsula of California and bends down to east and west of Mexico. It includes most of South America except the south, the central part of Africa (the northern limit being to the south of the Tropic of Cancer), and much of India, with Farther India, but merely skirts north-eastern Australia

Region II. Covers the desert part of North Africa and the Arabian and Indian deserts

Region III. Mediterranean Belt

Region IV. Northern Lands

Region V. Southern parts of Southern Continent:

Thus we get as a first region a Pantropic or Inter-tropical Belt stretching right across the globe (Fig. 33), but excluding most of Australia save a comparatively small area round the Gulf of Carpentaria and in Cape York peninsula. Within this Pantropic region, however, again as we might expect in view of what we have seen occurs in the case of mammals, the signs of affinity between the floras of tropical Africa and tropical Asia are much closer than between the former and the plants of tropical South America. So great are the contrasts indeed that most systematic botanists find it convenient to divide the Pantropic Belt into an Old World and a New World section. At the same time, and for us it is a significant fact, the sharpness of the contrast is blurred by finding that there are a few—a very few—genera common to

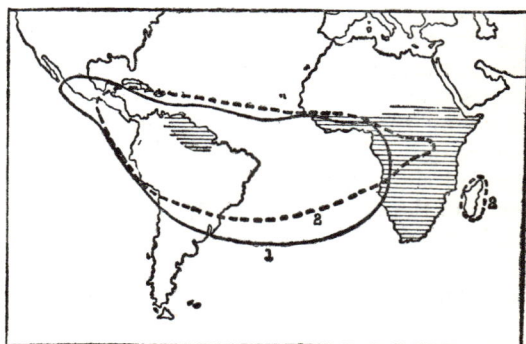

1 shows the range of Vismia, and 2 that of Symphonia. The amphibians shown are the tongueless frogs (Aglossa) widely spread in Africa and having a somewhat limited range in north-eastern South America

Fig. 34.—Indications of affinities between some of the trees (1 and 2) and certain amphibians (horizontal shading) of West Africa and Neogaea

West Tropical Africa and Tropical America but absent from other parts of the Old World tropics. Two examples are the related genera Vismia and Symphonia, tropical trees belonging to what is apparently a somewhat old-fashioned family. As Fig. 34 shows, Vismia has a fairly wide range in tropical America and a very limited one in West Africa, while Symphonia with a not dissimilar range in America is more widely spread in tropical Africa and reappears, after a gap, in Madagascar, but not elsewhere. There is a certain analogy to the range of a group of frogs (Aglossa), represented by two genera and several species in Africa and by a single endemic form, the Surinam toad, in the Guianas and lower Amazon area. The Aglossa possess certain primitive features and the living kinds are apparently related to a fossil form found in mid-Tertiary beds in Europe, suggesting that the group had

14

a northern origin. Such facts are important because they confirm the rather less definite evidence derived from the mammalian faunas that there has been in the geological past some kind of link between West Africa and Brazil despite the present width of the Atlantic here.

The second region shown on the map includes the southern part of the Sahara, much of Arabia and the continuation of this arid belt eastwards to the Indian desert. It may be called the Northern Palaeotropical Desert Region. From the floristic standpoint it is characterized by the negative feature of the absence of endemic orders, while even the genera are shared with the bordering areas to the north and south. On the other hand the species, remarkably few when the extent of the area is borne in mind, are mainly endemic. This means in effect that the region is now so arid that it supports plant life with difficulty but that the onset of the present extreme drought or the extension of the drought area or both must have been sufficiently gradual to make it possible for a certain amount of adaptation to take place, involving the rise of a number of new species.

It is only when we consider the subdivisions of Arctogaea that the full significance of this floral region becomes clear. Africa south of the desert (cf. Fig. 33, p. 208) forms for the zoologist the Ethiopian Region of the Arctogaeic Realm, but he draws his limit as a straight line, corresponding mainly to the tropic, across the Saharan and Arabian deserts. Straight lines of this kind, whether as political or administrative frontiers or as distribution limits, mean two things. They mean firstly that at the time of drawing there is little knowledge of detail ; almost always there is also a secondary implication that the detail is not worth troubling about. In this particular case the point which interests the zoologist is that to the north of the desert, in the lands bordering the Mediterranean Sea and sharing the Mediterranean type of climate, there are deer and sheep, both absent from the south, while the characteristic Ethiopian mammals do not occur. For him then the desert as a whole is a kind of no man's land separating areas with characteristic faunas and having too few mammals of its own to need special consideration. It is therefore very important that the botanists on the other hand emphasize rather the transitional or ' island ' character of the southern section of the desert belt, which at once links the Mediterranean flora of the north with the tropical flora of the south, and has also served as a minor centre of evolution. If, as the zoologist believes, the present mammals of Ethiopian Africa entered from the north, he has a problem to solve in the question of how the forest-haunting forms got across the desert.   Some botanists maintain that the 'European' element in the Desert Floral Region is so pronounced as to prove that during the height of glaciation the Sahara cannot have been nearly so arid as at present, and that there must have been at least relatively moist areas which served as migration tracks.   Clearly this view aids the zoologist in facing his own problem.

North of the Desert Floral Region the botanists recognize a Mediterranean one, using the term in a somewhat wider sense than is usual with climatologists.   That is, the Mediterranean Floral Region includes not only the Mediterranean Lands as usually defined but extends southwards to cover part of the Sahara and eastwards into Persia.   The essential floristic feature is the presence throughout of at least some of the plants charac-teristic of the true Mediterranean Lands, combined with the absence of the endemic species which distinguish the Desert Region.   The limits are thus necessarily somewhat vague, especi-ally to the east.   Southwards, however, there is a good deal of evidence to show that some of the mountain massifs of the Sahara form a kind of floral divide, the northern slopes bearing plants of definitely Mediterranean character and the southern ones endemic desert plants.

This enlarged Mediterranean Region is of much interest to the zoologist, who would fain recognize a similar zoological division if he could find a logical basis.   This is partly because, as we have already suggested, the American zoologists divide North America into a northern and a southern section, the one characterized by mammals with strong affinities to those of temperate Eurasia, the other by those common to Neogaea.   There are many analogies between North America and the extra-tropical Old World, and a desire for symmetry prompts a search for a similar subdivision in the latter.   There is no doubt that the mammals present round the Mediterranean Sea do differ from those found north of the Alpine chains of Europe and their continuations in Asia.   The difficulty is that this 'Mediterranean' fauna has neither the measure of unity which can be recognized in the southern or Sonoran section of the fauna of North America, nor that which can be recognized for the plants.   For example, Syria shares with Ethiopian Africa the rock coney (Hyrax) ; here we seem to have an obvious analogy with the peccary present in the southern United States and extending also into South America. As against this we find that the monkey, the so-called Barbary ape, found in the Atlas Lands and on the Rock of Gibraltar belongs to a genus (Macacus) found not in Africa but in eastern

Asia (India, Farther India and some of the Malay Islands with an extension into Tibet, China and Japan). Generally the mammals found round the Mediterranean Sea show a great mixture of elements, their nearest allies being widely scattered.

This is the more remarkable in that during the Pleistocene period the mammalian fauna of southern Europe and its border-lands was at once much richer than at present and the contrasts between it and that of the region north of the mountain belt much greater. It seems then as if we might say that the effect of the Pleistocene and post-Pleistocene climatic changes had been very different on the plants and on the mammals of the lands round the Mediterranean Sea. The pre-glacial mammals, aided it would seem by land-links, scattered widely ; many became extinct in their former habitat, a few lingered on in isolated areas, but great numbers found their way into Ethiopian Africa or into tropical Asia south of the mountain belt. The result is that while we have to-day very definite contrasts between the faunas of temperate Eurasia on the one hand and those of Ethiopian Africa and what is called the Oriental (see Fig. 33) Region of Asia on the other, the area which forms for the botanist the Mediter-ranean Floral Region is not zoologically a unit.

It should be noted that what is rather loosely called the ' migra-tion ' of plants necessarily takes place in a very different fashion from the actual migratory movements of mammals. Numbers of plants which once grew round the shores of the Mediterranean Sea, as well as farther north, have disappeared. But certain areas—the Balkan peninsula seems to have been one—served as refuges from which a measure of re-colonization of lost ground took place. The beautiful Judas tree (*Cercis siliquastrum*) seems to be an outstanding example of a plant which survived glacia-tion within the Balkan peninsula and spread westwards again as the climate improved. Such instances of survival are suffi-ciently numerous among plants to make it possible to define a separate Mediterranean Floral Region ; they are too infrequent among mammals for it to be possible to erect a similar zoological region.

Apart from these two intercalated Floral Regions in the eastern hemisphere there is no real difference between the botanists and the zoologists as regards the recognizable biogeographical regions of the northern extra-tropical lands. The botanists accept the view of the zoologists that despite minor and local differences temperate Eurasia shows remarkable resemblances in its life to North America. Many botanists indeed take over from the zoologists the term Holarctic to cover a wide belt in both hemispheres, the name being intended to emphasize the fact that the farther north one goes the closer are the resemblances.

Turning next to the southern hemisphere we find that all botanists separate off from the great Pantropic Region extra-tropical South America and South Africa and also, as already stated, virtually the whole of the Australian continent. Are these three separate regions or merely subdivisions of an inter-rupted Austral Region ? The point is debatable and we need only note that there are clear signs of affinity between the floras of South Africa and of Australia, and others between those of temperate South America and both Australia and New Zealand. Since South Africa has no marsupials and Australia no placentals the mammals of the two areas cannot show any relationship and there is no definite evidence of this among other faunal elements. On the other hand traces of affinity certainly exist between the faunas of South America and of Notogaea. Generally we may say that the distribution of plants in part confirms and in part supplements the zoologists' view that there has been at one time some kind of connexion between the now widely separated southern continents.

GENERAL SURVEY OF TAXONOMIC DISTRIBUTION

We may now sum up the general conclusions arrived at. Zoo-logists and botanists are agreed that it is possible to divide up the lands of the world on the basis of the taxonomic affinities of their plants and animals. There are also at least certain resemblances between the divisions recognized. The differences can be ex-plained in part by the fact that the zoologists have, so far as the mammals are concerned, far more fossil material at their disposal than is available for the botanists ; in part also by the contrasts between the modes of dispersal open to mammals and to land plants. The number of kinds of land plants is also much greater than that of land mammals so that the botanical problem is far more complex.

Because of the wealth of fossil material the zoologists in their first division of the globe into Realms lay stress upon the fact that a wide tract of land, including sections in both eastern and western hemispheres, and extending in Africa far south of the Equator, seems to have had some measure of unity throughout later geological time, and, so far as its northern section is concerned, to have served as the main centre of evolution for the higher living mammals. Notogaea has been long isolated and has served as the centre of evolution for the majority of living marsupials.

Neogaea was similarly for long isolated, and there special types of mammals evolved ; but at least since towards the close of the Tertiary era it has been connected with North America.

Arctogaea is so wide a Realm that it must needs be divided. To the north the contrasts between the eastern (or Palaearctic) sub-region and the western (or Nearctic) are much less marked than the resemblances. This leads to the recognition of one large Holarctic Region. In North America this passes, not without intermixture, into the Sonoran Region, where mammals with Neogaeic affinities are mingled with Arctogaeic ones. In the eastern hemisphere the desert belt on the one hand and the mountain chains, of which the Himalayas are the most conspicuous element, on the other, make the separation of Ethiopian and Oriental Regions an easier matter.

Neogaea scarcely needs subdivision, but partly to get a completely logical arrangement and partly to emphasize the fact that many of its most peculiar forms are limited to the tropical areas, it is regarded as including a single Neotropical region. Notogaea is more complex, for various island areas, including some of the Malay islands, which contain mammals, and New Zealand, the Polynesian Islands and the Hawaiian Islands, which have none, have to find a place here. For the moment it is sufficient to say that continental Australia, New Guinea and Tasmania form the Australian Region.

Turning next to Floral Regions we find that the botanists tend to simplify their problem by laying the first stress upon climate. A number of orders are virtually limited to the tropics, and, apart from the Conifers, which are geologically old, there is a general tendency both in the class of Monocotyledons and in those orders of Dicotyledons which are both tropical and temperate, for arborescent forms to predominate in the tropics and herbaceous forms in the temperate regions.

As against this tendency for the botanists to run their major divisions across the globe, and specifically to recognize a great (Holarctic) North Temperate Region as contrasted with an almost equally wide Pantropic one, they are constrained to separate off certain special regions. In the eastern part of the northern hemisphere we have a Northern Palaeotropical Region and a Mediterranean Region of more limited extension. The southern hemisphere presents difficulties. We cannot say that an Austral *temperate* region is recognized, for the Austral Floral Region includes tropical as well as temperate Australia. If we call this area ' Australian ' we have to remember that the botanist is not using the word in quite the same sense as the zoologist.

The divisions may be put for convenience in the following tabular form :

Floral Region	Zoological Realms	Regions
1. Holarctic (including Sonoran zoological Region)	I. Arctogaea	1. Holarctic.
2. Mediterranean		2. Sonoran.
3. Northern Palaeotropical Desert		3. Ethiopian.
		4. Oriental.
4. Pantropic	II. Neogaea	5. Neotropical.
5. Austral (a) Extra-tropical Neogaea		
(b) Extra-tropical Ethiopian	III. Notogaea	6. Australian and others.
(c) ' Australian '		

PRESENT AND PAST DISTRIBUTIONS AND LAND CONNEXIONS

ORIGIN OF EXISTING DISTRIBUTION

This brief summary sets forth the conditions we have to attempt to explain. It is clear in the first place that there is much evidence to show that while the evolutionary process has occurred in all parts of the earth's surface it has been more rapid and more continuous in certain areas than in others. Certain parts of the wide land-masses of the northern hemisphere, so far as the fossil evidence proves, appear not only to have served as the areas of origin of the main classes and orders of terrestrial plants and animals, but to have been the sources from which the world at large has been peopled with more and more highly differentiated types. Areas connected by land with these centres of evolution have been progressively occupied by such higher forms ; those like Notogaea which have been isolated during later geological time are devoid of some of these.

This enables us to divide our problem into three sections. There is first the question as to the reasons why these northern lands should have served as the main centres of evolution for terrestrial plants and animals. Then follow the further questions of how they spread to other areas and why this dispersal should have taken place. In regard to both these latter questions at least we have to set a limit in geological time to our inquiry. It is probable that throughout the eras defined by the different fossil-bearing rocks certain of the lands of the northern hemisphere have always been the main evolutionary centres. But to whatever extent this is true, our discussion of the how and why of dispersal must be restricted not only to certain forms of life but in essence to Tertiary and post-Tertiary time. This still leaves the problem a sufficiently complicated one.

It appears that the main reasons why parts of the northern hemisphere have been the chief seat of the great stages in organic evolution are to be sought, first, in the fact that the northern lands have shown throughout later geological time a measure of continuity denied to those of the south ; and, second, in the further fact that they have been subjected to a degree of tectonic and climatic change absent there. There has, that is to say, been ample room for evolutionary experiment and a constantly renewed stimulus owing to changes in relief and climate.

The study of the way in which dispersal from the centres of evolution has taken place involves some attempt to consider the distribution of land and water during Tertiary and post-Tertiary time. Leaving this for the moment we may turn to the question of why the dispersal has taken place. In one sense it is a natural consequence of the fact that all organisms tend to reproduce at a greater rate than is necessary to replace loss by death. But that universal tendency need not involve spread. For example, Welwitschia (p. 151) in favourable seasons produces vast amounts of seed, but there is no reason to believe that it is increasing its range.

It is usual to put the subject of dispersal in a general form by saying that any new type of organism, arising by hypothesis within a particular habitat and as a response to the local habitat factors, tends to spread outwards from the area of origin till a check occurs. Thus the problem of distribution for any type seems to resolve itself into the time factor, the length of time which has elapsed since its origin, and the checking factor, the causes which have prevented the tendency from attaining its full expression, or conversely have permitted virtually world-wide distribution to be reached. But the checking factors may act at any stage of dispersal so that an original wide distribution may be followed by a loss of territory.

This means that in theory, if not always in practice, we ought to be able to distinguish between two kinds of endemic species and genera. Endemics are organisms of limited range, restricted to some particular area. They may represent products of recent evolution and are then called new or neo-endemics. In that case the restricted range is due to the fact that time and opportunity have not permitted them to spread. Certain of the deeply cut valleys at the eastern end of the Himalayas are remarkable for their great numbers of endemic plants, especially species of Rhododendron, Primula and Meconopsis (including the blue Tibetan poppies). In some cases these species seem to be limited to particular valleys and not to extend beyond them. Such species are often very rigidly adapted to particular sets of conditions. An extension downstream is impossible because in that direction conditions change rapidly ; an extension across the bounding mountain walls, which rise to great heights, is equally impossible. Such forms are clearly neo-endemics. They might spread if the ordinary agents of denudation, for example, wore down the mountain slopes in such a fashion that they could spread upwards, or if local earth movements modified the relief and the incidence of the climatic factors.

On the other hand, the genus Eucalyptus, with a great number of species, is limited to a comparatively small part of the southern hemisphere. But it was once present in the northern hemisphere. Clearly the Australian Eucalypti are old or palaeo-endemics, for the genus must have found a refuge there when it disappeared from the north. The same sort of thing occurs with animals. Lemurs are represented in the island of Madagascar by a number of genera unknown elsewhere whether as fossils or as living forms. These are neo-endemic genera which have arisen there and have been unable to spread because of the island nature of the area. The New Zealand lizard (p. 20), on the other hand, is clearly like the genus Eucalyptus a palaeo-endemic, for its allies once lived in the northern hemisphere and have disappeared there.

Such illustrations lead us to ask a further question. Are time and physical opportunity in the form of a potential line of migration all that is necessary to ensure spread ? If a localized uplift connected Madagascar with the African mainland, as it must once have been connected, would the Malagasy lemurs occupy Africa ? In this case we may be fairly sure that they would not, for Africa contains kinds of carnivores absent in Madagascar, and lemurs are singularly helpless animals. Competition in its widest sense has had a great bearing on spread, and many kinds of organisms have doubtless arisen and been crushed out so rapidly that they have never spread far from their area of origin. But it is not with such failures that we are primarily concerned, but rather with the forms which have succeeded in conquering wide tracts of the surface, and with the factors which have aided their conquest.

Fossils suggest Arctogaea as the home whence Marsupials spread to Notogaea and Neogaea, to which they are now confined save that the opossum occurs in both South and North America. Notogaea's isolation gave opportunities for specialization and the Diprotodont sub-group has the lower incisors limited to one large forward-pointing tooth on each side. This sub-group is unknown, either fossil or recent, in Arctogaea but, while most important in

Notogaea, it is represented in Neogaea by Miocene and Pliocene fossils and by one living genus Coenolestes (in Ecuador) and would seem to have reached South America either by way of Antarctica or through a land connexion now lost, unless we accept the hypothesis of continental drift.   The absence of evidence for Marsupials, other than early and doubtfully related Mesozoic forms, from Africa south of the Sahara, is an interesting fact.

No placental mammals have reached Notogaea save in association with man, unless we allow a non-human factor to account for the occurrence of some of the species of rats and mice.   Neogaea lacks most of the Ungulates found elsewhere and its Insectivores are few while its Carnivores, except the Felidae, are rather a special assortment.   There is abundant evidence that Ungulates, Carnivores, Insectivores, Rodents and Primates, as well as Marsupials, in fact all the orders of the common and abundant living land mammals, originated in Arctogaea, and that Neogaean forms are often stragglers, such as the tapir (also found in south-east Asia), peccary, guanaco and its relatives, and the deer Cariacus. One also notes in Neogaea cases of local specialization such as the extinct Notoungulata and Litopterna, and the surviving and extinct Edentata.   The Edentata are a lowly and heterogeneous assemblage of survivors of ancient types of placental mammals and one cannot be too sure about the closeness of relationship of Old and New World forms.   We can say confidently that they prospered in South America and spread to the north of Mexico, as will be mentioned later.

Africa, south of the Sahara, called the Ethiopian region, like Neogaea, lacks certain types notably a number of Ungulates such as deer, sheep and goats (save in Abyssinia).   Two Edentates on the other hand, exemplify the ' refuge ' idea, though without the outburst of specialization characteristic of Neogaea, also a region of refuge for this group.   There has obviously been a succession of outflows of mammals from the northern continental masses, which have had varying but, on the whole, close relationships to one another.   Apparently periods of relative stability with only a trickle of migration have alternated with great outbursts intruding animals into new homes, where they might persist awhile as strays or become the ancestors of specialized groups.

We have already hinted at the apparent cause of that disturbed equilibrium of which post-Tertiary time affords so much evidence. Climatic conditions in the northern hemisphere seem to have become at once colder and more diversified locally in later than in earlier Tertiary time.   This change was followed by the northern glaciations, which had a double effect. They led to the evolution of a number of new forms adapted to the changing conditions. These in their turn exerted pressure upon the pre-existing forms. Many of these disappeared, others spread south-wards to areas where the conditions recalled those which had formerly prevailed in their area of origin. In other words, the existing distribution of plants and animals has been enormously influenced by the recent Ice Ages, and the effects of these extended far beyond the limits of the area actually glaciated.

The taxonomic distribution which existed prior to the northern glaciations must, on the other hand, have been greatly influenced by the Tertiary and pre-Tertiary form of the lands. Here we can only note a few outstanding points, for the subject is complex and there is little certainty.

It is generally accepted that throughout a long period of geological time a Mid-World sea, the Tethys of Suess and the Mesogaea of some other geologists, lay between the northern and southern land-masses. This underwent vast changes during the Tertiary era. At present two sections, an eastern and a western, retain in different degrees the original character, in parts, of a geosynclinal sea. The one is formed by the Mediterranean Sea and its continuations, the other is the American ' Mediterranean ' formed by the Gulf of Mexico and the Caribbean Sea, while the intervening section has lost its individuality in the Atlantic Ocean. But there are notable differences between the two shrunken remnants of the Tethys. To the west only the narrow isthmus of Central America, itself a possible track of organic migration, separates the American Mediterranean from the Pacific, and the Cordilleran Belt has a north-to-south direction. The Mediterranean Sea, on the other hand, has a limited eastward extension and has obviously greatly diminished as compared with its former size. Further, both on its borders and in the eastern area beyond, what were once the sediments of the Tethys have been uplifted to form the transverse mountain chains continued from the Alpine chains of Europe into Asia. The uplift has not only affected the areas which now form the actual mountain belt, but has also reduced the Caspian to an inland basin and still farther east, combined with sedimentation, has linked peninsular India by what are now the Indo Gangetic lowlands to the mountain belt. These Tertiary changes have thus increased the land surface of Eurasia, but at the same time the run of the mountain belt must have impeded southward migration, the check being most marked in India where the mountain belt is virtually complete.

Turning next to the land-masses separated originally by the Tethys, we find that the northern area has undergone great changes throughout geological time. What matters for us, however, is that there are at present only two water gaps within the great land-mass, neither of which appears to be old in its present form. Both gaps show a northward narrowing, and this in the case of the North Pacific is so marked that Bering Strait in lat. 66° N. is but 36 miles wide. It seems clear that even in post-Tertiary time there must have been some kind of connexion here. There is no comparable narrowing in the case of the North Atlantic in similar latitudes, but the great wedge of Greenland reduces the gap and there are various island ' stepping-stones '. No geologist now believes that the North Atlantic has maintained its present form throughout a very long period of geological time, even if there is still difference of opinion as to the period and nature of the last changes. It seems fairly certain that there was some connexion across what is now the North Atlantic during at least part, perhaps the greater part, of Tertiary time, but this connexion was in high latitudes. The intermingling of Eurasian and North American floras and faunas was limited by the latitude of the link, but nevertheless such intermingling did occur.

The real crux comes with the southern lands. Here we have very definite evidence that there was some kind of early connexion across what are now the South Atlantic and Indian Oceans. The difficulty lies in deciding what was the nature of the link and when and by what stages the break occurred.

Let us take first the known facts. A region mainly included in the Central Provinces of India, and having as its approximate limits lats. 18°–24° N. and longs. 77° 30'–87° E., is called Gondwana, or the Land of the Gonds, on account of its native inhabitants. Here there occur fossil-bearing sandstones and shales of freshwater and terrestrial origin, including coal-beds, of Permian age. The fossils include a number of characteristic plants, especially ferns and fern-allies, forming what is known as the Glossopteris flora from a particular genus present. The Glossopteris flora occurs also in the Permian beds of Ceylon, Africa, South America, Australia, and Glossopteris has also been found not far from the South Pole in Antarctica. This distribution is believed to justify us in assuming that during the Permian and some later periods these now separated areas formed a quasi-continuous land-mass to which the name of Gondwanaland has been given.

The presumably very ancient genus Peripatus, related to both segmented worms (Annelida) and Arthropods (Millipedes, Insects, Spiders, Shrimps, &c.) has species in New Zealand, New Britain, Australia, the Malay peninsula and Sumatra, South Africa, South America and the West Indies.   Again, the surviving members of the ancient order of fishes called Dipnoi are freshwater forms in Australia (Ceratodus), West Africa (Protopterus), and South America (Lepidosiren).   The Apoda or Coecilia, a presumably ancient group of worm-like Amphibia, still live in inter-tropical parts of America, Africa and south-east Asia, but not in Madagascar or Australia.   Among Chelonia the family Pelomedusae occurs in Africa (and Madagascar) and South America, while the family Chelydidae is found now in South America, Australia and New Guinea but not in Africa (compare the Diprotodont Marsupials), though it occurs fossil in northern lands.   These facts all imply ancient connexions between the various southern land-masses.

Lemurs still live in south-east Asia, Madagascar and inter-tropical Africa and have found a special opportunity of evolving new genera (nine are known) in Madagascar ; their ancient relatives are found fossil in northern lands.   Elephant, Rhinoceros and Scaly Anteater occur in Africa and south-east Asia but not in Madagascar.   The frogs of Madagascar and south-east Asia are apparently related, and land and freshwater shells in the Seychelles Islands (a continental fragment and not merely volcanic oceanic islands) are like those of south-east Asia and unlike those of Africa.   Wegener's theories of continental drift offer a hypothesis alternative to that of a lost land-bridge, Lemuria, in the Indian Ocean.

Connexions between North and South America were established only well on in Tertiary times with changes in West Indian and Central American mountain arcs.   Pine trees in the strict sense do not extend south of the Nicaragua lowland in America, but have spread from Central America into the West Indies, one species, *Pinus occidentalis*, being actually found in Cuba and even Haiti as well as in Central America.   Oaks have very numerous species in Mexico and stretch southward into the inter-tropical part of the Cordillera of South America, but, on the other hand, they do not reach the West Indies.   Among the true bears in the strict sense, one, Tremarctos, has spread southward along the Cordillera of South America.   The Edentates, as has been said, had a remarkable development in South America, and it is from that continent that, about the end of Tertiary time, the ground sloths now extinct spread into the south-western regions of U.S.A., while the armadillo also spread northward from South

America as far as Texas in post-Pleistocene times.   The relations between North and South America in fauna and flora thus include a number of migrations from each toward the other, a matter of which more will be said in the next chapter.

CHAPTER XII

THE ZOOGEOGRAPHICAL REALMS AND THEIR FAUNAS: NEOGAEA AND NOTOGAEA

IN the preceding chapter we have attempted, with the aid of a few illustrations rather than the customary lists of characteristic forms, to suggest both the basis of the division of the lands into biogeographical regions and the way in which the differences between them can be explained. Although the method seems to plunge the student straightway into problems of great complexity it is justifiable for our special purpose. For the zoologist, the fact that, e.g., sheep are mountain animals native only to certain ranges in the northern hemisphere and there confined to rather different types of country from those frequented by the allied goats, is part of the definition of the genus Ovis. It has, that is to say, direct zoological significance. But as geographers our concern is first to supplement a survey of the structure, relief, climate and so forth of the lands by showing that the physical factors influence the plant communities while these in their turn influence the animals, including man. Further, just as mere description of the surface features must be followed by an attempt to correlate and explain these, so also when the details of the local picture have been filled in by indicating the outstanding organisms, we have to try to find reasons for the presence of these in one area and not in another. Thus the total fauna and flora of any land area are of less geographical importance than are those members which either reflect best the physical conditions at the present time or throw most light on past conditions and connexions.

At the same time we must give at least a summary account of the faunas of the major regions in order to characterize these adequately. It is not easy to make such a summary interesting, and we may attempt first, by discussing a few examples of group range in time and space, to make clearer just wherein the interest lies and how the facts may be interpreted.

EXAMPLES OF GROUP DISTRIBUTION AMONG MAMMALS

Sheep. The members of the genus Ovis are confined to the northern hemisphere and eleven species of wild sheep are recognized. Less agile, as a rule, than the goats or some kinds of antelopes, they frequent especially upland country where large tracts of mountain pasture occur ; are more purely grass-eating than the goats and generally intolerant of high temperatures, especially of moist heat. Of the eleven species no less than five occur in the mountains of Central Asia, where some species ascend to heights of 10,000–12,000 feet or more. Of these Asiatic species the urial has a wide range, and its extension into Sind and the Punjab brings it nominally into the Oriental Region ; that is, it is one of the forms to which the Himalayas are no barrier. So far as their range is concerned, the remaining species fall into three groups. Three species have each a limited range in south-western Eurasia and seem to be nearly related. These are the Armenian sheep, the Cyprus sheep and the mouflon of Corsica and Sardinia. The Atlas Mountains of North Africa contain the so-called Barbary sheep, which extends into some of the mountain massifs of the Sahara, can tolerate very arid conditions, and appears to be more nearly related to the blue sheep of Tibet than to the other western forms. There is thus a curious analogy with the so-called Barbary ape (cf. p. 211) whose nearest allies are found in Eastern and Central Asia. Finally, the Kamchatka peninsula and the Stanovoi Mountains contain a sheep which is closely related to the Bighorn sheep of the Rocky Mountains, the latter ranging in suitable localities from Alaska to Mexico.

In time, sheep are not known till nearly the end of the Tertiary era and their present range seems easily explained. We may suppose that they arose within some part of the Central Asian area after the Tertiary mountain-folding had produced a variety of new physical habitat types, and after what appears to have been a widely distributed and fairly uniform Tertiary forest had given place locally to grass swards peopled by newly evolved herbaceous plants. The ensuing Glacial Period, by bringing mountain climatic conditions down to the low grounds, promoted a wide dispersal of the original sheep stock and the appearance of local specializations. As the ice retreated back to high latitudes and altitudes certain of the widely spread Ice Age sheep succeeded in surviving in particular localities, where they were either isolated in the literal sense (Cyprus, Sardinia and Corsica) or found suitable refuges in mountain ranges (Barbary sheep). In particular, the close relationship between the Kamchatkan sheep and the Rocky Mountain sheep suggests migration from the Old World to the New across the Bering Strait area, followed by southern spread of the latter along the axis of the range, accompanied by slight differentiation as interbreeding between the two stocks ceased to be possible. Thus the continuity of the North American Cordillera has favoured the continuous distribution of a single species, while the fracturing of the folded mountain belt of Eurasia has resulted in the rise of species peculiar to the separate parts.

The absence of sheep from South America is easily explained when we remember that the physically possible migration line through Central America leads through just that hot, wet, forested type of country of which sheep are so intolerant. Their absence from the Ethiopian Region may be explained in similar fashion. The fact that sheep occur in the Tibesti massif of the Sahara is part of the evidence that while northern Eurasia was undergoing glaciation parts of the Sahara were less arid than at present, but their farther southward extension must have been blocked by the presence of forested country of quite unsuitable type.

Generally, then, sheep are of geologically late origin, probably arose in Central Asia, and have not been able of themselves to spread beyond the limits of the northern hemisphere despite the fact that, as has been abundantly proved, the grassy plains of the southern hemisphere are perfectly suited to the domesticated breeds. The discontinuous distribution of the three species found in western Eurasia is paralleled by that of various other mammals, such as the chamois (a somewhat aberrant antelope) and the wild goats (ibex), and is readily explained as a result of the Ice Age.

Elephant Group. This group forms a great contrast with the sheep, for it can be traced back to early Tertiary times, and while there are but two kinds of living elephants many fossil forms and allies are known. The group is a dying one, keeping a precarious hold only within the palaeotropical belt though it once had a wide distribution.

Let us note first the kind of evidence available in this and similar cases as a means of tracing the history of a group and the lines of migration followed by its evolving members. In parts of Europe, Asia, northern Africa and the two Americas there occur Tertiary beds of various ages containing many mammalian fossils. Such beds afford positive evidence of the mammalian fauna at the time and place, and, where the same or closely

15

related mammals occur as fossils in beds of similar age in widely separated localities, we are justified in assuming that these were spread throughout the intervening areas, even if fossil-bearing beds are not known there. Again, when a particular mammal occurs in older beds in one area but only in younger ones in another, it is a natural deduction that migration occurred from the first to the second area. In parts of the areas named, such richly fossiliferous deposits are found as to enable us to draw well-founded conclusions as to the total fauna. On the other hand, within the inter-tropical and southern region of Africa, fossil-bearing deposits of known Tertiary age are as yet known from only a few spots. Dinotherium, an early member of the elephant group, is, however, known from East Africa, where apparently it survived into the Pleistocene, and East Africa has recently yielded a good number of fossil mammals.

The evidence available gives us the following picture of the origin of the elephant alliance, of the earlier range of its members, the lines of migration followed, and the progressive extinction throughout most of the area first occupied. In deposits of Upper Eocene and Oligocene Age in the Fayum region of Egypt there occur for the first time fossils of mammals which seem to mark the transition from primitive Ungulate types to elephant-like forms. Moeritherium and Palaeomastodon show in their teeth the beginnings of those features which distinguish the elephants from all other mammals. This suggests that what is now the lower Nile valley was either the area of origin of the elephant alliance or a part of that area.

The species of Mastodon represent, as it were, the next stage, and these occur first in beds of Lower Miocene Age both in Europe and Asia. In this genus tusks may be present in both jaws instead of only in the upper one as in the true elephants, and the cheek teeth are short-crowned and of far simpler structure. At the same time Mastodon shows a nearer approach to the living elephants than does Palaeomastodon. Mastodon is found in North America in beds of Upper Miocene Age and in South America in those of the succeeding Pliocene Age. We deduce, therefore, that the members of the genus migrated from the Old World to the New, and that the migration line was in a northern latitude, so that a further period of time elapsed before they reached South America, which in any case was not linked to the northern continent till near the end of Tertiary time.

The next point is that while Mastodon lingered in the Americas till the Pleistocene, apparently even till the human period, it disappeared from the Old World, save perhaps in Ethiopian

Africa, at the close of the Pliocene.   Its disappearance from Eurasia can be connected with the fact that, as is shown by certain Indian Pliocene beds, evolution within the alliance was proceeding rapidly there.   Series of fossils have been found linking Mastodon, with its relatively simple cheek teeth, with the true elephants, characterized by their single pair of tusks and massive, highly complex cheek teeth.   By Pleistocene times these true elephants were widely spread over Eurasia and its borderlands, a large number of species having been recognized.   One of these, the mammoth, as we have seen reached Alaska, but in America other forms evolved from Mastodon, including the Columbian elephant (*Elephas columbi*), which ranged well into the U.S.A., and *E. imperator*, which lived in the south-west of U.S.A., as well as forms difficult to identify, because only teeth and a few bones are available, recorded from South America.

The elephant group died out in America in Pleistocene times, and there was an analogous extinction of the more numerous elephants of temperate Eurasia during the same period, but the stock succeeded in reaching south-eastern inter-tropical Asia and there survived as the Indian elephant ; there was no analogous survival in isthmian or South America.

The Pleistocene elephants were the product of intense specialization, particularly as regards the teeth.   Some extinct forms also reached a size much greater than that of the living species.   The record of the rocks, and this whatever group we take (cf. the lost reptiles of Secondary time), suggests that in all such cases of large increase of size the adaptability of the stock becomes exhausted and extinction tends to follow.   Persistence seems to demand the power of adjustment to changing conditions and this power can apparently be lost.   Once it is lost, the stock may still linger on, as it were by inertia, until a changing environment stimulates evolution in some other group or groups ; then the senile stock dies out as a result either of direct competition for food or of attack by new kinds of enemies.   Thus we have to associate the disappearance of elephants both from temperate Eurasia and from North America with the rise of new types of Ungulates specialized along quite different lines, and of new types of Carnivores combining agility with powerful weapons and acute senses.   Of the varied Pleistocene elephant types in the Old World some, like the mammoth, seem to be nearly related to the living Indian elephant, others, found fossil in southern Europe and its margins (Spain, Algeria and various islands such as Sicily, Malta, &c.), to the living African one.   Lines of southward migration were apparently open to both, and with minor modifications of structure (loss of hairy coat) and of habit (avoidance of direct sunlight, frequent bathing, etc.), both types have succeeded in surviving within inter-tropical areas.

In South America old Ungulate groups, mainly of large forms such as the Litopterna and the Notoungulata, also the horses, died out in the Pleistocene as also did the elephants, while the large ground sloths at least diminished and have subsequently become extinct.   Elephants, horses and ground sloths disappeared from North America as well about the same time.   The immigration of the Felidae without their predestined victims such as oxen, sheep or antelope herds into South America, though llamas, guanacos and the Cariacus deer occurred there, may well have been a factor of the extinction noted.   The disappearance or reduction in numbers and range of very large mammals in the late Pleistocene is, however, almost a world-wide feature and needs further study with attention specially devoted to the much more comprehensive changes in the New World, for both elephants and horses survive in the Old.   Further reference to this will be made later in the present chapter.

This complicated story throws light on what is called discontinuous distribution, a phenomenon even more strikingly illustrated in the camel family and the tapirs.   The living elephants are found only in two separated areas in the Old World and are absent from the intervening belt.   The camel family is divided between the Old World (Arabian and Bactrian camels) and South America (guanaco, vicuña and domestic llama), while the tapir occurs in South America as well as far away in the Malay region.   In all such cases, as we have shown for the elephants, the members of the group can be traced back to a common source, and the present habitats represent the ends of the migration routes.   Generally, then, the existing range of a group requires to be interpreted in terms of its past history, and the longer this has been the greater the difficulty.

MAMMALS OF NEOGAEA

This preliminary survey makes it possible to treat the individual regions briefly, and we may conveniently begin with the Neogaeic Realm which is conterminous with the Neotropical Region.   As Fig. 33 shows, it includes South and Central America, with a northward extension into the ' hot lands ' (*Tierras Calientes*) which border the Mexican plateau to east and west, and also the West Indian Islands.   From the point of view of types of habitat, a notable feature is the large area covered by forest, especially of the hot, wet type, which is continued into the isthmian area. With this is associated a number of kinds of arboreal animals, such as monkeys and marmosets, rodents, e.g. the tree porcupines, Edentates (sloths, some ant-eaters), opossums and so forth. A second notable feature is the length and continuity of the Cordilleran range which has served as a line of migration, e.g. for the guanaco, and also itself forms the habitat of a number of peculiar forms such as the vicuña, the chinchilla among Rodents, the spectacled bear and many others. Areas of intense aridity occur, but true desert covers a smaller area than in Africa. Among the forms specially adapted to dry lands mention may be made of the long-legged Patagonian cavy, a peculiar Rodent ; but the Rhea, like its African ally the ostrich, frequents open, semi-arid country.

Most interesting of all from many points of view are the grass-lands, especially the pampas of the south-east. As contrasted with the variety of mammalian life found in the forested areas, they contained, at the time of European occupation, a comparatively small number of forms though the number of individuals was great. Ungulates were represented by the guanaco, the larger of the two wild species of llama (camel family), and the pampas deer, a member of the Cariacus genus (p. 203). Since the guanaco has a wide range in the Andes, accompanying its ally the vicuña in the mountains of Ecuador and Peru, and since its ancestors certainly entered from the north, it seems probable that its occupation of the pampas is recent. The pampas deer also differs in habitat and in details of habit from its congeners, which are woodland animals. Apart from these two, the chief animals of the pampas were Rodents, notably the social and burrowing viscacha, a somewhat marmot-like form related however to the chinchilla and not to the marmots ; and one representative of the Running Birds, the Rhea. Against all, and particularly the viscacha, the settlers have waged unremitting war, and they have replaced them by introduced domesticated stock animals of whose great numbers the student of geography does not need to be reminded. The remarkable point is that when European man introduced these herds of Ungulates into the pampas he was, in a sense, reconstructing conditions which had prevailed during Quaternary time. Beneath the existing plant cover there lie in many areas richly fossilized deposits containing remains of horses (genus Equus) as well as of many extinct Ungulates peculiar to the Realm. Cattle and sheep, it is true, were never present till the domesticated forms were brought in, but that the wild horses which entered from the north should have died out, and yet domesticated forms thriven apace when brought across the ocean is one of the great puzzles of distribution.

Many possible explanations have been put forward, none completely satisfactory. It may be that the solution will come through the studies which the ecological botanists are making of the effect of grazing on grassland types. Their work seems tending to show that, where pastures are grazed wholly or mainly by one kind of stock, degeneration, or retrocession as it is called, tends to occur, while differences in feeding habits appear to check this where the grazing animals are of varied types. It may be that the horses which found their way into South America multiplied after the disappearance of the more primitive original Ungulates to such an extent as to destroy the basis of their own subsistence, and that after a period during which the pastures had time to recover these were reoccupied by guanaco and pampas deer. It is at least clear that we must not overestimate the importance of the natural pastures of the pampas in connexion with the present stock industry, for its progress has been accompanied by the introduction of sown fodder plants of alien origin. There is thus no certainty that the pampas would have continued to maintain the introduced Ungulates if these had been left to depend on native grasses.

A negative feature of Neogaea is the absence of Insectivores, except for two peculiar shrews (Solenodon) in the West Indian Islands. These shrews are believed to be related to the tailless hedgehog (Centetes) of Madagascar and to the Cape Golden Mole (Chrysochloris) of South Africa, all primitive types. Their presence in the West Indies is the most striking example of affinity between the *living* mammals of the Neotropical and Ethiopian Regions.

It is usual to associate the persistence of a variety of opossums (some twenty-four species in addition to the aberrant water-opossum) with the absence of Insectivores, for many of the opossums are small, shrew-like and insect-eating forms. We can similarly associate the paucity of Ungulates with the fact that the Rodents are not only extremely numerous but specialized in a fashion unknown elsewhere. Almost every possible habitat is occupied, and the somewhat pig-like capybara of eastern South America, which is aquatic in its habits, is the largest living Rodent, though considerably smaller than some extinct forms found in the Tertiaries of the Argentine.

All the Carnivores are clearly immigrants. They include the widely distributed true cats, dogs and a bear, as well as a number of members of the bear alliance, such as raccoons and their allies and the skunks, apparently evolved within North America. Civets are absent as they are from North America. The few living Ungulates (peccaries, Cariacus deer, llamas, tapirs) seem likewise to be of northern origin. The Cariacus deer and peccaries are shared with North America at the present time, the latter having apparently evolved there from an early pig-like stock common to it and the Old World. North America was also the area of origin of the camel family, one set migrating to the Old World and giving rise to the camels while the other was the source of the South American llamas. Tapirs (p. 204) were once widely distributed in the whole northern hemisphere. Though the bison, closely related to the cattle of the Old World, is a great feature of North American life, neither cattle nor sheep nor the Cervus deer ever of themselves reached South America, which has also lost its original primitive types of Ungulates. Finally, it seems probable that the South American opossums also came from the north, for they were abundant in early Tertiary time both in North America and in Europe.

As contrasted with these immigrant stocks the New World monkeys and small and helpless marmosets have certainly originated within South America and are unknown elsewhere. They were probably evolved from a primitive lemuroid stock which reached the area through Africa. The marmosets and monkeys, together with the Edentates and the Solenodon shrews of the West Indies, constitute the most important survivors of the early Neogaeic mammalian fauna, and this suggests that the relative safety afforded by the dense equatorial forest against attack by the immigrant Carnivores, was of much importance in enabling them to persist. The very numerous Rodents present a more difficult problem. Some are certainly recent immigrants, but the endemic forms show somewhat ill-defined relationship to groups found in Africa, so it is possible that their far-off ancestors came by way of that continent. Finally, as already stated (p. 218), the rare marsupial Coenolestes presents a puzzle. A special reference to the South American Edentates must be added.

Fossil-bearing deposits within South America are sufficiently numerous to prove that Edentates of this kind have been present there from the very beginning of Tertiary time. Their story can also be traced through successive beds, making clear that continuous evolution has occurred in a number of directions, the process culminating in the appearance of the three divergent living families. As is so generally the case with ancient stocks, certain extinct forms reached a much larger size than any now living, some of which are small and rare.   Whole families also have died out completely.   Again, the living forms, comparatively few in number, combine in a remarkable way high specialization along certain lines together with features more primitive than those of any other living placental mammals.

Without elaborating the last point, we may note that the sloths, as already stated, are the most purely arboreal of mammals, intensely adapted to life in dense tropical forest.   Their immediate ancestors, the ground-sloths, reached a greater size and strength, but, owing to their terrestrial habit, must have been much more liable to attacks by Carnivores.   They were also devoid of those special features which enable the sloths to spend their whole life in the trees, and there to escape notice owing to their slow movements and the greenish tint of their coats.   The latter peculiarity, curiously enough, is due to minute algae which, in the damp atmosphere of the forest, lodge and multiply in special flutes of the shaggy hair.   This is a remarkable adaptation paralleled only by some marine organisms, such as certain crabs, which have seaweed growing on their backs and thus obtain the same kind of concealment as Macduff's soldiers.

Of the three kinds of ant-eaters two are arboreal with prehensile tails, one being not unlike a miniature sloth, though the diet is quite different.   The third, the great ant-eater, haunts wet lands where it finds shelter among the tall grasses.   The armadillos, again, not only have their protective shield of bony plates but are swift burrowers, some appearing to sink through the ground on an alarm.

Such facts, combined with the absence—with the exceptions still to be noted—of these Edentates from other parts of the world seem easily interpreted.   They suggest that many Edentate types have arisen within the Neogaeic Realm and, owing to their adaptive features and secluded habitats, have been able to maintain a somewhat precarious hold there, despite the late-Tertiary and post-Tertiary invasion of more highly organized northern forms. This suggestion appears to be confirmed by their late appearance in North America, where the first undoubted Edentate fossils occur in beds of Pliocene and Pleistocene Age.   Thus the fact that ground-sloths occur in Miocene beds in South America but not till the very end of Tertiary time in the northern continent, where the animals spread as far as Kentucky, suggests northern migration after the land-link was formed.   We can explain in a similar fashion the presence of one living South American armadillo in Texas as the product of a late, probably post-glacial, northern migration.   Thus it has been customary to say that, apart from a limited and late extension northwards, the living and extinct South American Edentates are characteristically Neogaeic and not found elsewhere. They, therefore, like the Litopterna and Notoungulata, seem to form an exception to the rule that orders of placental mammals have originated in the northern hemisphere ; their ancestors got into South America and, for a time, enjoyed considerable prosperity there. Possibly they may be descendants of the Eocene Taeniodontae of the northern hemisphere (North America).

NOTOGAEA, CONTINENTAL AND INSULAR

Between the continent of South America as representing the largest land-mass of Neogaea and Australia as the main element of Notogaea the contrast is great, Australia showing a persistent aloofness of which there is little trace in South America. The presence of the Solenodon shrews of the West Indies and perhaps of Neogaean Edentates may suggest an early connexion across the Atlantic with Ethiopian Africa, a connexion broken at the latest in early Tertiary times. On the other hand, many other living or recently extinct forms make it certain that the existing connexion with North America has prevailed since at least the later part of the Tertiary era. Again, the high specialization of certain elements in the fauna, particularly the Edentates and Primates and some at least of the Rodents, makes it clear that possible periods of union with other land-masses were separated by a long interval of isolation during which no immigration occurred.

There is still another point to be noted. The isthmus of Panama, the narrowest part of the land-link with North America, nowhere very greatly exceeds 100 miles in width and is in places much narrower. If we can assume that it has undergone no great recent changes, then we must suppose that along such a bridge animals so large as Mastodons, horses, llamas and ground-sloths can pass without difficulty. Possibly, in a geologically recent period, there may have been another more easterly link between the continents, as by Trinidad, Haiti and Cuba ; but even this is not likely to have been wider. This suggests that we need not give the hypothetical ' Western Gondwanaland ' continental proportions, for, by a parity of reasoning, quite a narrow land-bridge between Brazil and West Africa would have been sufficient to permit of the migration of early types of placentals from Ethiopian Africa to South America. Hypotheses of continental drift would alter the problem fundamentally.

Turning next to Australia we find that the absence of placental mammals, whether of primitive or of specialized types, makes it certain that the existing isolation is both geologically old and has been continuous. The break between Australia and the northern section of Eastern Gondwanaland must have occurred at a date so early that placental mammals, if they existed, had not yet had time to spread throughout the area, and there has been no subsequent connexion of a nature to permit their entrance. In itself this does not necessarily enable us to date the break, for if placentals originated to the north of the Tethys, they may have had but a limited southern extension when far eastern Gondwanaland broke up ; it is probable, however, that Australia has been isolated since the close of Secondary time.

The Austro-Malay Region.   Between it and the peninsulas of south-eastern Asia lies the great East Indian archipelago.   Even the student of geography is apt to be a little vague as to its actual extent and composition, for the implied analogy with the much smaller West Indian islands is very deceptive.   It may, therefore, be noted that the western extremity of Sumatra is separated from the eastern one of New Guinea by 55° of longitude, and that while the Philippines, a north-eastern prolongation of the archipelago, nearly reach 20° N. lat., New Guinea stretches to beyond 10° S. lat., making a total extension in latitude of some 30°. Where in this great stretch can we find a line of demarcation between the Oriental region with its wealth of placentals and the Australian one with its multitude of marsupials ? Alfred Russell Wallace drew it between Borneo and Celebes (Strait of Macassar), continuing it through the narrow but deep channel which separates Bali and Lombok, and, under the name of Wallace's Line (cf. Fig. 35), this has persisted in the literature of distribution. It is, however, in some ways unsatisfactory, particularly in that it throws Celebes into the Notogaeic Realms. Celebes has a rich and varied placental fauna, including a peculiar monkey, a remarkable lemur (Tarsius) which it shares with Borneo, Sumatra and the Philippines, a peculiar pig-like animal (Babirusa) and others, making a recent connexion with the Oriental region clear, while the marsupial element in its fauna is quite insignificant, including only one or two species of a kind of phalanger (Cuscus). Detailed problems of distribution in this area are also greatly complicated by the fact that it is the home of the Malays, at once great navigators and skilled in taming animals which they are fond of carrying about with them as mascots. They may, therefore, have been responsible for some puzzling details. As Fig. 35 shows, it is customary to

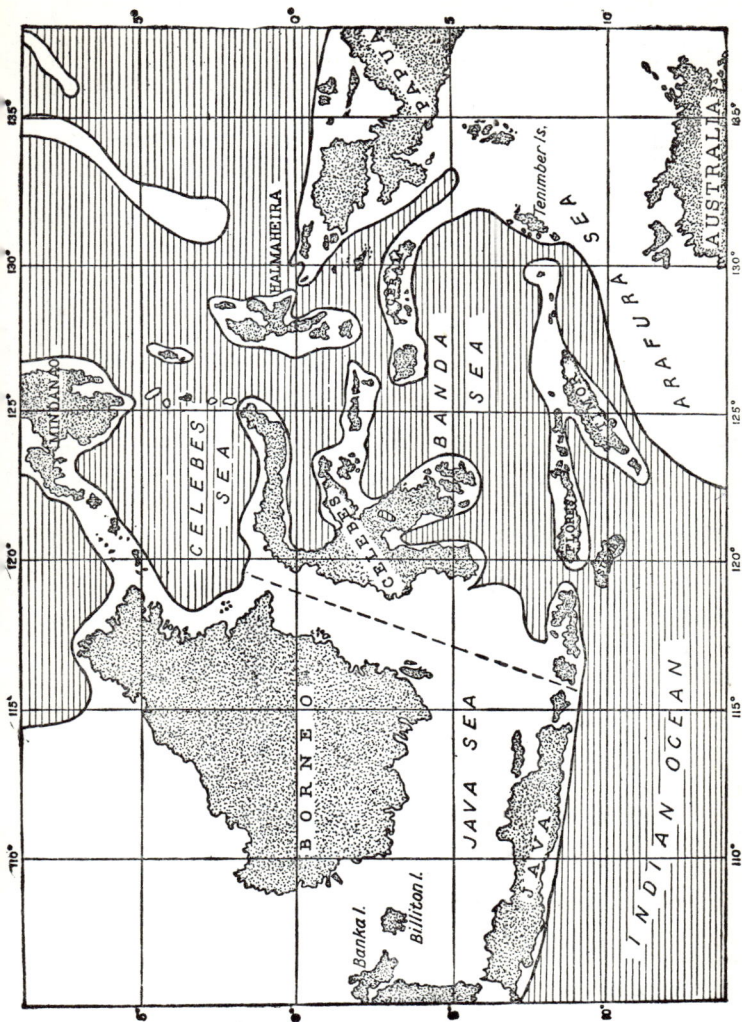

FIG. 35.—Austro-Malayan Region showing Isthmian Links

After Bailey Willis

Also shows Wallace's Line

emphasize the limited and partial westward extension of a few marsupials in the form of some arboreal cuscuses to the west of New Guinea by recognizing a transitional Austro-Malayan region, bounded to the west by Wallace's Line.

Does this transitional region cover in the main, if not in detail, the area within which the Secondary break occurred, and if so what was the nature of the earlier connexion ? Fig. 35 has been taken from an article by Bailey Willis, who is a strong supporter of the view that early connexions between the existing continents never had a ' continental ' aspect, but were merely what he calls isthmian links, that is, elevations of existing oceanic ridges regarded as the equivalents of mountain ranges on lands. That is, he retains in a modified form the older view that the continents and great ocean basins are essentially permanent features of the earth's surface. At the same time he holds that, just as in various geological eras the continents have shown in the great folded mountain ranges what he calls transient rugosities of the surface, whose foundations have at times subsided to great depths, so also similar cordilleras may have been raised temporarily from the ocean floor and served as lines of organic migration. Thus, in this particular case, he does not, as most European geologists do, regard the East Indian archipelago as a whole as the remains of a continental area linking up what is now south-eastern Asia with an enlarged Australia. Rather does he believe that there were only narrow and temporary bridges between the two continents which permitted the Glossopteris flora and much later early marsupial types to migrate southwards. The slightly marked ' return current ' indicated by the presence of a few cuscuses to the west of New Guinea would presumably be ascribed to accidental transmission.

As the figure shows, he regards New Guinea as having been formerly united to Australia ; Sumatra, Java, Bali, Lombok and Sumbawa, as well as Borneo, Celebes and the Philippines (Mindanao) are, on the other hand, assigned to south-eastern Asia. Three possible isthmian links between the two continents are suggested, one or all of which may have existed from Permian till towards the close of Secondary time. The three are : (1) by the Sumatra–Java arc through Flores and Timor to the Australian–New Guinea mass ; (2) by Celebes through Ceram to the same ; (3) by the Borneo–Mindanao area through Halmahera (Gilolo) to New Guinea. On the figure Wallace's Line, not shown in the original, has been inserted, and it will be seen that Willis's position is essentially a return to that held by Wallace, but with a definite shift of the line or lines of break to the east.

Fauna of the Australian Region. Of the marsupials of the Australian region little more need be said. Saved from the competition of the more intelligent placentals and stimulated by the ample space at their disposal, the original stocks which reached the area have evolved in a great variety of directions, and their descendants show a range of adaptive modifications of which there is little trace either in the living marsupials of Neogaea or in the extinct forms of the northern hemisphere. Since virtually all kinds of habitats, all possible modes of life, are open to them also, they show a curious parallelism to the placentals elsewhere. Thus the Tasmanian wolf recalls the placental wolf, the rare Australian mole the placental mole of Europe, and so on. Such resemblances, due not to common descent but to adaptations to similar modes of life, are described as convergent, convergence being a proof that similar conditions tend to produce a similar response even among organisms not nearly related.

New Guinea with its smaller area and more uniform environment has fewer kinds of marsupials than Australia, and some of those present show special features. Thus the true kangaroos of the open plains of Australia are absent in New Guinea, where the dense tropical forests contain the tree-kangaroos, extending also into North Queensland, which have proportionately longer fore-limbs and less specialized hind ones. The presence of a true pig has already been mentioned and the possibility of its introduction noted (p. 198). Both Australia and New Guinea contain a considerable number of rats and mice, but it is believed that these or their ancestors have been accidentally introduced.

Finally, it may be remarked that, apart from the indications already noted of affinities between the marsupials of Australia and South America, their amphibians seem also to show relationships. Thus (see Fig. 36) both areas are characterized by the absence of true frogs (Ranidae), which just reach the Cape York area in Australia and occur only in the north of South America. More striking is the occurrence in both and not elsewhere of frog-like forms belonging to the large family of Cystignathidae, apparently somewhat primitive creatures. The interpretation of these facts is difficult. Since the true frogs seem to be the most recently evolved members of the tail-less amphibians (Anura), and probably originated in the northern hemisphere, their absence from both Australia and South America is not unnatural. But whether or not the presence of the Cystignathidae in the two areas and not elsewhere is an indication of a former direct connexion between the two is an unsolved problem. As we shall see later, the plants show similar suggestions of affinity.

The Polynesian and Hawaiian Regions.   As Fig. 38 shows, it
is customary to attach to the Notogaeic Realm a somewhat
heterogeneous collection of islands characterized faunistically by
the absence of terrestrial mammals and amphibia (with rare
exceptions), and to divide these into two regions called Polynesian
and Hawaiian.   The latter includes only the volcanic Hawaiian
archipelago and has a unity of its own, for both the group and
the separate islands are marked by a high degree of endemism
affecting especially the birds and the land-shells.   On the other
hand, neither is the Polynesian region a unit nor are its limits
easy to draw.   Thus the Solomon Islands have several kinds of
amphibia, including a peculiar genus and one marsupial (a

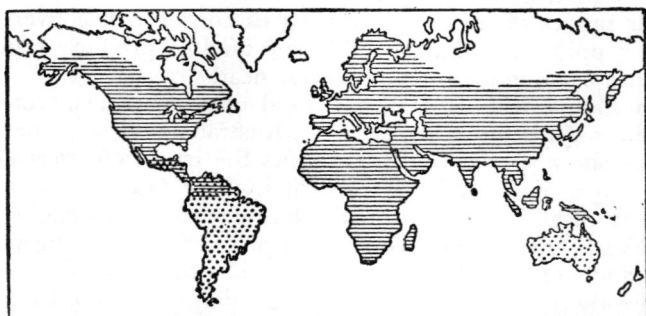

FIG. 36.—Distribution of true frogs (Ranidae) and Cystignathidae or Southern
frogs

The horizontal shading represents the true frogs which just extend into the north of South
America, are absent from Australia except for the Cape York peninsula, but are otherwise
cosmopolitan.   The dots show the range of the southern types, and while there is a slight
measure of overlapping it is clear that Australia and South America agree in the general
absence of true frogs, except in the extreme north, and in the presence of the more primitive
Cystignathidae

phalanger), suggesting that they should be included with New
Guinea rather than with the Polynesian Islands proper.   But the
New Britain (Bismarck) archipelago, which lies still nearer New
Guinea, contains four kinds of marsupials, and, moreover, the
flora of the Solomons seems more akin to that of New Zealand
and the intermediate islands than to that of New Guinea.   These
two facts have led to the drawing of the regional division line
between New Britain and the Solomons, bringing the former
into the Australian and the latter into the Polynesian region.
    The New Zealand group offers even greater difficulty.   It has
obviously at one time formed part of a continental area, for the
Glossopteris flora (p. 220) is represented in beds of Triassic Age,
and the absence of mammals must be ascribed to the early date

at which separation occurred. There is, it may be noted, a native placental rat, but this is regarded as having been certainly introduced by the Maoris, while a certain element of doubt exists as to the origin of the more numerous (about 26 species) rats and mice found in Australia which some systematists consider to have been present there for a fairly long period.   Of the other elements in the fauna of New Zealand we may recall the fact that its peculiar beaked lizard (Sphenodon) has its nearest allies in Permian and Triassic beds in the northern hemisphere, so that its presence speaks to early migration overland. Of other terrestrial reptiles it contains only geckoes, supposed to be the oldest group of the ' modern ' lizards and practically cosmopolitan in warmer latitudes, being found even in such islands as the Hawaiian archipelago.   No special significance can be attached to their presence, for these little lizards cling tightly to branches and brushwood and are extremely resistant to starvation, so that in calm tropical waters they might easily be carried great distances on floating trees.   It is believed that their wide distribution in island groups is due to such ' accidental ' transmission, their (relative) age having given time for the process.   There is but one amphibian in New Zealand, a small and rare frog-like creature. The birds are remarkable, particularly in the presence of Running Birds, the living kiwis and extinct moas : the ancestors of these must presumably have come by an overland route.   In inverte-brates the islands are poor.   Generally we can but say that apart from a possible connexion with South America through Antarctica, it would appear that New Zealand had only some early land-link with the north, broken before the period when New Guinea and Australia received their characteristic fauna.

The Polynesian islands proper are either of volcanic or of coral origin, and like the Hawaiian islands are characterized by extreme poverty in kinds of terrestrial and freshwater animals.   Such animals as do occur are those which, like birds and bats, may have reached them by flight, or, like insects, may have been brought by air currents, or have possibilities of accidental trans-mission over water by floating trees.   In the case of minute forms there is also the possibility that eggs or resting adults may have been carried by birds, which often have mud attached to their feet.   Such islands are, therefore, according to the old definition ' oceanic ', as opposed to the continental types, like the Seychelles, which have once formed part of a larger land-mass.   In this case it may be noted that the problem of the permanence or otherwise of ocean basins does not seriously affect the issue so far as the present faunas are concerned.   Whether or not a ' Pacific continent ' ever existed matters little, for we can scarcely suppose that, if it did, its organisms, if any, had much influence on the existing island faunas.   Whether of volcanic or coral reef origin, the islands in their present form represent ' new ' land, and beyond being reasonably sure that their organic life came either through the air or over water we have little means of tracing its source. The interest of their faunas lies mainly in the evidence offered of the effect of an island environment ; but before dealing with that subject we may note some points in regard to the general question of the absence of mammals and amphibians in such island types.

Mammals present no great difficulties.   Even in the case of small forms, and except where the separating water belt is narrow, transmission over water must be difficult if only on account of the food problem.   It is possible, however, that some of the minor anomalies of marsupial distribution in, e.g., the Austro-Malay islands and the Solomons may be an indication that marsupials are more easily carried passively than most placentals apart from rodents.   Amphibians are, however, cold-blooded and remarkably resistant to starvation, and one might expect that they would be more likely to be disseminated passively. Their extreme sensitiveness to salt is, however, a notable inhibiting factor, for even on a bulky natural raft the chances that they could escape contact with sea-water are not great.   At the same time, according to Gadow (*Camb. Nat. Hist.*, Vol. VIII, p. 72), ' undoubtedly many individuals have made long and successful voyages across the seas on floating trees '.   Though made generally, the statement must be meant to apply mainly to the Anura or frog-like forms.   As Fig. 37 shows, the worm-like burrowing Apoda are confined to the pantropical belt, excluding both Madagascar and Australia.   They are unknown as fossils, and their burrowing habit makes over-water carriage unlikely. The Urodeles (salamanders, newts, &c.) seem to have originated in the Holarctic Region, and though they are abundantly represented in the Sonoran Region, and have even succeeded to a small extent in reaching South America, as well as the confines of the Oriental Region in the Far East, they are, broadly speaking, northern forms.   The Anura, on the other hand, are cosmopolitan as a group, even if, as Figs. 36 and 37 show, the families may have a limited distribution.   We can offer no explanation of the presence of a single frog-like form in New Zealand, of a toad in the Hawaiian group, of frogs in the Fiji Islands, and so on, beyond supposing that these are cases of accidental transmission by drift-wood.   It is perhaps worth note that, if this hypothesis is correct, the peculiar distribution of the tongueless frogs (Aglossa), as shown in Fig. 34, need not necessarily involve a continuous land-bridge between tropical Africa and South America. Anura are not known as fossils before about the Middle Eocene, and the European fossil ally of the existing Aglossa dates only from Mid-Tertiary beds. If the ancestors of the Surinam toad (Pipa) crossed the Atlantic by land, this carries Western Gondwanaland down to a very late date. But if, as Willis suggests, the land-link was always narrow and of an isthmian rather than a continental character, early breaking up into islands linked by shoals, then perhaps the ancestors of Pipa may have been carried from island to island till they reached the coast of South America.

FIG. 37.—Distribution of the limbless (Apoda) and tailed (Urodele) amphibians

The Urodeles are shown by horizontal shading. Although they do not reach very high latitudes, and thin out in the arid areas of Central Asia, they are broadly limited to north temperate regions, with a limited southern extension into South America. Apoda (shown by dots) are pantropic apart from the Australian region

Turning next to the outstanding features of island faunas, we have to note first the characteristic tendency to endemism, as shown, for instance by the peculiar monotypic genera of amphibians found in New Zealand (Liopelma) and the Solomons (Ceratobatrachus), and particularly by the land-shells (Achatinellidae) of the Hawaiian Islands. That such forms must have arisen within the areas where they occur from ancestors brought overseas by 'accident' seems clear. Since the access of new stocks with which the first successful immigrants might inter-breed must be a very rare phenomenon new characters seem to become fixed with relative rapidity. The process is analogous to that by which man produces new breeds of domesticated animals. His method is to prevent blending by control of mating, allowing only those forms to interbreed which possess

16

the characters desired. In islands a similar effect is produced
by the fact that the occurrence of interbreeding with unrelated
stocks is rare or impossible, so that any variations which appear
are not swamped by intercrossing.

A second feature is that flying forms tend to lose the power
of flight, as is illustrated by the flightless burrowing parrot
(Stringops) of New Zealand and by many of the insects of the
Hawaiian Islands.   Various explanations, not wholly incompatible
with one another, have been offered.   Thus it may be a result
of the fact that in storm-swept and small islands forms with
much power of flight are apt to be swept out to sea and lost,
leaving those with degenerate wings to propagate their kind.
The tendency for the wings to degenerate may again be a result
of inbreeding, perhaps, an indication of failing vitality resulting
from the rarity of the introduction of new blood.   Again, in the
case of birds, the absence of predatory mammals doubtless
permits flightless birds to persist in a fashion impossible in
continental areas with their rich mammalian fauna—that is, the
struggle for existence is not so keen.

A third peculiarity is that, especially in small islands with a
limited food supply, there is a general tendency for dwarf forms
to appear, as is well illustrated by the small insects and land
molluscs of the Hawaiian Islands and by many of the mammals of
small continental islands.   Thus Malta once contained a pygmy
elephant, Madagascar had till recently a pygmy hippopotamus,
and so on.   In such cases degeneration due to inbreeding doubtless plays a part.   Conversely, large islands of varied relief and
plant cover are sometimes characterized by giant forms, exemplified by the extinct Moas of New Zealand.   Generally, we may
say that remote islands have acted as minor centres of evolution
and represent, as it were, laboratories in which various experiments have been carried out which shed much light on the
evolutionary process.

CHAPTER XIII

ARCTOGAEA AND ITS REGIONS

GENERAL FEATURES OF ARCTOGAEA

THAT the Arctogaeic Realm displays certain major contrasts with both Neogaea and Notogaea is obvious enough. It covers an area much greater than either of the other two and, although it extends to and beyond equatorial latitudes, includes most of the temperate lands of the globe. Further, during the whole period when the distinctively modern types of organisms were evolving, it has shown a measure of physical continuity. This is indeed its fundamental feature. While Notogaea seems to have been isolated since the close of Secondary time, and Neogaea, whatever the nature of its earlier connexions, was not linked directly to North America until late in the Tertiary period, both the present and the past faunas of Arctogaea show that the existing separation between the eastern and western land-masses of the northern hemisphere is of quite late origin. It appears certain also that during at least parts of the Tertiary period there was a connexion between the two across what is now the North Atlantic.

Thus the first important point about Arctogaea is that its wide Holarctic Region contains a broadly similar fauna throughout. This fauna includes, notably in its Ungulates, some of the most specialized of placental mammals, while there are few organisms which can be justly described as primitive. Clearly the struggle for existence has been exceptionally keen, losses in the immediate past have been great, and there have been few opportunities for that evolution of adaptive features in old stocks which is so marked in, e.g., the Edentates of Neogaea. This region shows mountain building in a great latitudinal belt, as well as extensive Pleistocene glaciations, so we are justified in saying these sequences of events were largely responsible for giving the Holarctic fauna its present features.

Attached to the broad Holarctic Region are three others displaying notable contrasts both with it and with each other. Of these three the Sonoran Region, as we have seen, is remarkable because no obvious physical feature separates it from the Nearctic or western section of the Holarctic Region.   The recognition of a distinct Sonoran Region is due to the fact that within it there appear mammals such as the peccary, the armadillo of Texas, the opossum, the Virginian (Cariacus) deer—which has, however, a limited extension beyond it to the north—the prongbuck (Antilocapra), also with a limited extension to the north, and various Rodents, all of these animals wholly alien to the Old World. The fact that, because of the absence of any physical barrier, a certain blending of the Sonoran and Holarctic faunas should have taken place is inevitable ; but this slight intermixture does not obscure the recognition at the present time of two distinct faunas within the single physiographic unit of North America.   The one is essentially the same as that of temperate Eurasia and includes a number of forms of quite recent origin.   The other, more original, includes forms like Antilocapra and some of the Rodents which appear to have originated within the area and scarcely succeeded in spreading beyond it, and others like peccary, armadillo, and Cariacus deer, common to it and to Neogaea.

The interpretation of these facts is fairly clear.   Because the link with Neogaea was established before the end of Tertiary time and has been maintained since, and because it was of such a nature as to serve as a migration track for certain kinds of mammals in both directions, the effects of Pleistocene glaciation have been in part neutralized in southern North America.   Apparently as the ice advanced from the north, lines of southward retreat for many of the pre-glacial mammals were open.   During interglacial periods and also during the final retreat of the ice a return current set in, so that some of the lost ground was recolonized.   In other words, the present fauna of the Sonoran Region is at least in part a reconstruction of the pre-glacial fauna of North America.

As already suggested, the American zoologists have made very elaborate attempts to find climatic limits to the range of particular mammals within the continent, in the hope of being able to give a rational explanation of the contrast between the Sonoran and Holarctic faunas.   In the main these attempts have resulted only in showing that, before man interfered, readjustments were in the act of taking place.   On the physical side we have the fact that considerable areas of North America as well as the Arctic Archipelago and most of Greenland still remain under Ice Age conditions.   On the biological side we have the conflict between

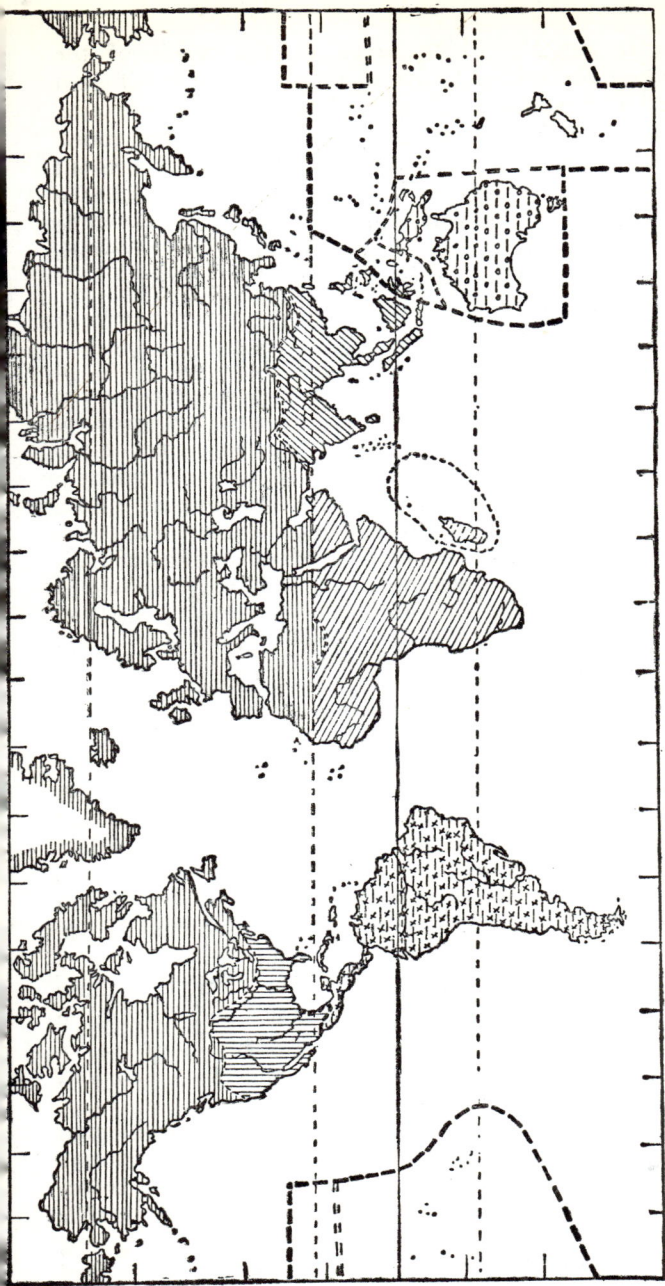

FIG. 38.—I. Outer limit of Notogaeic Realm. II. (a) Inner limits of regions in Notogaeic Realm; (b) boundary between Oriental and Holarctic; and (c) boundary of Ethiopian in middle of Sahara (boundary otherwise being the Tropic). III. (a) Northern boundary of Sonoran; (b) boundary of Malagasy.

1. Holarctic Region.   2. Sonoran.   3. Ethiopian.   4. Oriental.   5. Neotropical.   6. Australian.   7. Malagasian.

the plants and animals which arose as the result of the great change and the earlier forms adapted to a quite different environment. The absence of any physical transverse (i.e. latitudinal) barrier, and the fact that the earlier forms had found a refuge to the south from which they could return without difficulty, mean that a struggle is in progress, though European man has of course brought about great changes. Thus while the actual division line between the Sonoran and western Holarctic (Nearctic) areas is largely artificial, the fact that a distinction between the characteristic mammals of the two can be recognized is of much importance.

In the Old World conditions are very different, for the Ethiopian and Oriental Regions are not in any sense analogous to the Sonoran. The Ethiopian is essentially a persistent part of Gondwanaland ; and this is also at least partially true of the Oriental, which includes in peninsular India the area wherein the Glossopteris flora (p. 236) was first recognized. Both regions are therefore attached to Arctogaea rather than constituent elements of it. Because of the virtual absence of beds containing fossil terrestrial vertebrates of Tertiary age in peninsular India and in large parts of Ethiopian Africa, we know little of the period in which, or the stages by which, these fragments of Gondwanaland became attached to the northern lands in such a fashion as to permit free inter-migration of land animals. In other words, the details of the process by which the Tethys shrank to form the existing Mediterranean are obscure. What is clear, however, is that during the Pleistocene period the desert barrier in the west had not the same effect as at present, so that Ethiopian Africa then received a number of forms which had previously lived farther north. The giraffe is a conspicuous example ; in Pliocene times it occurred in Greece, Persia, northern India and China, but now it is confined to Ethiopian Africa. But whatever were the tracks by which modern types of mammals reached Africa south of the desert, it is clear both that those routes were not suited for all kinds of mammals and that in the last stages they were essentially one-way tracks. For refugees like the giraffe there was no return to the lands they had left, such as occurred in the Americas.

Thus the essential features of the present fauna of the Ethiopian Region are that it includes a mixture of apparently primitive forms, such as the Aard-Vark (Orycteropus), Hyrax, some Insectivores such as the Cape Golden Mole, lemurs, &c., with a number of essentially modern types like many of the true Ungulates, most of which apparently originated farther north and entered comparatively late. At the same time some modern forms like bears, deer and sheep never succeeded in reaching it.

Similar statements, with certain differences, can be made in regard to the fauna of the Oriental Region. The primitive element is on the whole less noticeable, doubtless in part because the breaking up of the area into peninsulas and islands left fewer refuges than did the compact mass of Ethiopian Africa with its great extension to the south. The resemblances to the existing Palaearctic fauna are on the whole greater because the northern mountains form a less complete barrier than the desert belt. On the other hand, again probably because of the smaller and less compact area, a number of forms once present have disappeared from the Oriental Region while persisting in Ethiopian Africa. Among these, in addition to the giraffe, mention may be made of the hippopotamus and chimpanzee.

Generally then, the Ethiopian and Oriental Regions have a fauna which includes many forms which once lived in the Palaearctic area but have disappeared there from Pleistocene times, plus an earlier element which recalls in more or less obscure fashion the time when they were linked to each other and to Brazil, and were separated from the northern lands by the Tethys. The differences between them may be explained in terms of the contrasts between the barrier belts which have bounded them to the north since later geological time, and the contrasts between their present geographical features.

It is a natural result of the sum-total of these conditions that few general statements can be made about the mammalian fauna of Arctogaea as a whole. We can indeed hardly say more than that, while the contrasts with Notogaea are obvious, Arctogaea differs from Neogaea mainly in that Ungulates, now so scantily represented in the latter, are abundant throughout, while Insectivores, virtually absent from Neogaea, occur everywhere, even if the types differ in the Regions. Another point of some interest is that Ganoid fish, absent from both Neogaea and Notogaea, are found throughout, though their range in Ethiopian Africa is limited and the African forms are peculiar and apparently not nearly related to the Holarctic Ganoids. The last point is of some importance, especially when we remember that Ethiopian Africa is the only part of Arctogaea which contains a living Running Bird and a Dipnoan fish. Not only as regards its mammals but in the fauna as a whole, we can discern dimly an ancient aloofness blurred beneath the imprint made by late-Tertiary and post-Tertiary migrations.

THE HOLARCTIC REGION

This is much the largest of the world regions and particularly in the eastern section displays the greatest variety of relief and range of climate. In the American section the range of climate may be said to be much more limited if we divide off a Sonoran Region in latitudes which in the Old World are included in the Holarctic. Further, both in height and extent, the ' Alpine ' chains of the Old World surpass greatly the folded mountain chain of North America and the latter has nothing to correspond to the lofty plateaux of Central Asia. Because of its relief, ' glacial ' conditions persist in Eurasia in the lower latitudes to an extent with which North America shows little analogy. Thus the greater area of the eastern part of the Holarctic Region is, as it were, counterbalanced by the effects of relief, which provide countless habitats for animals adapted to cool, and especially to cool and dry, conditions. If then we ask how it is that the faunas of the two parts of the Holarctic Region resemble each other so closely despite the apparent differences between the two, part of the answer is as follows. Both areas are occupied by animals adapted to the conditions which developed as the Pleistocene Ice Sheets retreated, and in both the earlier pre-glacial and inter-glacial fauna has largely disappeared. In the Old World many members of the earlier fauna survive in the Ethiopian and Oriental Regions, but their return to the north has been often prevented by the combination of a wide desert belt and transverse mountain chains. In North America the area re-colonized is separated off as the Sonoran Region, so that both sections contain a fauna which is in the main of definitely ' northern ' type.

Before noting its special features we may emphasize one point as a natural consequence of what has just been said as to the size and greater variety of the eastern section. This is, that while the resemblances in groups and genera are great, it is generally true that the characteristic forms are more numerously represented in the Old World section than in the New World one. For example, the account given on p. 224, of the distribution of sheep shows that in North America only the Cordillera offers a suitable habitat, and there is but one species. In the Old World, on the other hand, there are a number of species widely spread over a variety of mountain areas. The same sort of thing is illustrated by the goats. North America has but one somewhat aberrant goat, restricted to the Rocky Mountains, and with a limited southern extension to about lat. 36° N. in California. In the Old World, goats of many kinds occur with a wide range in both latitude and longitude. A similar statement might be made concerning oxen, deer, and others.

Turning next to the characters of the Holarctic fauna as a whole we have to note that Edentates are absent throughout. Primates are absent in the west and represented in the eastern section only by a few monkeys on the southern border. The characteristic placental mammals of both are members of the orders Ungulates, Carnivores, Rodents and Insectivores. Neither section contains Marsupials. Identical or closely related species occur in both sections. Thus among the Carnivores we find that the lynx of Europe is closely related to the American lynx, while wolf, fox, Arctic fox, brown bear, polar bear, pine-marten, weasel, wolverene and so forth are common to both. Among the Ungulates, the reindeer of Eurasia is apparently identical with the caribou of Arctic America, the American bison is a near ally of the European bison, a species of deer in central Asia is allied to the wapiti, while the elk of Europe seems to be the same animal as the moose of Canada. Among Rodents we have as common forms beaver, lemmings, Arctic vole, hares and so on. Of Insectivores the shrews occur in both areas and the mole-shrews are represented by one species in Japan and another in North America.

The contrasts between the faunas may be noted by taking a few examples. In the Mediterranean Lands the civets, otherwise characteristic of the Oriental and Ethiopian Regions, are represented by a mongoose (though this name is sometimes restricted to the Indian species of the genus Herpestes) and a genet, both of which must be regarded as survivors of the pre-glacial fauna. There are no civets in North America and they appear never to have been represented there. On the other hand the Nearctic section contains the common raccoon belonging to a family with a wide distribution in both Americas. It is probably a form which has succeeded in re-colonizing ground lost during the Ice Age. The family appears to have been of American origin. During the Pliocene, however, there lived in Europe an allied form, the panda, represented now only by the panda of the eastern Himalayas (Oriental Region). This suggests that some raccoon-like form found its way from North America to the Old World, probably by the Bering Strait area, developed into the panda and spread widely. It disappeared from the Holarctic Region in post-Pliocene times but has succeeded in persisting on the north-eastern border of the Oriental Region. As a third example among the Carnivores we may take the hyaenas. These are unknown in the New World and the three living species are in the main Ethiopian

(2) and Oriental (1).   But the Oriental form, the striped hyaena, occurs also in Persia, Mesopotamia, Syria and Palestine, i.e. in the Holarctic Region.   During the Pliocene and Pleistocene it lived in Europe.   Its present limited range within the eastern Holarctic Region may be explained as due to survival, though there is the possibility of a post-glacial migration from the Oriental Region.   Curiously enough, the spotted hyaena, now confined to Ethiopian Africa, lived in Europe during Pleistocene times. There was presumably a southward migration into Africa across what is now the desert belt, but a return has proved impossible.

Similar conditions are illustrated by the Ungulates of the eastern and western sections.   Thus while the horses have had a very complicated history, there is some evidence to show that they originated in the New World, certain members finding their way into the Old World, apparently by the Asiatic route.   But while both the Americas lost their horses at a geologically late date, the eastern Holarctic keeps both wild horses and the wild ass, while the striped forms (zebras) found their way into Ethiopian Africa.   The camel family certainly originated in North America and while the llamas found a refuge in South America and have been unable to return, the ancestors of the camels migrated to the Old World.   Fossil camels occur in the Pliocene of India and the Pleistocene of Algeria, suggesting that the ancestral forms entered by the Asiatic route.   No truly wild camels occur at the present time, but the single-humped or Arabian camel is presumed to have originated in Arabia and the two-humped or Bactrian camel possibly in some part of central Asia.   In contrast to these two cases we find that the musk-ox occurs in Arctic America and is absent from the Old World.   But it was widely spread in Europe in Pleistocene times, as well as in Asia.

A further contrast between the Ungulates of the two sections is seen in the presence of antelopes in the east.   These were of Old World, probably Asiatic, origin and never reached the New World, for the Sonoran Antilocapra seems to have originated independently from a deer-like ancestor.   At the present time antelopes are especially characteristic of the Ethiopian Region, but a certain number occur in the Palaearctic area and on its margins.   The details of their distribution illustrate in an interesting way the effects of the complicated climatic changes which accompanied the final retreat of the ice.   Thus the large saiga antelope is now limited to the steppes of eastern Europe and western Asia, but had an earlier range throughout western Europe ; the chamois, once widely spread over the lowlands of Europe, has found ' island ' refuges in various mountain belts (Pyrenees, Alps,

Carpathians, Caucasus, Taurus, and the mountains of southern Georgia). The gazelles, which are slender, extremely agile forms, mostly small and therefore not demanding much food, tolerant of extreme aridity, have been much more successful both in keeping their hold and extending their range. For them the arid belt which stretches from the Atlantic to the confines of India and is continued into central Asia is no barrier but a preferred habitat. Thus they are numerously represented within the Holarctic Region, penetrate into the western part of the Oriental Region and have colonized Africa throughout.

Generally we may say that prior to the onset of glaciation the antelopes were in the evolving stage. As the climate grew colder there must have been large-scale migration into Ethiopian Africa, giving rise to a wealth of new species there. At the same time in the north various forms were able to adapt themselves to the changing conditions and spread widely, though some, like the saiga and the chamois, have lost ground since.

Without multiplying examples we may sum up the reasons for the existing differences between the faunas of eastern and western Holarctica as follows :

1. Although at various times during the Tertiary period the two were linked together, and this by more than one migration track, the blending of their faunas was never complete ; some of the initial contrasts have persisted as shown, e.g. by the absence of antelopes in the west.

2. The greater area and more diversified relief and climate of the eastern area permitted certain immigrants of American origin to persist there while they died out in their birthplace ; the camel family and the horses form an illustration.

3. While in the Old World there is little evidence of that return current in post-glacial times which makes it possible to separate off a distinct Sonoran Region in the New, yet a few of the members of the earlier fauna, among which civets, the hyaena and macaque monkeys are outstanding, have persisted and provide a small ' southern ' element not recognizable in the same way in the American area.

Of the Region as a whole we may say that close resemblances between the faunas of the two sections, involving identity of species, occur especially with regard to forms characteristic of the higher latitudes. Some of the differences are explicable in terms of geologically recent extinction in one or other area ; but this is not invariably true. In the latter case—that is, where certain forms have been continuously absent in one area while occurring in the other—we must suppose that the land link or links which have existed since the origin of such forms have never been of a nature to permit them to migrate from one area to another. It is generally true that such forms are not adapted to life in the higher latitudes, and it is this fact which leads us to believe that the Tertiary land-links were in those northern regions where, both in the North Pacific and the North Atlantic, peninsulas and islands seem to stand like the piers of broken bridges.

THE ETHIOPIAN REGION

The Malagasy Sub-region. Madagascar is sometimes made a separate region because the difference between its fauna and that of Ethiopian Africa is so great, but this seems needless in view of the small total area included. Terrestrial mammals are absent from the Seychelles, Mauritius and Réunion, and though a few occur in the Comoro Islands, which form a kind of broken bridge between the north end of Madagascar and the mainland, yet essentially the sub-region includes only the island of Madagascar. In latitude it shows a general correspondence to Portuguese East Africa though it is not much more than half the size. The contrasts between its fauna and that of Ethiopian Africa are, however, far greater than can be explained by any difference in area or latitudinal range.

Those contrasts are in part negative, for Madagascar lacks many mammals found in Ethiopian Africa. But, and this is the essential point, the faunal type is entirely different. To make this clear it is necessary to go into some detail.

It has been pointed out above that the number of kinds of Ungulates is one of the characteristics of the Arctogaeic Realm. From this standpoint Madagascar is quite exceptional. Of living Ungulates it possesses only a bush-pig, related to the bush-pigs of Africa, while the hippopotamus occurs in the sub-fossil condition. Both are semi-aquatic in their habits and are believed to represent late immigrants, which reached the island across the Mozambique Channel at a time when it was narrower than at present and probably studded with islands. If this explanation be accepted, we may say that truly terrestrial Ungulates, so extraordinarily abundant in Africa, are absent from Madagascar.

Three placental orders are represented by a number of genera including species of some size, these being the Primates, Carnivores and Insectivores, while there are also seven small, mouse-like Rodents. All four orders show as a common feature the fact that their higher members, well represented on the mainland, are absent from the island. Thus all the Primates of Madagascar belong to the lemur group ; Africa has a few lemurs, but the dominant members of the order there are monkeys and anthropoid apes. All the Carnivores of Madagascar belong to the civet group ; Africa contains a number of civets, but its dominant Carnivores are the true cats (lion, leopard, hunting-leopard, &c.) and dogs (jackals, foxes, hunting dogs, &c.). Except for one small musk-shrew (Crocidura), belonging to a widely distributed Old World genus, found in Africa, Asia and Europe, all the Insectivores of Madagascar belong to a curiously old-fashioned group which, from the nature of the teeth, has been regarded as forming a link between the early fossil marsupials of the northern hemisphere and the placentals. This group includes four families so remarkable both in their distribution and in the varying number of genera and species which they contain as to demand special consideration. The four families are the following :

1. The Centetidae or tenrecs are entirely confined to Madagascar, and include the genus Centetes and five others, some ten species in all being recognized. The most striking, and the largest of all living Insectivores, is the tail-less hedgehog (Centetes) which reaches a length of some 16 inches.

2. The Solenodon shrews (two species) occur only in the West Indian Islands (p. 230).

3. The Cape Golden Moles (genus Chrysochloris) are confined to South Africa, some seven species being recognized.

4. In West Africa occurs a peculiar water-shrew (Potamogale), to which a small mouse-like creature (Geogale), found in Madagascar, seems to be related.

Thus except for its musk-shrew (possibly accidentally introduced), all the Insectivores of Madagascar belong to a very primitive stock, once widely distributed but now represented outside the island only by one genus in the West Indies, one in West Africa and one in the Cape area. The family Centetidae has apparently arisen within the island and never existed outside it ; it is the only family represented by more than one genus. To it belong the larger, more abundant and dominant Insectivores of Madagascar. On the other hand, the West African water-shrew and the Cape Golden Moles form a quite insignificant element among the Insectivores of Ethiopian Africa, which contains in addition hedgehogs, jumping-shrews and true shrews, all clearly of later origin and devoid of the primitive features found in the group to which the Centetidae and their allies belong. This means that Madagascar has served as a refuge for a very early type of Insectivore which has there undergone secondary evolution. Elsewhere that early type only lingers on in three widely separated areas.

All the Rodents of Madagascar, again, belong to peculiar genera and to a somewhat primitive and widely distributed sub-family, represented on the mainland only by a single genus. On the other hand Africa is rich in more specialized Rodents of many kinds.

Bearing in mind what has been just said as to the Insectivores, we may note next the special features of the lemurs. Numerous both as individuals and as kinds, they seem to run steadily into local races so that there is some difference of opinion as to the precise number of species. But it may be said that of some fifty living species of lemurs well over thirty are confined to the island of Madagascar, and these belong to a number of genera. Ethiopian Africa has ten or twelve species belonging to two genera ; the Oriental Region as a whole only three or four belonging to three genera. Thus Madagascar at the present time is the chief home of the lemurs just as it is the chief refuge of primitive Insectivores. Lemurs indeed constitute more than half the terrestrial mammals of the island and include in the Indris the largest living form. The Indris reaches a length of about 2 feet while a much larger extinct form occurs in the sub-fossil state. Since both lemurs and the tenrecs are helpless and primitive animals, the fact that they occur in large forms points to the absence of competitors and the paucity of enemies.

Somewhat comparable conditions are shown by the civets. All the six genera present are endemic, but three show relationship to the African mongooses, while a fourth mongoose-like form is very peculiar and seems to have become specialized for a diet of insects. The fifth genus, represented like the last by a single species, seems to be related to the rasse, an Indian civet. Finally, the most remarkable and largest form falls into the genus Crypto-procta, also with a single species. It is a fierce animal with sharp retractile claws and almost cat-like teeth, and, while most civets are comparatively small animals, here the head and body together reach a length of nearly 3 feet. It is probable that the cat-like features are an instance of parallelism in development and not of direct affinities with the true cats. That is, as the chief predatory animal of the island Cryptoprocta has become specialized for a diet of flesh while elsewhere civets, exposed to the competi-tion of the higher Carnivores, are mixed feeders constrained to depend largely on small birds or mammals, reptiles, insects and so forth.

Thus this detailed survey of the mammals of Madagascar

brings us back, with fuller knowledge, to the conclusions outlined in Chapter XI. During middle Tertiary times both Africa and Madagascar had apparently a somewhat limited and primitive fauna, consisting mainly of lemurs, civets and early Insectivores, such as occurred in Europe and Asia during the early Tertiary period. When the connexion between Africa and Madagascar was broken, probably in Miocene time, that earlier fauna was saved by isolation in Madagascar, and there underwent secondary evolution leading to the development of endemic genera. In Africa, however, few of those earlier forms succeeded in surviving the inrush of more highly organized forms which occurred presumably during late Tertiary and Pleistocene time. Though positive evidence within Ethiopian Africa is lacking, we must suppose that this means that during much of Tertiary time communication between it and the lands to the north of Tethys was difficult, so that Africa tended to have an ' old-fashioned ' fauna as compared with that of Europe and Asia, which was undergoing rapid evolution. With the close of the period communication at once became easier and the approach of glaciation furnished an impulse to southern migration. Thus the present fauna of Ethiopian Africa is similar to that which occurred in the Mediterranean Lands and southern Eurasia during the Pliocene and part of the Pleistocene ; but that of Madagascar recalls the early Tertiary fauna of the northern lands. This means in effect that Ethiopian Africa was late in becoming an integral part of Arctogaea while Madagascar has remained aloof.

Ethiopian Africa. Here the primitive element in the fauna is completely overshadowed by modern types abundantly represented both as species and as individuals, and including all the larger and more powerful mammals. Such of the earlier forms as have been able to survive are arboreal, lingering in the dense forests, or frequenting mountainous country, or have evaded competition in other ways as by burrowing or taking to an aquatic mode of life. While lemurs seem to be relatively numerous, the count of species is increased by what are perhaps not much more than local races of the genus Galago, the members of which are widely spread throughout various types of forest in equatorial Africa with a southern extension along the east coast. The galagos appear to be related to some of the Malagasy lemurs, while the two species of Potto (Perodicticus) found in the West African forests appear to be related to the slow Lorises of the Oriental Region. In this case the discontinuous distribution suggests that the ancestral forms were widespread but that the living forms, extremely sluggish and purely nocturnal, have been able to persist only where dense forest offers a secure refuge, in two separate areas.

Among the primitive members of the Ungulates the members of the genus Hyrax are interesting. In Syria, Palestine, Arabia and the Sinai peninsula, that is, on part of the borderland between the Holarctic and Ethiopian Regions, the Syrian rock-coney occurs. All the other living species are confined to Ethiopian Africa, where they are especially characteristic of Abyssinia and South Africa, except that three species, differing from the others in being arboreal rather than inhabitants of rocky country, occur in equatorial latitudes. The living genus is unknown in the fossil state, but allied forms occur in the Oligocene deposits of the Fayum (p. 226). It may be that the genus Hyrax was evolved in the north and has persisted there continuously in the form of the Syrian rock-coney, while during the later Tertiary some forms migrated into Africa and there gave rise to the African species. That would mean that early Hyrax-like forms died out in Africa. Conversely, the genus may have originated in Africa, in which case the Syrian Hyrax would represent a late immigrant.

Orycteropus, the Aard-Vark, has two living species in Abyssinia and South Africa respectively, and occurs in fossil form in the European Lower Pliocene.

The Old World Edentates are also represented in Ethiopian Africa by the pangolins or scaly ant-eaters, of which there are four Ethiopian species, while three others occur in the Oriental Region. Allied forms occur in the Oligocene and Miocene beds in Europe. The African species are mainly confined to West Africa, the home of so many strange animals, and are either burrowing or partially arboreal.

Rodents of the Porcupine group (Hystricomorpha) have five out of eight families represented in America. Those not represented include the Hystricidae (the Old World Porcupines), the Ctenodactylidae and the Thryonomyidae (Cane-Rats, &c.), which are African forms, related, however, to the South American Octodontidae. What are believed to be fossil allies occur in Oligocene beds in Europe. The Octodont Rodents thus give a hint of a possible former connexion between Africa and South America.

Apart from anomalous and early forms, the mammals of Africa show a close resemblance to those now living in the Oriental Region, many of which occurred also in the eastern Holarctic Region during Pliocene and Pleistocene times. Where differences exist they can be readily explained in one of two ways. First, the Ethiopian Region reaches a greater area and shows a greater variety of habitats, large desert tracts and wide savannas being added to forests of various types. In consequence, many forms which have died out in the Oriental Region have been able to survive and even to become differentiated in various directions. As against this, however, we find that the northern belt, now a singularly arid desert, seems to have acted as more or less of a barrier during the latest period. This means that certain kinds of mammals have failed to effect an entrance into Ethiopian Africa while they form a part of the Indian fauna.

A few examples may be given under both headings. Equatorial Africa has two related anthropoid apes, the gorilla and chimpanzee, both absent from the Oriental Region. The chimpanzee occurs as a fossil in Indian Pliocene beds, but has become extinct there since. Among its monkeys, which are numerous and varied, Africa contains peculiar forms absent from the Oriental Region, though again Pliocene fossils show that the differences are of geologically recent origin. Among its very numerous large Ungulates Africa includes forms like the rhinoceros, which occurs also in India ; and others, like the hippopotamus, the giraffe, okapi and many kinds of antelopes, which are unknown there. Of the giraffe we have spoken above, while the hippopotamus occurs in fossil form in India as well as in Europe. A curious small point about one of the two African species of hippopotamus is that in West Africa there occurs a pygmy form which in captivity, e.g. in the London Zoological Gardens, breeds freely and seems hardier than the common form. It is believed to be very nearly related to a dwarf form found in Pliocene beds in Sicily and Malta. If this is so, it suggests that the dwarfing, apparently in the first instance an adaptation to a limited island habitat, has persisted as a fixed characteristic, despite the long migration southwards to West Africa and despite the great difference in climate.

The African antelopes reflect rather different conditions. They are characteristic especially of the vast savanna lands, and the extent of these, no less than the way in which they extend across the Equator in East Africa, permitting seasonal migration to occur, has made it possible for great secondary evolution to take place within the continent. India, on the other hand, is poor in antelopes, having but three living kinds, apart from the widely distributed gazelles. Though the contrast is again partly blurred when fossil forms are taken into account, there is no doubt that many of the Ethiopian antelopes have originated within the continent and never spread outside it.

Africa has a wild ass of its own in Somaliland and the striped

17

horses elsewhere, while, except that an Asiatic wild ass **extends** into the arid lands of western India, the Oriental Region is now devoid of horses. But fossil forms occur in Pleistocene deposits in central India and Madras, so that the animals were formerly more widely distributed in the Oriental Region. To the west of the Indian desert area the physical conditions are not well suited to horse types, a fact which helps to explain their absence.

Since mention has been already made incidentally of the chief kinds of mammals which have failed to reach Ethiopian Africa across the desert barrier, little more need be said of these. We need only recall that among the most important absentees are the deer, sheep, goats, except for one deer in Abyssinia and another in south-eastern Arabia, bears, the Himalayan panda, tapirs, the tiger among Carnivores, and so on.

THE ORIENTAL REGION

One of the major contrasts between this region and the Ethiopian one is that the former has no precise equivalent of the Malagasy sub-region. That is, there is no appended area with a prolonged history of isolation within which early Tertiary types of mammals have accumulated and undergone secondary evolution, uninfluenced by later migrants. But although the fauna of the nearer Indo-Malay islands includes anthropoid apes, monkeys, higher Ungulates (e.g. oxen) and other elements which prove quite definitely that connexions with the Asiatic mainland must have existed in late-Tertiary and even post-Tertiary times, yet the fauna of these islands is complex. It includes forms absent or but slightly represented in India proper, some of which have allies in the earlier Tertiaries of Europe, while others appear to have originated within the islands.

Thus, on the one hand we have evidence that the islands must have had connexions with each other and with the mainland in later geological time, while on the other the endemic mammals speak to a measure of isolation. Of those endemics some, like the orang of Sumatra and Borneo, are what are called palaeo-endemics or survivors, for the orang seems to have lived in northern India during the Pliocene—that is to say, it has lost ground. Others, like the remarkable aberrant lemur called *Tarsius*, i.e. the Tarsier, confined to certain of the islands, especially Sumatra, Borneo, Celebes and the Philippines, are apparently neo-endemics, or local products of evolution which have originated within the archipelago and never succeeded in extending outside its confines.

The prevalence of endemism in the islands seems to suggest that the connexion with the mainland may have been transitory, union and separation alternating perhaps more than once. But there is another aspect. To some extent the narrow Malay peninsula shares with the islands the feature of containing peculiar mammals absent from the remainder of the Oriental Region. Now both the islands and the peninsula resemble West Africa in that the equatorial climatic type, with its organic response in the hot-wet forest, occurs in its most characteristic form. West Africa, as we have seen, is the home of a number of peculiar mammals, and indeed such areas are well fitted to serve as refuges for relatively helpless creatures unable to face competition in more open country. Whatever measure of physical isolation the Indo-Malay islands may have experienced at different times, then, their climate and vegetation have probably favoured both the persistence of stocks which have died out elsewhere, and the rise of new types too well adapted to the local conditions to find it easy to extend into regions where these are not present in the same accentuated form.

The presence of a number of endemics in the Malay peninsula and the islands is not, however, the only remarkable feature of the Oriental Region. To a considerable extent the great inlet of the Bay of Bengal, penetrating farthest north just where the Himalayan chains begin to change direction, forms a partial dividing line within the Region. That is to say, India proper contains various kinds of animals which are absent from Burma, Farther India, South China and the islands, while the converse is partly true. Of this contrast we can offer a fairly clear explanation.

As has been shown, there is direct fossil evidence that the early Tertiary placental mammals of Europe—and presumably of Asia north of the Tethys—were mainly lemurs, civet-like Carnivores, and very unspecialized kinds of Insectivores. These or their descendants drifted, by what routes we know not, in course of time into the fragments of Gondwanaland represented by Ethiopian Africa and peninsular India. Meantime, evolution went on rapidly to the north of the Tethys, giving rise to the more modern and highly varied types of mammals. Near the end of Tertiary time, communication with these southern lands seems to have become easier, and this, combined with climatic change, led to a great inrush of modern types which largely overwhelmed the earlier fauna in both areas, driving its representatives to seek refuge where they could or wiping them off the face of the earth.

As has been said, we know little of the migration tracks which led into Ethiopian Africa. It is generally held that the main one lay to the east. Some have thought that the pygmy hippopotamus is a descendant of the dwarf form of Sicily and Malta, and this would imply a western route southwards, but this view is said to be improbable. In the case of the Oriental Region we have much more certainty. Here the lofty central Himalayas with the Tibetan plateau behind form a real barrier. But in the north-west the actual mountain wall is lower and less continuous, while the Afro-Asian arid belt is continued into India. By this north-western gate certain of the recently evolved mammals got into India without difficulty. Clearly it would be most likely to be used by forms tolerant of arid conditions or adapted to mountain life. Far to the east again the coastal strip of Asia is now, and has been with various changes throughout a long period of geological time, clothed with forest, while at the same time no imposing transverse mountain barrier exists. Here, therefore, animals adapted to wooded country could spread southwards to ' land's end '.

Thus we have the concept of two streams of specialized mammals moving towards what is now the Oriental Region, one with a general west-to-east direction and the other flowing southwards farther east, the tendency to keep this direction being accentuated by the trend of the mountains of Burma. Burma and India are, however, physically continuous, though the connexion, regarded as a highway, is constricted to a bottle-neck because of the approach of the head of the Bay of Bengal to the Himalayas, which, if the analogy may be pursued, is partially plugged by the forested hill country of Assam with its copious rainfall. The relatively difficult task of negotiating the gap has tended to keep the two streams apart, though it should be noted that normally it was easier for the members of the eastern group, adapted as they were to damp wooded country, to push westwards than for the western forms to extend their range to the east. The latter would indeed tend to turn southwards within India because of the greater suitability of the plateau area.

Thus India proper may be conceived as having two converging streams of immigrants, one coming from the north-west and the other represented by the forms which were able to force an entrance from the north-east. Bearing in mind how the peninsula narrows southwards we could hardly expect that many members of the early Tertiary fauna could survive within it. Farther India in the large sense, that is, the area to the east of the Assam ' neck ', seems to be more favourably placed in this respect, for in the main there was only one stream, few of the western forms being able to pass the gap. But if we think of the members of the earlier fauna being pushed southwards by the incomers into an area of equatorial climate, it is not difficult to see that survival would be possible mainly for such forms as could adapt themselves to the very special conditions by secondary evolution. Even so, their opportunities were limited by the fact that adaptation to equatorial conditions was also taking place among the immigrants. The net result is that the primitive element in the fauna is much less marked in the Oriental Region than in the Ethiopian one. There are much fewer kinds of lemurs, there are no Insectivores allied to the West African water-shrew and the Cape Golden Moles. The fact that lemurs do occur, however, no less than the abundance of members of the civet group, and certain curious features about the Insectivores, is a clear proof that such a primitive element did once exist. We may, therefore, note some points about the lemurs, Insectivores and civets, before passing on to illustrate the statement about the difference between the mammals found east and west of the Assam area.

Among the lemurs two, only, occur in the mainland area, both being lorises. One, and much the larger, is widespread in the eastern area and extends southwards to Sumatra and Borneo ; the other or slender loris is confined to the forests of southern India and Ceylon. The common loris extends, as one would expect, into the Assam area—but no farther—while a variant which is found in Java is sometimes regarded as a distinct species. The only other living Oriental lemur is the Tarsier, of whose history nothing is known, though it presumably originated within the islands from some early lemuroid stock.

The so-called flying-lemurs (Galeopithecus), leaf-eating arboreal mammals with a parachute which enables them to glide from tree to tree, seem to be aberrant Insectivores. Of the two species one is spread throughout the Malay peninsula, Borneo, Sumatra and Java, while the other is confined to the Philippines. Again the history is unknown, but the animals have presumably originated within the islands from some Insectivore stock.

More typical Insectivores are the tree-shrews (Tupaiidae) entirely confined to the Oriental Region, but apparently, like the jumping-shrews of Africa, derived from certain fossil forms found in European Miocene beds. The type genus (Tupaia) is widespread, but endemic species occur in various of the islands, while another genus occurs in Borneo. More interesting is the range of the members of the hedgehog family. In the Oligocene of Europe there occur early hedgehog-like types mingled with more primitive allied forms. The true hedgehogs, perhaps because of their armour of spines and their power of rolling themselves into a ball, have been very successful in keeping their hold.   They are found throughout the Old World part of the Holarctic Region, in Ethiopian Africa and in India.   To the east of the Assam gap, however, they are absent and are represented by spineless, rat-like forms, with long naked tails (genus Gymnura), apparently the descendants of the forms found in the European Oligocene associated with the early hedgehogs.   If these rat-like forms ever existed in India they have disappeared there, but they are spread throughout Burma, the Malay peninsula and the islands of Sumatra, Borneo and Java.   They are unknown elsewhere.

The civets illustrate the same sort of thing, but in less striking fashion.   While the Region as a whole is rich in representatives, the Malay section has peculiar genera of its own, apparently evolved there from early stocks.

As illustrations of the fact that the modern types of mammals in the islands show the same tendency to run into endemic genera or species which we have noted among the lemurs, insectivores and civet-group, we need only mention that Borneo has a peculiar monkey (Nasalis) with a proboscis-like nose, while Celebes (if it be included in the Oriental Region, cf. p. 234) has a number of strange endemics including the pig-like Babirusa, with its huge tusks, and a small kind of ox.   The gibbons (Hylobates), the only other kind of anthropoid ape within the Region apart from the orang, also show curious modifications. Only one species reaches the confines of India and there only in the Assam area, while the largest living species is confined to the island of Sumatra, and Java seems also to have a species of its own.

As contrasted with the anthropoid apes, monkeys of many kinds are widely distributed throughout the whole Oriental Region.   Like the deer, monkeys have been so successful in colonizing the whole Region that they offer no special points of interest in connexion with lines of migration.   It is the forms with a limited range which are of most importance in this connexion.

Particularly interesting are the two great cats, the lion and the tiger, the one a western and the other an eastern immigrant. The lion has now almost disappeared from India save in parts of Kathiawar and Rajputana, but till recently it extended towards Central India, though no farther.   The tiger is widely spread throughout temperate Asia, and extends southwards to Burma, the Malay peninsula, Sumatra and Java.   Further, since the

Assam area forms for it no barrier, it has spread into Bengal and so, perhaps quite recently, southwards through peninsular India. Its absence from Ceylon is part of the evidence that it is a late immigrant into India proper. We must note, however, that the limited range of the lion in the Oriental as compared with the Ethiopian Region, and its replacement throughout most of the former by the tiger, is in part explained by the difference in habits between the two animals ; for the lion in the main haunts open and dry country, while the tiger is a jungle animal. It must, however, be borne in mind that such dominant and specialized forms, endowed with high intelligence, can show much adaptability. It was easy for the tiger to enter the Oriental Region from the Holarctic one by the eastern forested belt, and once there it could extend its range. But the great Afro-Asiatic arid belt formed a barrier to its westward extension, while this, on the contrary, could be easily crossed by the lion. The latter found its way into Ethiopian Africa and there spread widely. The result is that two great Carnivores, one apparently originating in western warm-temperate Eurasia and the other in eastern, are now found especially in two widely separated inter-tropical areas. We cannot doubt that, could it have reached Ethiopian Africa, the tiger would have found perfectly suitable habitats there ; but the arid belt formed a barrier. On the other hand, the lion, once it found its way into Ethiopian Africa in the wake of the great Ungulates, was able to occupy a great variety of habitats. It is by no means confined now to the dry, sandy tracts to which adaptation is suggested by its tawny colouring, so different from the striping of the tiger.

Among other Carnivores whose range makes it clear that they entered from the north-west, mention may be made of the striped hyaena and the Indian wolf. Neither occurs in the lands to the east of the Bay of Bengal.

Some striking examples of contrasts between western and eastern immigrants occur among the Ungulates. Sheep, true goats, and horses, limited to those north-western parts of India where the physical conditions resemble those prevailing in their Holarctic habitats, are clearly mere intruders. Of the antelopes the nilgai is absent from Ceylon and does not extend to eastern Bengal or Assam ; the black-buck reaches Lower Assam but no farther east ; the four-horned antelope has a more restricted range within India. The Indian gazelle, a fourth Oriental antelope, found also in Baluchistan and Persia, is within India limited to the plains of the north-west and centre. Such facts, taken in conjunction with the range of antelopes elsewhere, leave no doubt that they are western immigrants for which the Assam ' neck ' has formed an insuperable barrier.   Conversely, certain Ungulates called serows, believed to link the antelopes with the goats, seem to be eastern forms and have but a limited extension to the west.   One Himalayan species does range as far west as Kashmir ; but, of the remaining three, one extends from the eastern Himalayas to Burma, Siam, the Malay peninsula and Sumatra.   Another occurs in Formosa and still another in Japan. The Malayan tapir, restricted to the Malay peninsula, Sumatra and Borneo, affords a further example of the group of eastern immigrants.   The rhinoceroses fall into the same group but have a wider range and reach north-eastern India.

It should be clear from this description that the Oriental and Ethiopian Regions form an interesting contrast.   In both, an earlier fauna was replaced by one coming from the north ; but because of their respective geographical relations to the northern lands, the immigrants were not identical in the two cases, and their subsequent history has followed somewhat different lines, the Oriental Region having lost many forms which the Ethiopian one has kept.   The student of human geography will not fail to note that there are some curious analogies between the history of the higher animals and of man in the two areas.

PART IV

FACTORS OF PLANT GEOGRAPHY

CHAPTER XIV

DISTRIBUTION OF HIGHER LAND PLANTS

GENERAL FEATURES OF FLORAL REGIONS

OUR somewhat detailed study of the mammalian faunas of the Zoogeographical Regions has shown that in each Region the fauna has a certain unity of its own ; and this despite the minor differences between the parts, such as the eastern and western sections of the wide Holarctic Region. There are also certain general resemblances between widely separated Regions, e.g. the Ethiopian and the Oriental. We have seen, further, that differences or resemblances between the Regions or their parts can be explained in terms of hypotheses concerning past relations of the land-masses combined with facts of migration and extinction or survival. It has been made abundantly clear that the great migratory movements have been from the wide land-masses of the northern hemisphere towards the narrower and discontinuous southern ones, and that extinction of early stocks has been most marked in the Holarctic Region, while the survival of members of these is especially characteristic of some of the southern lands.

In the main, and allowing for the great differences in the available means of dispersal and for the much less complete fossil evidence, the past and present distribution of the higher plants confirms the conclusions derived from the study of mammals. Sometimes the correspondence is curiously exact. For example, it was shown that all the mammalian evidence goes to prove that South America was separated from North America during much of Tertiary time, and had then a very peculiar fauna of its own. But after the isthmian connexion made southward migration possible, some northern forms, e.g. the panther, took advantage of the line of migration afforded by the Andes to penetrate the whole length of the southern continent. The range of the genus Ribes (gooseberry) affords us an almost parallel phenomenon among plants. Its members are North Temperate, being especially abundant in North America, but they extend also along the line of the Andes into South America. Here they are clearly recent immigrants, while no similar extension into the southern hemisphere occurs elsewhere.

Other illustrations could be given, but the point is simply that the general correspondence between the facts brought out by a study of the geographical distribution of mammals and a similar study of the higher plants is sufficient to make it unnecessary to discuss in detail the floras of the Phytogeographical Regions named on p. 215. We may limit ourselves, therefore, to discussing some cases where the plant evidence is either fuller or illustrates points not brought out so clearly by the animals. Because the range of plants is so much more definitely controlled by the physical habitat factors than is that of mammals, the influence of the late-Tertiary and post-Tertiary variations in climate is more readily traced with them. So far we have largely taken it for granted that the advance and retreat of the continental ice sheets was one of the major causes of those great changes in the recent distribution of mammals of which there is such abundant evidence. Some notes on the plants of the wide Holarctic Region will help to make clear how great have been the changes in the flora there since Tertiary time, and those changes in their turn must have exerted great influence on the mammals.

THE HOLARCTIC REGION IN TERTIARY AND POST-TERTIARY TIMES

There is much evidence to show that during Tertiary time forest was at once more widely distributed and more uniform in character in what is now the Holarctic Phytogeographical Region than it is at present. Individual genera of woody plants, many of which to-day have a restricted range, occur as fossils in a number of different areas in a fashion which suggests a wide distribution then. Some of these areas now lie outside the tree limit in the Arctic region. In other cases, as notably in southern England and parts of continental Europe, we find that trees occur in the fossil state which are entirely absent as native living plants, though many will thrive when introduced. In certain fossil-bearing beds in Greenland assigned to the Miocene period we also find a remarkable mixture of forms at present characteristic of different types of forest. Thus laurels and magnolias, now characteristic of the east coast mesophytic forest, are mingled with tropophytic trees like ash and beech and with certain types of conifers which are now highly localized and seem to demand very special habitat conditions. While we must not assume that the Tertiary representatives of such genera necessarily required the same kind of climate and soil as the living species, yet it does seem that the widespread Tertiary northern forest did not display that definite division into coniferous, tropophytic, sclerophyllous and mesophytic belts which is so obvious at present. Further, its extension into what are now Arctic latitudes suggests not only that there was an undifferentiated forest type, but that such communities as Arctic pastures, tundra and probably temperate grasslands did not occur in their present form. There is, that is to say, little evidence that the existing zoning of vegetation prevailed during certain parts of Tertiary time.

Without attempting to discuss the general features of that Tertiary Holarctic forest, we may select the Magnolia family and certain of the gymnosperms for special treatment. From their past and present range we can deduce certain facts of interest in regard to the influence of the post-Tertiary climatic changes.

The Magnolia family includes only woody plants, trees or shrubs, which form ' probably the most ancient types of existing Dicotyledons ' (Hutchinson). In Tertiary times they were undoubtedly widely distributed in the northern hemisphere, occurring in Europe, including England, as well as in Greenland and Spitsbergen. The existing genera and species, not very numerous, are mainly North Temperate but have a remarkable distribution in detail (Fig. 39). They are entirely absent from Europe, the Mediterranean Lands and Africa, occur in Asia only in the eastern and south-eastern area and have a limited range in North America. They are especially characteristic of the mesophytic (laurel) forest of eastern North America, which reaches its northern limit along the Canadian shore of Lake Erie, say about lat. 43° N., and of the similar forest in eastern Asia, which has northern outliers in the Korean peninsula and the Japanese islands in similar latitudes. On the other hand, the southern limit of the family transgresses notably the limits of this forest type. In eastern Asia its members extend into the Indo-Malay islands (Philippines, Borneo, Celebes, Sumatra, Java, &c.), and within India and Farther India have that sporadic and discontinuous range which we have already noted as characteristic of many of the mammals there. In the New World a similar discontinuous distribution is discernible outside the area occupied by the mesophytic forest. Thus Magnolias extend throughout Florida and reach Haiti but not Cuba. They are found in parts of Texas and on the Mexican plateau and reappear in southeastern Brazil in the neighbourhood of Rio de Janeiro.

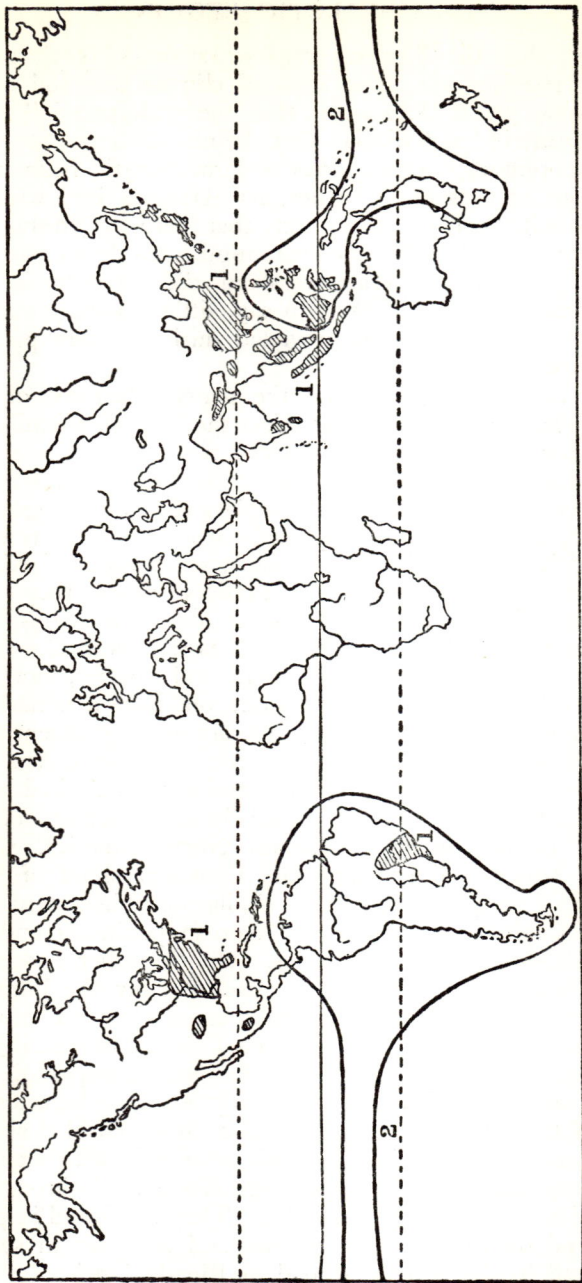

FIG. 39.—Distribution of (1) Magnoliaceae, (2) Drimys (Winteraceae)

After Hutchinson

But while they thus extend into inter-tropical and even (Indo-Malay islands) equatorial latitudes, the type of climate to which they are especially adapted is one of summer rain and warmth, many being quite tolerant of low winter temperatures. Both deciduous and evergreen forms occur, the latter being less resistant to low temperatures than the former. Their southern extension would appear to be limited less by climate than by the competition of the nearly related but slightly more specialized family Winteraceae, the range of which overlaps that of the Magnolias in south-eastern Asia and Florida, though its members are mainly intertropical. Fig. 39 shows the range of the genus Drimys, and its southern extension in both the Old and New Worlds will be noticed. Like the Magnolias the Winteraceae are entirely absent from Africa, a fact suggestive of their probable relation to the former family.

The present restricted range of the Magnolias within the Holarctic area (which, it will be recollected, includes the Sonoran Zoological Region), as compared with their former wide one, is fairly easily explained. In eastern Asia lines of southern ' retreat ' were open to them as the climate grew colder in the Pleistocene Age or before, the Malay Peninsula and islands being particularly important. Much the same statement can be made of eastern North America where the Bahamas form a link between Florida and Haiti, while the latter (cf. p. 269) may have been further linked to South and to Central America. On the other hand, the combination of the Alpine chains and the Mediterranean Sea prevented a similar southern retreat in Europe, and there the family died out in post-Tertiary times. As the climate improved after the final retreat of the ice, we must suppose that the Magnolias, less fitted to hold their own in inter-tropical latitudes than their allies the Winteraceae, readvanced towards the north. They have, however, proved unable to reoccupy all their former territory, notably in Europe and in the lands which are now Arctic. But there is an important difference between these two areas. The present climate excludes absolutely from Greenland or Spitsbergen any living member of the family, but Magnolias are among the most prized ornamental trees and shrubs throughout much of Europe and the Mediterranean Lands. The North American tulip-tree (Liriodendron) grows to fine proportions in parts of Scotland, and generally we may say that under cultivation a number of Magnolias thrive, flower and fruit in latitudes considerably north of their range in temperate Asia and North America. Their absence as wild plants must therefore be regarded not as a direct effect of the existing climate, but as a result of the fact that they found no place of refuge in Europe or its borders during the maximum glaciation and have not been able to return of themselves to the area since.

It is not quite such a simple matter to explain the present range in North America.   There, roughly west of a line drawn from Chicago through the lower Mississippi, Magnolias occur only in the two isolated areas named above (Fig. 39).   It is not clear why these two areas should not coalesce with each other and with the southern part of the eastern belt.   Doubtless local soil and climatic factors do exert an influence, but it seems as if there must be something else.   It is usually assumed that the element of competition comes into play and that the Magnolias are less fitted to the sum-total of the conditions than are some other kinds of plants.   They can keep their hold only where specially favourable habitats are present, and are unable to spread beyond.

Thus, so far as the Magnolia family is concerned, we find that its wide distribution in Tertiary times in the northern hemisphere has been replaced by a much more localized one at present. In some cases it would seem that the areas once occupied have changed so completely as to inhibit re-colonization not only by Magnolias but by trees of any kind ; in other cases, as in Europe, the absence of the family is apparently due to the historical accident that they were exterminated within the area and have found no migration track by which they could get back ; more puzzling is their absence from areas to which neither of these explanations seems to apply.   There we are forced to believe that recent and modern competition is different from that of Tertiary times, forms better adapted to present conditions being able to hold the Magnolias in check.

Some very striking contrasts between the range of particular genera in Tertiary times as compared with that of the present day occur also among the conifers.   Looking at the Holarctic Region as a whole we find that certain forms, such as larches (*Larix*), spruces (*Picea*), firs (*Abies*), pines (*Pinus*), and so on, are widespread throughout and occur near the tree limit both in altitude and latitude.   Although it cannot be said that particular species show the circumpolar range which is so marked among some of the northern mammals, yet the coniferous forest belt has a generally similar aspect in Europe, Asia and North America. As against such widely ranging genera we find in the lower latitudes in eastern Asia and in both eastern and western North America endemic types whose few living species are often sharply localized.   These endemics have always aroused great interest.

Quite often they display marked peculiarities of leaf-form or mode of growth which make them appear exceptional even to those with little knowledge of systematic botany. There is, however, more than this, for palaeontological observations which prove that they were once widely distributed are of long standing and thus their present limited range constitutes a challenge which can hardly be ignored.

Of various possible examples we select three, the genera Taxodium, Glyptostrobus and Sequoia. They occur together in the Greenland Miocene beds already mentioned and are also present in Tertiary deposits in many other parts of the northern hemisphere. To-day there are but two living species of Taxodium, one being the swamp cypress of the southern United States, while the other is found in Mexico. Both of the two living species of Glyptostrobus occur in China, while the geographer hardly needs to be told that the two living species of Sequoia are Californian, the big tree (*S. gigantea*) being found in the Sierra Nevada and the redwood (*S. sempervirens*) in parts of the coastal belt. It is customary to use the range of the two species as a means of emphasizing local differences of climate and especially fog penetration in California. This makes it all the more remarkable that the Sequoias, more familiar to tree-lovers under their old name of Wellingtonia, grow without difficulty in the British Isles, where they are common ornaments of parks and pleasure grounds. In this case, as with the Magnolias, the gardener has little difficulty in reconstructing at least in part the earlier Tertiary forest in our islands, but he has to go far afield to find its surviving elements.

The evidence available is not sufficient to tell us whether the three genera have been continuously present since Tertiary times in the areas where they now live, or whether they have reached these by a migration process. It is noteworthy, however, that Sequoia occurs fossil in beds of reputed Miocene Age in California, as well as farther inland in Colorado and also in the north in Alaska. This suggests the possibility of a gradual contraction, both from north to south and from east to west, of a former wide range in western North America. But since the genus also occurred in Tertiary times in Siberia and Manchuria, it is not clear why it should have disappeared in Asia while Glyptostrobus, with which it is associated in Greenland, has survived in China. The disappearance of all three genera from Europe is paralleled by that of the Magnolias and many other forms, but it is puzzling why Taxodium should linger in southern North America and nowhere else.

18

Behind all such difficulties of detail, however, certain broad facts stand out. These localized coniferous endemics, now confined to areas of warm temperate or sub-tropical climate, represent early types which seem to have been caught as it were between two difficulties, when the warm and apparently fairly uniform climate of earlier Tertiary time gave place gradually to the colder, more varied and fluctuating conditions which prevailed with the rise of the Tertiary mountain chains and the onset and passing of the Ice Age. On the one hand, certain kinds of conifers became adapted to unfavourable soil and climatic conditions and were able to colonize vast tracts, whether in the northern lowlands or on the mountains. On the other, some kinds of dicotyledonous trees and both dicotyledonous and monocotyledonous herbs likewise adjusted themselves to the new conditions, and, while unable to compete effectively with the hardier conifers on the terrain occupied by these, spread widely and formed new types of communities elsewhere. The more conservative Tertiary coniferous genera found little opportunity in this changed world and have been able to persist only in certain isolated areas where specially favourable habitat factors enable them to withstand the double pressure.

How intense that pressure has been is illustrated by the history of the much more old-fashioned and earlier genus Gingko (p. 35), also present in the Greenland Miocene beds. It once had a similarly wide range, but was able to linger on only in China, where it appears to have died out as a wild plant but was preserved for posterity by the pious care of early Chinese gardeners who appreciated its decorative qualities.

Europe, still more than eastern Asia and both eastern and western North America, has lost many types of trees which it once possessed. At the same time, there is nothing in the present climate of the west-centre and south to inhibit the growth of many forms which linger on elsewhere in the warmer areas of the northern hemisphere. One result has been a multitude of introductions, especially from eastern Asia and eastern North America. Such forms as species of Catalpa, Paulownia, Gleditschia, Robinia (false acacia), Ailanthus (tree of heaven), Sophora, and so on, are familiar by sight, if not always by name, to those who have visited Europe's beauty spots. There is, however, another point of some interest. Southern (i.e. Mediterranean) Europe does contain a few native trees which to the northerner, accustomed to the endless repetition of oak, ash, beech, maple, lime and so forth, strike an alien note. It is generally true that these belong to genera represented also, usually by a number of species, in both eastern Asia and North America. Thus the beautiful Judas tree (p. 212) belongs to a genus (Cercis) three other species of which occur in North America with others in Asia. Similarly, the nettle tree, so abundant in Provence, is the only representative in Europe of the genus Celtis, which is numerously represented in the northern hemisphere outside Europe. Both the nettle tree and the Judas tree, however, owe their present range in southern Europe largely to man's influence, for he has planted them extensively and they have spread in what is called sub-spontaneous fashion.

The floras of Ireland and the west of the Iberian peninsula have common features which illustrate other points, and these have been discussed in another connexion in Part I, Chapter V.

THE MEDITERRANEAN FLORAL REGION

So far we have spoken of Europe as a whole, but it was shown in Chapter X that the botanists, as contrasted with the zoologists, recognize a separate Mediterranean Floral Region (Fig. 33). This is characterized by the enormous number of endemics, some hundreds of endemic genera and thousands of endemic species being present within the wide belt included. These endemics are undoubtedly of very varied origin. Some are the modified descendants of Tertiary types which have been able to maintain themselves *in situ* throughout the series of climatic changes which must have occurred in the area during late Tertiary and post-Tertiary times. Others, again, are the modified descendants of boreal forms pushed southwards as land ice invaded the northern part of the continent. But, while the Scandinavian geologists have been able to work out with some measure of certainty the climatic changes which followed the final retreat of the ice in north-central and Alpine Europe, we know as yet little of the sequence of events near the Mediterranean Sea. It seems certain, however, that throughout the whole of Quaternary time the climate, at least in the Balkan peninsula, was such as to permit some members of the earlier flora to persist, either unmodified or with but minor modifications. An interesting example is the conifer *Picea omorica*, which seems to have been fairly widespread in Europe before the onset of glaciation but is now limited to a few stations within the Balkan peninsula. But of the endemics of the Mediterranean Region comparatively few are forest trees. The reason seems to be twofold. In the first place, as has already been emphasized, the losses in tree genera, owing to the limited possibilities of a southward retreat, were very heavy.   But such facts as that *Picea omorica* has never been able to reoccupy the ground lost during the Pleistocene, and that genera like Celtis and Cercis are represented each by only a single species, suggest that the present climatic conditions over much of the area are relatively unsuited to tree growth. The majority of the endemics are either shrubs or undershrubs adapted to withstand the accentuated summer drought and bright sunshine, or herbs which are able in one way or another to evade this combination of difficult conditions.   Another remarkable feature is that while some of the endemics have a very wide range, and this despite the notable differences in the climates of the parts of the Region, others show intense localization.   We may take an example of the latter group which offers several points of interest.

All rock gardens of any pretensions include a small plant called *Ramondia pyrenaica*.   This consists of a flattened rosette of hairy crumpled leaves from which rise flower-stalks bearing purplish flowers curiously exotic in aspect.   The plant belongs to the order Gesneriaceae, most of the members of which are tropical. A familiar example is the large-flowered Gloxinia of our hothouses. The Pyrenean Ramondia is rigidly confined to the Central Pyrenees, but other species of Ramondia, and also the closely allied genus Haberlea, occur in the Balkan peninsula (Bulgaria and Greece).   Outside these two areas both genera are unknown, and, further, no species of Ramondia has been found between the two areas named.   The nearest allies of Ramondia are found in China and Japan, and in lower Pliocene beds in southern Europe there have been found fossils believed to link, both in morphology and in distribution, the genera Ramondia and Haberlea with these Asiatic forms.   The ancestors of the living European forms thus probably constituted an element in the widespread Tertiary forest.   As the conditions which favoured the existence of that forest changed with the onset of the northern glaciation, those ancestral forms presumably underwent evolution along lines which enabled some descendants to withstand the whole series of climatic variations between the Pliocene and the present.

The next point is to note the special features of *Ramondia pyrenaica* which limit its present-day range.   It occurs only in rock crevices of vertical cliffs facing north.   Such cliffs if well fissured may appear to be clothed with plants from base to summit ; but immediately one passes to a similar cliff exposed to direct sunlight the plants disappear.   Under cultivation it is found that, unless a nearly vertical position is given, moisture lodges in the crown and kills the plant. Shelter from direct sunlight is also desirable, though not so necessary in higher latitudes as in the native habitat. The Balkan forms show similar features, if not quite so accentuated.

It would seem, then, that the living Ramondias were differentiated in response to a climate which was not identical with that now characteristic of the Mediterranean Region. We can hardly explain their intolerance of direct sunlight except on the hypothesis that when they arose the skies were cloudier than at present, while their reaction to stagnating moisture suggests that precipitation took the form of mists and light rains rather than of heavy showers. If such a climate prevailed beyond the limit of glaciation during part of Quaternary time, we can suppose that the Ramondias ranged then throughout much of Mediterranean Europe. Their present discontinuous distribution and limitation in the west to a very restricted area would presumably be the result of changes of climate following the final retreat of the northern ice sheet.

There is some other if not very definite evidence derived from plant distribution to show that during Quaternary time considerable climatic variation occurred within the Mediterranean area. Thus, as we shall show in speaking of the British flora, not a few ' Mediterranean ' plants extend northwards through western Europe, especially along Atlantic-facing coasts. At present the climate on these resembles the Mediterranean one in that the winters are mild and wet, but differs notably in the diminished summer sunshine and much greater summer precipitation. While it is true that many of these northward-ranging forms have their chief centre in the north-western and western Iberian peninsula, where the summers are damper and cloudier than elsewhere, this is not invariably the case. The northward spread shows that dry, sunny summers are not essential to permit the plants to thrive and multiply, and this suggests that they became differentiated before the climate took on its present features. On the other hand, there is a good deal of evidence that forms which do require summer heat and drought have spread from the south-east to the west, which suggests that ' Mediterranean ' conditions developed progressively in this direction. Generally, despite the fact that the area which constitutes the Mediterranean Floral Region was outside the limits of the Pleistocene glaciation in the strict sense, it is clear that it was influenced by progressive climatic changes during the period, and these in their turn affected both the evolution of the endemic forms and their range at the present time.

FLORA OF THE BRITISH ISLES

Our island environment affords an excellent opportunity of studying the flora of a small tract of land forming a definite entity and yet representative of a much larger area.   Floristically the British Isles fall into the Holarctic Region, and all the orders and genera present have a wide distribution in temperate latitudes in the northern hemisphere.   But the range in latitude is considerable, and there is a notable diversity as regards both climate and relief.   The members of the flora also are far from being uniformly distributed throughout.   Further, there is clear evidence that the complete separation of the British area from the adjacent continent occurred, geologically speaking, at a very recent date, so that there has been little opportunity for local differentiation to take place.   It is perfectly true that the botanists, no less than the zoologists, recognize a certain number of British endemic species.   So far as the plants are concerned, however, these are mainly what are called minor endemics, that is, forms which differ only in minor points from related species elsewhere, and their numbers are not in any case large.   As regards the vast majority of British species we can name areas outside the islands in which they are also found, these being usually in some region of the continent of Europe, though, in a number of cases, the range is even wider, including parts of Asia and even North America.   At the same time, and this despite the relative poverty of our flora, there is a marked absence in it of uniformity.

This want of uniformity has two aspects.   If we limit ourselves to direct observation within the islands we find that, whether we travel from east to west or from north to south, careful scrutiny shows minor differences in the plants present, so that those which are common in one area are absent from another.   In a sense, of course, that is to be expected in any part of the earth's surface, in view of the extreme sensitiveness to the habitat factors shown by all plants—we do not expect to find mountain plants in the lowland areas, or conversely.   But the differences in Britain from place to place are not all so simply explained. Some of the mountainous areas possess in abundance plants absent from other hilly areas of similar height ; some of the mountain plants of Highland Scotland reappear in the lowlands of Ireland, and so forth.   That is to say, there are traces of an intense localization of certain kinds of plants which it is not easy to explain wholly in terms of differences in the existing habitat factors.   Clearly, the presence of a wild plant in any particular area is a proof that the conditions there are suitable ; but a definite problem arises when we find that it is absent from other areas where, so far as we can see, the conditions are quite as suitable and where it can be ' naturalized ' without difficulty.

Again, these localized British plants can be studied in another way by considering their range outside the British area. Most of our plants are present on the adjacent shores of the continent, where they are mingled with others alien to our islands. But parts of England, Scotland and Ireland contain plants which are absent from the nearer parts of the continent yet reappear in more remote areas, notably Scandinavia, the Alps, the Mediterranean Lands and even, in a few cases, in North America. Thus a number of questions at once arise. How did such plants reach their British stations ? What enables them to survive there ? Why are they unable to spread ? In the long run, all such questions resolve themselves into the major problem of the reasons why the flora of the British Isles has certain special features which suggest that it has had a complex history.

Before going further, let us take a few examples of these exceptional plants. In Wales a small ally of the stonecrops with remarkable shield-shaped leaves and greenish flowers, the pennywort (*Cotyledon umbilicus*), is extraordinarily abundant, being found in almost every old wall. It is as prolific in the Isle of Man and, in a somewhat luxuriant form, is present in the islands of the Clyde estuary, where it finds the joints of the volcanic rocks a favourable habitat. But although the Firth of Forth has similar volcanic islands and though the distance between Clyde and Forth is so short, pennywort is absent from the entire area. Outside western Britain, the plant extends southwards along the coasts of western Europe to the dry Canary Islands and eastwards throughout the greater part of the Mediterranean area, mainly as a littoral plant, the shape of the leaves enabling it to grow on vertical surfaces.

Again, Arbutus, found growing wild only in Killarney and at Glengariff on Bantry Bay, is a plant characteristic of southern Europe, especially the Mediterranean coasts, but it occurs also as far north as Brittany. *Actaea spicata* (the baneberry or Herb Christopher), though widely distributed in Continental Europe, Asia and North America, grows in the British Isles only in a small area in north-east England. A few plants also are very remarkable in that they occur in North America and in western Britain, but not elsewhere on this side of the Atlantic. Examples are the blue-eyed grass (*Sisyrinchium angustifolium*) found in Kerry and Galway, and *Eriocaulon septangulare*, a jointed rush, which grows in lakes in Skye and a few Hebridean islands and

also on the west coast of Ireland.   Similar examples have already
been discussed in another connexion in Part I, Chapter V.

Other curious examples of localization of species will be given
later in the chapter, but meantime it is necessary to take a more
general survey.   It must be noted first that the phanerogams of
the British Isles show two outstanding features, of which the
first is poverty of species as compared with adjacent parts of the
continent.   Thus there is no native larch or spruce, and great
numbers of the common herbs of France are absent here.   Such
poverty is a usual feature of island areas and is accentuated here
by Pleistocene glaciations.   This must have led to the extermination within the area of large numbers of pre-glacial species—
some, indeed, believe that all or almost all of these disappeared
and that the existing flora is the result of post-glacial immigration.
If so, more than one explanation might be offered of the nature
of the existing flora.   The absence of many species common on
the continent may be due either to difficulties of migration (e.g.
across the enlarged Rhine believed to have occupied part of
what is now the North Sea), or to the fact that the habitat proved
unfavourable to some continental species ;   for instance, the
introduced European larch is here particularly liable to canker.

The second characteristic of the British Flora is that it includes
diverse elements of highly localized distribution.   If the greater
number of British plants advanced across the Narrow Seas
after the passing of the ice, pushing on till habitat factors checked
their migration, then we should expect a richer flora in the south-
east and increasing poverty of species towards the north and west.
There is, in fact, some evidence of this ;   for instance, though
oaks are found at least as far north as central Scotland, it is
chiefly in southern England that they set abundant fertile seed
year by year, this being rare to the north, where climatic factors
apparently put a limit to the spread of the tree.

On the other hand, in spite of the poverty of the flora towards
the north and west, these areas contain plants absent not only
in the south and east but also on the nearest part of the continent,
and this seems difficult to explain.   Those who believe that the
flora is mainly of post-glacial origin assume changes of climate
during the period of migration.   Thus, as the ice retreated and
conditions became more favourable, a flora of Arctic or northern
type invaded Britain and was at one time widespread.   As the
climate improved other immigrants, adapted to warmer conditions,
came in and drove the first immigrants to the higher and more
remote regions, just as is supposed to have happened in the case
of human invaders.   But this theory does not explain the presence

in Ireland of plants of ' Mediterranean ' or southern type (in many cases altogether absent from England), in addition to those of the Arctic or northern. Why, for instance, is arbutus absent from Cornwall where, as well as elsewhere in southern England, it grows and seeds freely when planted ? Explanations suggested are that such plants entered the country during a brief period of warmer climate or (assuming that many pre-glacial forms survived the Ice Age) that the rarer and highly localized members of the flora were saved in particular areas in spite of glaciation not far away owing to special habitat conditions, but in some places have been unable to withstand the competition of post-glacial immigrants (see also Part I, Chapter V).

Leaving these interesting if apparently insoluble problems, let us now consider some points about the main features of the country as regards climatic, edaphic and physiographic factors. In the first place it is to be noted that the area as a whole is one of temperate climate and lies on the western margin of the continent of Europe. We should, therefore, expect the flora to show a general resemblance to that of the great continental masses in similar latitudes. Again, the Lowlands lie mainly to the south-east, a region of younger rocks and moderate relief and one which was in parts (especially south of the Thames–Severn line) outside the glaciated area. Eastern England, however, has some ' continental ' features in climate ; there is low relief and the rocks are largely Tertiary and post-Tertiary, producing loose soils. In the south-western area, on the other hand, there is an accentuated ' Atlantic ' type of climate, the relief is varied and the rocks are old. In the north and west, especially of Great Britain, there are upland areas with older rocks and marked relief, and the climate is modified by elevation. In Scotland and also, though less notably, in north England and in Wales, there is an area of elevation sufficient to ensure an approach to ' Arctic ' conditions, since there is a heavy winter snowfall persisting sometimes for weeks or months.

These different types of habitat have fairly well-defined floras, and the botanist Watson, about a hundred years ago, attempted to make a classification of these on a distributional basis. It is, however, difficult to get suitable terminology without begging the question of the origin of the different elements. Watson described as

(a) *British* plants widely distributed throughout Great Britain and in other lands. For instance, bracken, which is cosmopolitan ; goldenrod, which occurs also in continental Europe, Asia and North America ; and the ox-eye (or dog) daisy, which is found both in Europe and in Asia. Obviously these examples throw no light on the problem of the origin of our flora.

(*b*) He called those plants *English* which are common in the English lowlands and decrease to the north. Examples (all found also in Europe generally) are the following : the arum (lords and ladies), which is abundant in southern England, rare in northern and doubtfully native in Scotland ; the fetid iris, which is absent in Scotland and Ireland but abundant in southern England, though rare in northern ; and the lily of the valley, which is locally abundant in England but not found in Scotland or Ireland.

(*c*) The name *Scottish* he gave to plants rare or absent in England, such as the Scots pine and juniper, the bearberry or Arctostaphylos (found also in northern England and in Ireland) and the cloudberry (found also in northern England and in Wales, rare in Ireland, but extremely abundant in Norway).

(*d*) Examples of *Highland* or *Mountain* plants are : *Saxifraga oppositifolia*, quite common on the higher Scottish mountains, but somewhat rare in northern England, Wales and on the higher Irish mountains, and the reticulate willow, which is confined to the higher Scottish mountains.

(*e*) *Germanic* plants, according to this classification, are eastern forms diminishing towards both the north and the west ; they are often halophytes (salt-loving) or steppe plants. The two following are examples : *Frankenia laevis* or sea-heath, here found only on the coast from Yarmouth to Kent but widely spread on the coasts of Eurasia ; *Artemisia campestris*, here occurring only on the coasts of Norfolk and Suffolk, but widely spread in the dry, sandy wastes of Eurasia.

(*f*) An example of the *Atlantic* or *Western* type is *Cotyledon umbilicus* already mentioned (p. 279).

(*g*) Finally, there are *Local* forms with no obvious habitat factor, such as Arbutus (p. 91) and Herb Christopher (p. 279). Another example is *Saxifraga umbrosa*, a wild form of ' London Pride ', found in western and south-western Ireland and also in Portugal, western Spain and the higher Pyrenees (p. 91).

This scheme of classification, despite its detail, is in many ways unsatisfactory. Thus the (*c*) *Scottish* and (*d*) *Highland* plants are closely related, differing mainly in the fact that the latter occur as a rule at greater elevations. Yet the Arctic *Dryas octopetala*, a mountain plant in most of Scotland, comes down practically to sea-level in the extreme west and is ' lowland ', or partially so, in Ireland. The last group (*g*) *Local*, includes plants of very different types, while the distinction between

(b) *English* and (e) *Germanic* seems largely one of habitat, members of the latter group being found mostly on dry sandy soils or near the coast.

In most general discussions of the British Flora three main sets of elements are recognized :

1. Widespread species, represented in central Europe but often with a much wider range, extending to Temperate Asia and North America.   These throw little light on the origin of our flora and are probably to a large extent post-glacial immigrants, though some may have survived the glacial period in southern England or locally elsewhere.

2. Western or Atlantic or Hiberno-Lusitanian species (Lusitania being the old Roman province which included Portugal and part of western Spain, that is, the part of the peninsula which has a more or less ' Atlantic ' type of climate).   Some believe that south-western Ireland formerly extended farther into the Atlantic, in an area since submerged, and that in such an extension beyond the limits of the ice this western element may have survived the period of maximum glaciation.   In any case, moistness and mild winters seem to be important habitat factors (see p. 89).

3. Arcto-alpine plants, mostly common to the Alps and the northern area but with affinities that appear to be definitely northern.   Perhaps some of these plants were present in the country before the Ice Age and survived it.   It is noteworthy that an area round the upper valleys of the Tees, Tyne and Wear is believed to have remained ice-free, and that Upper Teesdale in particular is remarkable for a number of rare species growing together, including *Gentiana verna*, only found here in England, though it also occurs in western Ireland.   Possibly some migration may have taken place during the glacial period across the North Sea, for the presence of mammoth bones over the Dogger Bank suggests that there may have been a land bridge.

4. Finally, there are American forms, interesting because they seem to suggest the Wegener hypothesis of the drift of Europe and North America away from one another or perhaps an early migration via south Greenland and Iceland when the region of the Wyville-Thomson ridge still included much more land surface than it does now.   In this connexion it is worth noting that both European and American eels spawn in the same area near the Bermudas, a fact which suggests that the Atlantic Ocean has widened since the migratory habit was established among them.

ECOLOGICAL ASPECTS OF BRITISH FLORA

When we turn from the study of the actual composition of the British Flora to its ecological aspects, two facts at once emerge. The first is that, as one would expect in view of the small size of the islands, climatic changes, dense population and the prolonged period during which they have been peopled, plant associations have been deeply altered. Speaking broadly, the nature and number of these is a matter of deduction only, based upon comparison with less modified areas, and upon the persistence of minor members of associations in areas where the dominants have disappeared. Nor is the investigation of climax communities purely a matter of scientific discussion, for, especially in Scotland, it has been complicated by political and even religious feeling. Thus many maintain that the dry and wet moors so widely spread in Scotland are not throughout climax communities at all, but successional series created and maintained by those whose interests lead them to prefer that the land should be left to game animals rather than that it should support a settled population dependent on pastoral industries with some agriculture. Again, Catholic landowners, desirous of obtaining Government aid for re-afforestation and maintaining that many of the drier heaths could be made to carry forest, have been accused by ardent Protestants of being influenced by the desire to keep Catholic tenants settled on the land.

Secondly, just because the climax communities have been so largely destroyed, British ecological botanists have tended to lay great, perhaps excessive, stress on successional series (seres). Since these occupy sites, for instance, on the sea coast or around inland lakes, of little direct use to man, at least in the earlier stages of their development, the natural conditions can be studied with a wealth of detail and a certainty of inference not possible in lands constantly subject to man's influence. Thus sand-dunes, shingle beaches, fens and so forth, have been the object of far more elaborate investigations than is possible in the case of our scanty remnants of original forests, although this latter study has progressed greatly in the last decade. Contrast, for instance, the comparative difficulty of access to Scottish moors with the ease of access in the case of maritime communities, which is associated with the further fact that coastal areas offer opportunities for intensive study of natural flora.

ASSOCIATIONS

Three main associations can be recognized, apart from minor ones.

I. The Tropophytic or Summer Deciduous Forest. Owing to the latitude, the low grounds of England and Wales, together with the limited lowlands of the southern part of Scotland and large parts of Ireland, fall within the Tropophytic Forest Belt of the northern hemisphere. It is to be noted, however, that Scotland and Ireland at least are so near the limit of this great community that comparatively small elevations above sea-level exclude its characteristic members, and edaphic factors are of vital significance. It has to be remembered that our conception of winter temperatures here is apt to be obscured by the constant use of sea-level readings. The higher hills of Scotland, though never, technically speaking, rising to the snowline, retain some snow through normal years, and a winter snowcap is always present even on hills of comparatively low elevation. A slight rise of the land or lowering of mean temperatures would cause an ice sheet to form on Ben Nevis and elsewhere.

Again, as has been already seen, some of the common trees of the continental deciduous forest have either failed to reach the British Isles or have there only a very limited distribution. At best, therefore (that is, before man interfered), the British Tropophytic Forest must have been an impoverished one.

In theory the dominant trees of this association are the two British oaks, the pedunculate (found on damp clay soils, especially in the south and the Midlands, but not much in the far west), and the sessile, most characteristic in west Wales ; but, in point of fact, even in north Northumberland the oak grows with extreme slowness and in most of Scotland (as already stated) it is at least rare to find the tree setting fertile seed. In southern England, especially over chalk and on the oolite of Gloucestershire, the beech forms, or formed, much of the woodland, but has a limited distribution, and its origins and spread are subject to discussion. It is, at any rate, not native in Scotland (though it sets fertile seed there), nor in Ireland. Ash has a similar preference for calcareous soils, and the limited distribution of beech allows for the development farther north (in the Pennine area) of pure ash-woods in a fashion not paralleled on the Continent. Similarly, the fact that in the north the oak is near its limit allows birches to grow with a freedom unknown where oaks flourish better. On wet grounds the alder and willow may form pure woods, and the yew may perhaps do this also. Finally, the hornbeam, found in southern and central England and in Wales, is not native to Scotland.

Of the associations generally we may note that tier formation is present to some extent, hazel being an important member of the second tier. Climbers are comparatively rare, honeysuckle and ivy being the commonest. As elsewhere, the ground vegetation is marked by the very early development of plants which need to avoid summer shading ; for instance, the wood anemone, primrose, dog's mercury, celandine, squill and so on. Autumn flowers, so common in Mediterranean areas, are at least rare, though fungi commonly develop in that season, as also rather earlier do flowering root parasites and saprophytes.

II. The second main formation is the Northern Coniferous Forest, of which some remnants believed to be original (the Caledonian Forest) persist in Scotland (for instance, the Rothiemurchus Forest). In these areas a noteworthy feature is the extreme poverty in forest-forming coniferous species, the only tree of this kind that is found being the Scots pine, which is native neither in England nor in Ireland, though it is sub-fossil there. This tree is mingled extensively with birch, and the undergrowth is largely juniper. It is exceedingly difficult to decide whether this Coniferous Forest could be reconstructed over large areas of the Scottish Highlands or not ; and, if so, whether Scots pine or spruce or North American conifers (especially the Sitka spruce or Douglas fir) would be the best agent.

Where strong winds check the growth of coniferous forest, or where the soil, because of its dryness, shallowness or acidity, prevents the growth of forest trees, the Heath Associations, dominated by ling or heath (bell heather), are predominant. It is a very doubtful question how far these heaths or dry moors are a climax community. It is still more doubtful how far ' wet moor ', or true moor, which develops over great thicknesses of peat, is a climax or a successional community. Its characteristic plants are Sphagnum, cotton grass and other sedges, bilberry and ling where the soil is drier, and various grasses.

III. The question whether or not truly natural grasslands occur in Britain is not fully settled. They possibly do so over some chalk hills and on some other hill or plateau areas, but most of our grasslands are artificial and due to forest destruction.

SUCCESSIONAL SERIES (SERES)

This subject has already been mentioned in Part I, Chapter I. Of Successional Series (Seres) the most interesting are the maritime examples, especially sand-dunes and salt marshes. Plants which grow within reach of the tides are halophytes, that is, show marked xerophytic characters, having reduced leaves or imbricated leaves or inrolled leaves, or a waxy covering, and so on, because salt prevents the ready absorption of water.

In a wet climate like that of the British Isles the sand of dunes does not contain much salt, for this is rapidly leached out. Plants growing on sand-dunes, however, in their earlier stages also show xerophytic characters, for the following reasons : surface layers of sand have little power of holding water ; humus is either absent altogether or present to a very small extent ; rain water runs through with great ease ; and, finally, sand has little capillarity, that is, little power of lifting water from lower layers. On the other hand, for similar reasons, deeper layers of sand are generally moist, for the dried-out surface layer forms a mulch, protecting the deeper layers from evaporation. Thus the plants of such an area have the deep roots that are characteristic of desert vegetation. As the dune becomes fixed the xerophytic characters of the plants diminish in intensity but tend to be still present. It is noteworthy that many dune or seashore plants can also grow on mountain-tops, where the cold diminishes the power of absorption and xerophytic characters therefore reappear. Familiar examples are *Armeria maritima* (sea-thrift), *Silene maritima* (bladder campion) and *Plantago maritima* (sea plantain). Similarly, *Saxifraga oppositifolia* (purple mountain saxifrage) extends to the seashore. Some botanists believe that part of the explanation of this is the fact that gulls and some other shore birds may nest inland in mountainous areas.

On the shores at or near the limit of the highest spring tide such forms as sea couch grass (Agropyrum), sea rocket (Cakile), orache (Atriplex), saltwort (Salsola) and sea sandwort (Arenaria) can tolerate occasional submergence in sea water and help to heap up small piles of sand. The chief agent in silting estuaries (especially in America) is the Spartina or cord-grass, which is native only in southern and eastern England (particularly Hampshire), though it is now spreading to Wales and being introduced in the ' stoblands ' of the Forth.

The most important fixing plant of drifting sand is *Ammophila arenaria* (marram grass), which will not tolerate prolonged submergence but can push up buds after being buried and makes a felt of roots and rhizomes in the sand. A noteworthy feature—which it has in common with esparto grass—is that its leaves curl inwards, so protecting the stomata and diminishing transpiration.

Once the sand is fixed, other species can appear. Lichens and mosses are often among the first colonists and help to make humus.   Common features of others which appear early are long tap-roots penetrating deeply into the soil, the mat form and hairs or fleshy leaves.   Examples are the restharrow (' liquorice ') with its long root-stocks, ladies' fingers (often with fleshy leaves), thyme, bedstraw, sedum, and so on.   Bracken often appears, and there may be both ling and bell-heather.   On some parts of the east coast sea-buckthorn (Hippophae) occurs, but as a rule the plants of the seashore and of dunes in this country are herbs, whereas in the Mediterranean area shrubs and undershrubs of *maquis* colonize the shore and in the tropics true trees (mangrove) are common.

The development of grasses may lead to the formation of close turf, and thereafter the sand-dune passes into either a grassland association or a heath, forming the climax community.

INDEX

Authors' names in italics

19   289